Spirit of Enterprise

The 1990 Rolex Awards

Spirit of Enterprise

The 1990 Rolex Awards

Foreword by

Jean Dorst

Director, Laboratory of Zoology, French National Museum of Natural History
Member of the Institut de France

Preface by

André J. Heiniger

Chief Executive Officer and Managing Director, Montres Rolex S. A.

Edited by

David W. Reed

BURI Buri Druck AG, CH-3001 Bern

Photographs and artworks have been submitted by the entrants except where indicated in the captions

This book was produced in Switzerland for Rolex
by Buri International
Production co-ordinator: Rolf Montag

Typeset by Elgra Ltd. Bern/Zurich
Printed by Buri Druck AG
Bound by Buchbinderei Schumacher AG, Schmitten

First published in 1990 by
Buri International
Eigerstrasse 71
Bern
Switzerland

ISBN 3 7169 2103 3

Rolex Laureates

The Rolex Awards for Enterprise 1987 Members of the Selection Committee

Contents

indicates a Rolex Laureate

indicates an Honourable Mention

Juan Antonio Bravo-Perea, Peter Brock, Antonio Iodice D'Enza, Prasanna Upali Weerawardane, Ian Meadows, Zvi Ben-Avraham, Jean Luc Sanchez, Alan Henri Simmons, Denise Lore Herzing, Eduardo Raffaelli, Bernadette Guyot-Jullien, Diana Joyce Moe, Tiberio Petro-León, Dragos Gheorghiu, Jesus Angel Ortea Rato, Michel Roggo, Sophie Anne Marie Labruhe, Anthony John Mills, Malcolm Brian Pittwood, Thomas Hewitt Rich, Jambalyn Shagj, James Brady, Claudio Stampi, Bessel Jan VandenHazel, Li Bang-Yan, Walter Edwin O. Ominde, Peter S. Winn, Shigetaka Tomotoshi, Luis Javier Rodriguez y Silva, Michał Domański, Zuraina Majid, Rebecca Ann Covalt, Antonio De Vivo, Dominic Anthony Addario, Jr., Gordon McGregor Reid, H. Stephen Green, Sandro Roberto Scarioni, José-Germán Cárdenas, Crisologo Ondoy, Marie Christine Levine.

Foreword

Our present era is an exciting one, though fraught with innumerable difficulties for the men and women who are living through it. Does it not bring into question principles we thought were untouchable? There is no doubt that it will take its place amongst the great turning-points in the history of humanity, one of those moments when the course of events accelerates like a river which, after wending calmly on its way, suddenly thunders over the rapids. Certainly, this is a consequence of the progress of our technology. Computers are opening up prospects that were unknown until now, giving external scope to our brains in the same way machines did to our muscles in the 18th century. Advances in our knowledge of the biology of the molecule, the cell and the vast ecological systems which form our biosphere – that slender envelope of living matter which surrounds the core of our planet – permit us to master living matter in ways that were previously unknown. These are factors which have profoundly changed our behaviour and have led us to a crisis point in our civilization.

It might be feared that humanity is increasingly placing its trust in machines and science and that, in the end, we could become no more than robots. And that would put an end to the individual initiative, the spirit of enterprise which Montres Rolex S. A. is so aptly encouraging.

However, a glance through the pages of this book will show that such is not the case. The urge to seek, to find out and to understand – in a perfectly disinterested and often totally individual way – what was previously unknown is just as alive 56amongst our contemporaries as it was for those who lived in earlier centuries when life was less dictated by technology. In our universe dominated by the computer and the biologist's test-tube, the yearning to know and innovate is just as vital as it was when our distant ancestors drew bison and horses on the walls of their caves in the Dordogne and Spain.

Creativity and the spirit of enterprise will continue to be essential and exclusive qualities of humankind and ones which will for ever distinguish us from the living world around us dominated as it is by instinct or a very rudimentary apprenticeship. Yet this does not exclude research on our own past – a past from which we draw our future.

The projects that the Selection Committee for The Rolex Awards for Enterprise 1990 had the difficult task of deciding on offer striking proof of this unending process. The range of subjects is vast and extends across all spheres of knowledge and research. Yet all have a common denominator: the progress of humankind. Many of the candidates have as their objective to improve the lives of their fellow men, many of whom are still in great need. Others aim to extend our knowledge of the mysterious world around us and the vastness of space which we have, as yet, scarcely penetrated. Many are devoted to the environment, in the widest sense of the word – one of the most pressing problems of our time. All of them should receive closer consideration on the part of our political leaders than do short-term subjects of dissension.

These are subjects which are of vital concern to our candidates because the world of nature around us is seriously threatened. The survival of humanity depends on its preservation. Materially we are dependent on it. Yet, in general, we equally need the moral qualities necessary to live in harmony with those beings that have their place on the same genealogical tree as our species – derived as it was from an obscure branch of the primitive primates. For the candidates of The Rolex Awards, the human element is a matter of constant concern – and this has profoundly heartened me.

Of the important lessons I have learnt from my participation in this Jury, the first and foremost is that the spirit of enterprise is still marvellously alive amongst the young, and even the less young – which is extremely encouraging in our century encumbered with technology where the machine should be in the service of man, and not dominate him.

Without this spirit of enterprise, we would have remained what we were in the age of the cave-man. To quote the words of the great French biologist, Jean Rostand: Man, this "grandchild of the fish, great-nephew of the snail... From a line of animals that in no way seemed intended for such a destiny, there came one day that preposterous animal which was to invent integral calculus and dream of justice".

Here we have the great concept that acts as a permanent driving force for humanity. Moreover, the fact that it is an ongoing tradition has once again been proven by the candidates who have participated in this international competition organized by a major company pursuing the course of universal humanism. For me this has been a great source of joy.

Paris,   Jean DORST
November 1989   *Institut de France*

Preface

With this, the fifth round of The Rolex Awards for Enterprise, I feel there is scarcely any need to introduce you to this incredible world of endeavour and achievement that we at Montres Rolex S. A. have the privilege and pleasure to explore anew every three years. Nevertheless, for those of you who are encountering The Rolex Awards for the first time, a word of presentation will certainly not go amiss.

It all started in 1976, on the occasion of the 50th anniversary of a "first" that occupies a very special place in our traditions – the invention and patenting in 1926 of the Rolex Oyster Case which was immediately acclaimed as the world's first waterproof watch. This was a particularly important moment for us since the Rolex Oyster has been an eminent example of our own enterprise in the field of fine watchmaking, and its 50th anniversary seemed to us an appropriate occasion to share and celebrate what we have long called "The Spirit of Enterprise".

The Rolex Awards were therefore inaugurated in 1976 and granted for the first time in 1978. The response was immense, worldwide and exciting; it far exceeded our wildest imagination but revealed that our initiative had struck a response amongst the public at large and that our concept of the "spirit of enterprise" is one that is shared by a vast number of people of unusual talents and capabilities. The first Awards Ceremony held in Geneva, Switzerland, in 1978 consecrated five Rolex Laureates, and subsequently 26 Honourable Mentions were suitably celebrated at ceremonies in their countries of residence throughout the world.

In view of the remarkable response to our first call, we decided to maintain the Awards which – now having been organized sequentially in 1981, 1984 and 1987 – have become a tradition. Over this period, 20 enterprising individuals have become Rolex Laureates and over 100 have been granted an Honourable Mention.

The fifth and latest round of The Awards, which is the subject of the present book, has had nothing to envy of its predecessors. The level, variety and quality of the projects submitted by our candidates have filled us with pleasure but at the same time have rendered the task of the eminent Members of our Selection Committee even more difficult than on previous occasions.

Right from the start in 1976, we realized that the granting of five Laureates and thirty or so Honourable Mentions could not do justice to the quantity and quality of our candidates. We therefore undertook to present to the world at large a wider panorama of this wealth of enterprise by publishing a book describing and illustrating a number of the projects that had most vividly captured our imagination – both for the pleasure of the reader and to ensure that these candidates could demonstrate their ideas to the largest possible audience and, perhaps, gather the wider support they need to bring their projects to realization.

Our expectations have not been unfounded and the response given to the four previous editions of *Spirit of Enterprise* has been generous and effective, with many of the candidates whose projects have been published informing us of the opportunities that have presented themselves.

I feel convinced that this fifth edition of *Spirit of Enterprise* will have a similar impact. The projects that you will read about on the following pages demonstrate the panorama of achievement and the profound sensation of human generosity that are for us so typical of our candidates. They will take you into new and amazing realms of human endeavour and will, I am sure, leave you with a renewed admiration at human aspirations.

In Geneva, on 26 April 1990, I will be proud to welcome to the podium the five Laureates of The Rolex Awards for Enterprise 1990 and present each of them with a cheque for 50,000 Swiss francs and a specially engraved gold Rolex Oyster Day-Date Chronometer. In the days that follow, a total of 35 Honourable Mentions will similarly attend special ceremonies organized around the world at which their successes will be acknowledged by the presentation to each of them of a steel and gold Rolex Oyster. Finally, we are once again publishing this book and other documents to ensure that, in 1990 too, the spirit of enterprise has the largest possible hearing around the world.

The Rolex Awards for Enterprise 1990 have, in the same way as their predecessors, given myself and all those involved in them considerable pleasure and gratification. They have also strengthenend us at Montres Rolex S. A. in our estimation of the intrinsic value of the Awards that we have conceived and of our vision of the programme's future. We hope that your appreciation will match ours. So please allow me to take this opportunity of announcing that the next Rolex Awards for Enterprise will be launched in 1991 and of inviting you to join us in them.

Geneva,
November 1989

André J. Heiniger
Chief Executive Officer and Managing Director
Montres Rolex S. A.

Introduction

What is it that drives men and women to go where nobody has ever gone before, to adopt a cause and tenaciously persevere until the grievance has been righted, to give generously of themselves to help those less privileged than they, to undertake a crusade to protect the animals and plants of our environment? There is, of course, no single answer to such a question but there is a universal thread which links them together and which results in many of the most outstanding of their kind figuring in this volume. That thread is the "spirit of enterprise" – a quality that has been a fundamental force helping humankind to ever-greater achievements over the centuries and a quality that Montres Rolex S. A. has decided to honour and encourage in five consecutive rounds of The Rolex Awards for Enterprise.

The 267 people who will be recounting to you their hopes and ambitions from the pages of this book are uncommon but incredibly stimulating. They come from all the corners of the globe, and they represent an amazing range of disciplines. Yet they have all been chosen for their spirit of enterprise. Five of them were selected by a distinguished Selection Committee to become The Rolex Laureates for 1990 and a further 35 were designated Honourable Mentions. Yet they all have an exciting story to tell and this book has been created to ensure that the stories are broadcast as widely as possible.

On 26 April 1990, the five Laureates will come to Geneva to take part in the Awards Ceremony and each receive from the hands of Mr. André J. Heiniger, Chief Executive Officer and Managing Director of Montres Rolex S. A., a cheque for 50,000 Swiss francs, a specially inscribed gold Rolex Oyster Day-Date Chronometer and a scroll attesting their selection. This will be followed shortly afterwards by similar ceremonies throughout the world at which the 35 Honourable Mentions will be celebrated and each receive a steel and gold Rolex Oyster and a scroll.

However, as in previous years, Montres Rolex S. A. has agreed to extend further support and encouragement to many of the other candidates whose projects were of outstanding merit. It was therefore once again decided to publish a book containing descriptions of the award – winning projects and of a further 236 projects that were considered to merit a wide audience.

Since the project descriptions that the candidates submitted on the Official Application Forms for The Rolex Awards for Enterprise were of widely varying lengths, it has proved necessary to condense many into a more concise form. This has had the added advantage of allowing even more projects to be presented than in the four previous Rolex Awards books.

As before, the book itself is divided into three sections, each being devoted to one of the categories of The Awards: Applied Sciences and Invention; Exploration and Discovery; and The Environment. However, the individual projects are presented in a random order and the sequence is in no manner intended to indicate a rating on the part of Montres Rolex S. A. or the Editor.

This book has a dual purpose. It provides a vehicle for the world to appreciate the qualities of many of those who have participated in The Rolex Awards for Enterprise 1990 – their inventiveness, tenacity, courage and perseverance. But it also offers you, the reader, the opportunity of participating in the efforts that are being undertaken. We would therefore encourage you to reach out to these individuals and offer them your encouragement. Better still, write to the candidate whose project has particularly appealed to you and offer your own support in return for further details.

Last but not least, we hope that the endeavours that you read of in the following pages will incite you to give free rein to your own "spirit of enterprise" and encourage you to put your own project down on paper and submit it for The Rolex Awards for Enterprise 1993.

Geneva,
November 1989

David W. Reed

Editor

Applied Sciences and Invention

The projects described in this section were submitted under the category "Applied Sciences and Invention" which was defined in the Official Application Form for The Rolex Awards for Enterprise 1990 as follows:

Projects in this category will be concerned primarily with science or technology and should seek to achieve innovative steps forward in research, experimentation or application.

Solar-wind power system

Eduardo A. Sampayo

Gaboto 3713, 1826 Remedios de Escalada, Buenos Aires, Argentina

Argentine, born 20 July 1943. Project engineer in Agua y Energía Eléctrica,
Sociedad del Estado. Educated in Argentina; Dipl.-Ing. (Hydroelectric
Engineering) from University of Buenos Aires in 1972.

There is widespread agreement that the sun is the energy resource of the future,
and it has been calculated that the sun radiates to the earth about 3,000 times
more energy than is currently consumed by humanity. The equatorial zones are
those that are the best suited to exploit this form of energy; however, by
resorting to the exploitation of combined solar and wind energy it becomes
possible to use solar energy in regions which, although less sunny, have the
compensating advantage of higher levels of wind energy available. In fact,
experience gathered in the United States has shown that the wind energy
available in the winter is some 50% greater than that available in the summer
months; consequently, a combined solar-wind system should be able to ensure a
reliable source for electricity generation throughout all the seasons of the year.

Solar chimneys to exploit sun and windpower

The atmospheric solar chimney that we have designed can be driven by both the
sun and the wind and brings together and exploits three physical principles: the
greenhouse effect in which solar radiation, absorbed under a large and translucent horizontal roof, heats vast quantities of air; the chimney effect in which the
interior air – which is both warmer and lighter than the atmospheric air – flows
to the chimney and rises up it, causing a suction force; and the wind turbine,
which changes the pressure difference into mechanical energy. The initial studies
on atmospheric solar chimney power plants were commissioned by the Ministry
of Research and Technology of the Federal Republic of Germany, and the work
itself was carried out at the Kernforschungsanlage Jülich GmbH.

In my attempts to develop the original concepts of solar energy exploitation, I
am currently investigating two fundamental innovations which may have the
potential to significantly increase the efficiency and reduce the cost of generating energy in solar chimneys. These innovations are the development of a chimney to exploit a combination of solar and wind power; and a high-speed chimney
with a larger air flow and greater efficiency. The research programme that we

have undertaken to this effect has received the support of Agua y Energía Eléctrica, Sociedad del Estado, and the Universidad Nacional de la Plata.

Construction of a prototype model

In February 1987, we began construction of the actual model for the solar-wind chimney and laboratory testing was commenced in July of the same year. The model has now been extensively tested, and various modifications that the trials indicated were necessary have now been carried out. The results that we have obtained have fully justified our commitment to the approach we have developed and indicated that the development work should be continued.

The system itself consists of a horizontal canopy roof made from translucent plastic, which is open along its periphery, and positioned somewhat above ground level. The solar radiation passes through the translucent plastic panels, strikes and heats the ground underneath; in this way, the temperature of the fresh air flowing inwards from the periphery rises constantly as it approaches the chimney tower. The warm air produces an updraught in the chimney duct, and this air flow turns the turbine which drives the generator. The operating system is simple and has the added advantage that the collector exploits not only direct but also diffused solar radiation (i. e. it also operates when the sky is overcast). Moreover, the collector has also been designed to act as a wind-capturing system and, in this way, the generator will be driven when there is wind but no sun.

The chimney is a very high tower, and its generating power is directly propor- tional to its height. The tower is reinforced with annular trussed beams uniformly

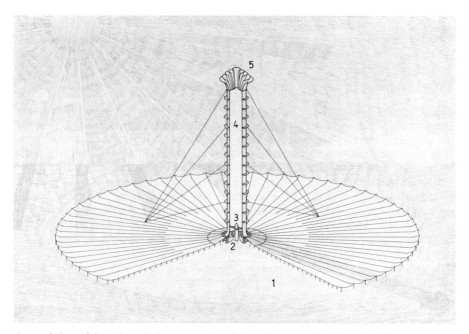

General view of the solar-wind power system design developed by Eduardo A. Sampayo.

The wicket gate of Eduardo A. Sampayo's solar-wind power system; wicket gate fitted with movable vanes below; wicket gate partially closed above.

distributed throughout its height, and guyed vertically at four levels, and in three different directions to foundation blocks to ensure maximum stability.

A multi-cone diffuser on top of the tower has the double purpose of allowing operation as a high-speed chimney and of acting as a draft tube for any wind blowing. The system operates as a solar chimney when the sun shines, and as a wind power plant when the wind blows.

Size-dependent costs

The technical and economic feasibility of the solar-wind chimney generator project was developed upon the basis of a 5.4 MW power plant; with increasing output, the specific costs decrease. We have estimated that the power plant's generating costs over a period of 20 years of amortization are lower than those for conventional solar chimneys. In addition, the solar chimney wins out in any comparison with other types of solar power plants. Calculations show that a solar-wind power plant with an installed capacity of over 5 MW can generate electricity economically. The calculated costs are achievable today and are not dependent on the development of new technologies or the advantages of mass production.

The Trickle Up Program, Inc.

Mildred Robbins Leet

Trickle Up Program, Inc., 54 Riverside Drive, PHE, New York, New York
10024–6509, United States

American, born 9 August 1922. Co-Director and Co-Founder of the Trickle Up
Program. Educated in United States; B. A. from New York University.

The unique philosophy and design of the Trickle Up Program (TUP) is based on 40
years of international development experience by co-founders and co-directors,
Glen and Mildred Robbins Leet. The combined experience of the Leets led them
to the foundation of the Trickle Up Program as a means to promote their belief
that self-help, grassroots development was the path to the successful elimination
of poverty and the generation of economic growth within the developing world.
In 1979, they invested $1,000 of their own money in ten businesses in Dominica.
They also designed an innovative computer programme to reach an expanding
global population of aspiring entrepreneurs and, by the end of 1988, a total of
over 10,000 businesses had been started.

Trickle Up versus Trickle Down

The Trickle Up Program operates on the reverse of the "trickle down" theory.
Trickle down involves the massive transfer of capital at the top through government and industry. Although this approach proved successful in Europe under
the Marshall Plan, when applied to Third World economies it has not produced
similar results, and in some cases, the poorest of the poor are poorer than ever.
Often trickle down activities have served to concentrate production in urban
areas, producing population concentrations with adverse environmental,
economic, and social consequences. As the trickle down method provides capital
for centralized production, it has, in some situations, made it difficult for decentralized, labour-intensive production to survive. This results in unemployment
and underemployment, as what little capital remains in small communities has
been drained away to pay for goods and services produced centrally.

The Trickle Up Program is targeted at those in the informal sector who are
generally overlooked when development plans are made. In contrast to traditional development programmes, TUP involves people directly in working, selling, saving and reinvesting. By helping to initiate local businesses, TUP creates a
multiplier effect, generating increased productivity and commerce. This expands

Fruits and vegetables, Cebu, Philippines. The fruit and vegetable harvesting group consists of ten women. Some 67% of the profits were reinvested, and the group's success allowed these entrepreneurs to expand by buying and selling chickens. They reported that the group members were spending their time more productively.

local employment opportunities and markets, causing communities to grow and prosper from within. As this process spreads, benefits can truly "trickle up" through a country's economy.

Traditional development programmes often train people for skills they may not be able to employ effectively in their existing economies. TUP does not tell people what to make or how to market it, but helps them to start businesses they decide will be successful, based on *their* knowledge of *their* markets. Businesses started through the Trickle Up Program relate principally to community needs. They produce food (64.3%), clothing (10.6%), household goods (15.8%), crafts (5%), and miscellaneous supplies and services (4.2%). It is common for successful TUP entrepreneurs to start one business and use the profits to expand into larger, often different, enterprises. Trickle Up goes beyond the mere generation of employment. By encouraging entrepreneurs to reinvest in their businesses, TUP promotes the accumulation of savings that allow them to not only expand their businesses and improve their standard of living, but to gain a new sense of confidence, security, and the belief that they can positively affect their futures.

The TUP proposition

The Trickle Up Program strategy is based on respect for the ability of men and women to plan and work together and on the assumption that people already possess the skill and ingenuity to create income producing enterprises. What they need is confidence, business insight, and start up capital. TUP provides conditional $100 grants in two $50 instalments to groups of five or more people who have joined together to start a business. Grantees are required to complete TUP's simple business plan, in which they commit to begin a business enterprise: that they have planned themselves; for which they have or can secure any necessary approvals or resources; where the 1,000 hours of self-employment can be completed within three months; where a profit is anticipated; where not less than

20% of the profit will be reinvested; where continuing and expanding levels of self-employment are anticipated; and for which they will send reports on their enterprise and results to TUP.

Trickle Up projects are initiated and monitored by community based co-ordinators who find that TUP can advance the work of their own organizations. They include over 1,400 individuals and professional personnel of local and international voluntary organizations, governmental agencies, the United Nations Development Programme, UNICEF, UN Volunteers, and the Peace Corps. Although the grant given to each enterprise is only $100, the impact is great. By following TUP's carefully designed forms, grantees learn the basic skills which enable them to build self-sufficient businesses. Reports from the field indicate that the resulting increase in income and confidence has not only directly improved basic family needs such as nutrition, health, shelter, clothing and education, but has indirectly spurred community development.

TUP's results are achieved without a large or expensive administrative structure. As was stated in a UN publication, "the Trickle Up Program has developed carefully designed forms and simple procedures, and with its creative use of microcomputers, TUP is able to manage a widely spread programme of activities with a minimal staff, resulting in impeccable financial accountability and solid records and reports of accomplishments".

Long-term plans

The Trickle Up Program will continue to start businesses using its simple formula for success: businesses started with $100 grants, planned and managed by those who will do the work and reap the benefits. Funding will continue to be sought from individuals, foundations, and governmental and non-governmental agencies. The growing interest and participation of organizations involved in development will expand the TUP philosophy and system as it is incorporated by them for use in their own programmes.

Zudzi basket weavers, Zudgazi, Ghana. The basket weaving and selling group consists of two women and three men. The members reinvested 60% of the profits into the business, and were able to buy raw materials in bulk and to increase their inventory.

Systematic studies on the corrosion casts of the ocular vessels and retinal vascular diseases

Zhang Huirong

Department of Ophthalmology, Third Hospital, Beijing Medical University, 100083 Beijing, People's Republic of China

Chinese, born 2 November 1931. Chairman and Professor. Educated in People's Republic of China; M. D. from West China Union University in 1953.

The ocular vessels which supply oxygen and nutrients to the eye play a significant role in microcirculation, and vascular diseases often lead to blindness. To research the mechanism of retinal vascular diseases, we have studied the structure of the ocular vessels and explored the causes and the therapy of retinal vein occlusion.

Systematic studies of the ocular vessels

From 1984 to 1988, we systematically observed the architecture and three-dimensional distribution of the ocular vessels of 148 eyes by using the corrosion cast technique and scanning electron microscopy. Among the specimens studied, there were 80 human eyes, 10 eyes of Macaque monkeys, 48 cats' eyes and 10 eyes of rabbits and rats. We have observed the characteristics of each portion of the ocular vessels, such as retina, choroid, iris, ciliary body, sclera, conjunctiva, extra-ocular muscle, lachrymal gland, as well as Zinn's circle and the vortex vein. So far, we have taken 1,453 electron microscopic photographs.

Some findings in studying the structure of ocular vessels

We observed the retinal angio-architecture in humans, monkeys and cats and found that the retinal vessels have a laminated structure. The radial peripapillary capillaries (RPCs) form the innermost layer; they originate from the central retinal artery and drain into the central retinal vein. RPCs can be divided into the long-chain type and the sparse-net type; they anastomose with one another and also with the deeper capillaries. We found that a constriction occurs at the site where an arteriole branches off from the parent artery. This exists in human and cat eyes and possibly regulates the retinal blood flow.

First, we checked that the anastomoses exist not only between arteries, veins and arterioles, but also between capillaries. The choroidal vessels show a segmental distribution. We observed the vessels of the iris and the ciliary body in the eyes

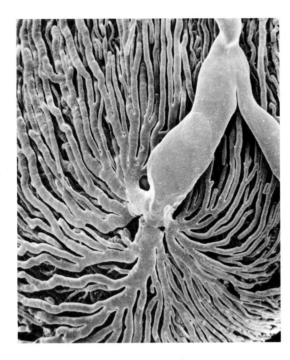

The vortex vein of the human eye. The choroidal veins converge and enter the vortex vein that forms a sack-shaped dilatation (ampulla) before leaving the eyeball (x19).

of humans, monkeys and cats and compared the different distribution between them.

Injection-corrosion and electron microscopy are new techniques in the study of ocular vessels, and to disseminate information about them, we organized a workshop in May 1987, and also published a collection of slides of the ocular vessels.

Retinal vein occlusion and its complications

For an ophthalmologist, it is an easy and gratifying task to carry out surgical operations such as cataract extractions, with or without intraocular lens implantation. Within just one week or so, the patient may recover his or her visual acuity and both doctor and patient are extremely satisfied. However, treating a retinal vein occlusion is a far more difficult task and the results are not so certain. I have examined a relatively large number of patients with retinal vein occlusion from all over China who have become blind because of the complication of neovascular glaucoma.

The treatment of retinal vein occlusion is a major problem for the ophthalmologist, and patients often lose their sight due to the complication – neovascular glaucoma. We have studied the potential of certain traditional Chinese medicines and were pleased to find that the therapy we developed reduced the incidence of neovascular glaucoma from 19% to 6% in the patients we treated. Subsequently, we simplified the treatment procedure and now, instead of a complicated decoction, we have been able to combine the effective drugs into a tablet form. I now wish to treat retinal vein occlusion by combining Chinese medicine and western medicine, and continue to study the therapy of its complications.

Improving the treatment of retinal vein occlusion

To further explore the causes of complications in retinal vein occlusion such as neovascular glaucoma, cystoid macular oedema and preretinal membrane, etc., we plan to do vascular endothelial cell culture, to make models of neovascularization, and find more effective therapies for retinal vein occlusion. My hope is that we can treat this disease with surgery and further study the causes of neovascularization which is not only due to retinal vein occlusion but also due to other diseases such as ageing macular degeneration, diabetic retinopathy, hypermyopia, etc.

My plan is also to compile an atlas entitled *An Atlas of Ocular Vessels – Corrosion Casts and Scanning Electron Microscopy* and a book by the name of *The Ocular Microcirculation and Its Related Diseases*.

Although we are proud to know that we have made a certain degree of progress, we recognize that our knowledge is still very limited. Nevertheless, my assistants and I will continue to intensify our studies in this field in spite of the difficulties that we know we will continue to encounter.

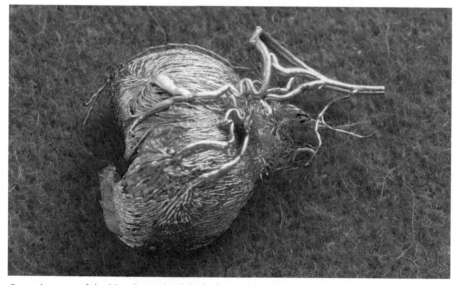

Corrosion cast of the blood vessels of the lachrymal gland of the human eye (x4).

A new technique of colour cartography – the associative chorographic map

Anna M. C. Bednarz

Honourable Mention
The Rolex Awards for Enterprise – 1990

Grolmanstrasse 32, 1000 Berlin 12, Federal Republic of Germany

German, born 19 November 1948. Freelance cartographer and consultant. Educated in the Federal Republic of Germany; B. A. (Geography) from University of Berlin in 1978.

A chorographic map is a map representing large regions, countries or continents on a small scale. During recent years, there have been several attempts to create maps showing the different regions of our globe in a "natural" way. The most striking features of the landscape are ground cover – including natural vegetation, land use and bare ground – and relief. Traditional "physical" maps can no longer meet our need since they do not feature ground cover, and they evoke incorrect associations due to the so-called "hypsometric tint scale": greens for lowlands and browns for high altitudes. For instance, green is associated with fertile grasslands or wooded areas, yet it is used to represent the low areas of the Sahara desert. Therefore a procedure was sought to combine relief and ground cover in one map, in order to render a natural impression.

However, up to now there did not exist a combined representation of relief, altitude, ground cover and climate, enabling topographic orientation, evoking the intended associations of the depicted areas, and capable of standardized production. My project envisages the development of such a system.

Concept, design and technique

It is impossible to give a "real" picture of landscape in a map. The vegetation varies due to climatic and seasonal effects, so that – dependent on the scale – it is necessary to summarize, simplify, and select individual features, i.e. to generalize. Therefore the representation of map elements must be carried out in an abstract and symbolic way. In order to aid perception and intuition, the colours to be used should be selected taking into account human colour association, for example greens for forest, oranges for tropical desert, and browns for land use.

Continuous features should logically be represented as continuous, and discrete features as in a mosaic. The system of traditional hypsometric colours is illogical since it divides the landscape into layers of different colours, creating an impres-

A section of the tropical-zone map (Nigeria and Cameroon) produced by Anna Bednarz using her new technique of colour cartography.

sion of discontinuity and reducing the effect of hill shading. More logical and more graphic is a monochromatic range for the hypsometric scale: low altitudes are darkest and high altitudes lightest, promoting the three-dimensional impression, which is achieved by hill shading. Customarily this shading is superimposed in grey or brown, falsifying the underlying colours. Shading in the same colour (integrated hill shading) avoids this unfortunate effect.

The associative chorographic map, a new type of map developed by me, meets the requirements set forth above and supplies a solution for the problem of combining the mosaic of ground cover with relief, altitude and climate in such a way that a clear legible, harmonious, and aesthetic representation results. Furthermore the process is economical, it can be standardized and it produces facsimile quality. Applying modern techniques, the production costs are reduced although the quality is improved.

This has been achieved by a new cartographic technique, the so-called colour-original technique with standardized colours and integrated hill shading using a new cartographic method – the mosaic-continuum method – reproduction by colour scanning with three colour separations only, and trichromatic printing. A special generalization permits more detailed information about the character of the countries while improving the clarity of the map.

Reproduction and printing

Colour separation is done with a colour scanner resulting in solely three colour separations in yellow, magenta and cyan with a given density. The coloured lines and symbols are exposed photographically onto the corresponding colour separations. Because all colour tones show the same brightness for the same altitude, it is possible to produce a separate shading by colour separation and transformation of colour into grey.

As yet five map sections – examples for the different climates – have been produced on a scale of 1 : 5,000,000. The examples are as follows: I, Polar, subpolar and cold temperature zone – Iceland; II, Cool temperature zone – Scandinavia; III, Warm temperature and Mediterranean zone – Iberian Peninsula; IV, Arid zone – Mauretania/West Sahara ; V, Tropical zone – Nigeria/Cameroon. Four of the five prepared map sections have been printed so far.

Future progress

Further studies, especially with regard to the reproduction process are necessary to optimize the results. Nevertheless, my work shows very clearly that my new system presents the possibility of producing high-quality multicolour maps with modulated colour at low cost. This new map type has been accepted for patent application and it can be applied not only to small-scale maps, but also to all thematic representations and even to non-cartographic subjects (graphics, art). With maps produced in the new system, it is intended to create a new type of patented loose-leaf world atlas with a new kind of binding.

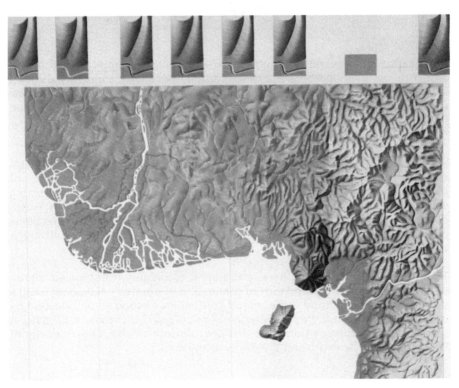

The southwest area of the warm-temperature and Mediterranean-zone map (Iberian Peninsula) produced by Anna Bednarz. Photograph of the colour original.

14

Ultra-light aircraft for monitoring Indonesian volcanoes

Michel Halbwachs

Laboratory of the Geophysical Institute, Université de Savoie, route de l'Eglise, B. P. 1104, 73011 Chambéry, France

French, born 24 July 1943. Professor of Physics at the Université de Savoie, Chambéry. Educated in France; Doctorat d'Etat (Solid Physics) from University of Grenoble in 1977.

Over the past 20 years, we have carried out a number of geophysical and other surveys in Indonesia and have had the opportunity of exploring active and inactive volcanoes including various little-known ones in eastern Java and the small Sunda Islands. During the Dutch colonial era, the authorities had closely monitored active and inactive volcanoes throughout the territory both from the air and the ground. However, nowadays only a limited number of imminently dangerous volcanoes are regularly monitored and the footpaths cut to give access to volcano craters by the Dutch have been allowed to grow over and become impracticable.

During our explorations, we were able to cut our way through these paths with the help of an experienced guide and also to overfly volcanoes which, although considered inactive or extinct by the Vulcanological Survey of Indonesia (VSI), were actually found to be active. Although the value of aerial monitoring of, in particular, the remoter volcanoes became apparent even during our earliest missions in 1978 and 1980, we were forced to abandon any long-term project of surveillance because of the organizational difficulties and the prohibitive costs.

Unforeseen volcanic activity

During a five-month stay in Indonesia in 1988, one of the volcanoes I climbed with friends was the huge 3,500 m high Gunung Slamet situated in the highly populated central plain of Java. This volcano was classed as inactive but, on the basis of our observations, we reported to the VSI next day that we expected activity to be imminent. The volcano erupted 10 days later, without any seismic forewarning.

The same spring, also without seismic precursors and after 80 years of inactivity, Banda Api, the small cone-shaped island in the sea of Banda, suddenly reawakened. Luckily the eruption was mainly effusive, so that although two large flows of lava totally buried the principal town, there was only one casualty as the other inhabitants had sufficient time to seek refuge on a neighbouring

Near to Lake Segara Anak, the G. Baru which is still active. In the distance the G. Agung on Bali.

island. Much more devastating was the eruption of Makian in July on an island in western Molucca. A cataclysmic explosion destroyed in seconds all of the towns and villages on the island. The 10,000 inhabitants had evacuated the island after having felt earthquakes a few days before.

From these three examples it is clear that although seismic surveillance may be sufficient in most cases, it certainly cannot be seen as a universal solution. The craters of these three volcanoes were never visited, but it is highly unlikely that the awakening of Banda Api and Makian had not been preceded by visible modifications of activity in the craters of the kind we had witnessed in Gunung Slamet.

The use of ULA in volcano surveillance

As we have already emphasized, the difficult ground access for a large number of potentially dangerous Indonesian volcanoes makes their regular surveillance a problem even for simple visual or photographic observation, let alone for measuring rudimentary physical or chemical parameters. The use of single or twin-engined airplanes is hampered by the lack of development in either civil or commercial light aviation. Moreover, the present availability of airplanes and aerodromes in Indonesia is not sufficient for rapid deployment of volcanic surveillance aircraft. Furthermore, the high hourly cost of flying has thus excluded airplanes from all routine volcanic monitoring programmes in the countries concerned. By the same argument, the use of helicopters, despite being the ideal machine for this type of work, remains, and will remain for some time to come, virtually out of the question.

Ultra-light aircraft have a manoeuvrability comparable to an airplane, a low speed capacity (25 to 50 knots), and an adequate maximum flying height, that is 4,000 m, but with incomparably lower running costs. The short training time for pilots, approximately 10 hours, is also a not negligible benefit. The rapidity with which the ULA can be brought into operation, being deployed from the foot of the volcano to be observed, means that advantage could be taken of favourable flying conditions.

We have developed earlier the importance of the visual observation of volcanic activity at a regular and sufficiently high frequency. In addition an experienced pilot is able to land on a very restricted area, for example a clear field of 50 m, which can generally be found on the volcanoes we have visited. It means that a ULA can be used to reach inaccessible (or almost inaccessible) edifices or calderas and to make measurements or take samples as far as is possible with light equipment.

We are convinced that the ULA, as an observation or transportation vehicle, will be an unsurpassed tool in third world countries. In addition to permitting visual observation, the ULA may be have a role to play in the following more sophisticated applications: carrying out airborne sampling of volcanic plumes, since changes in the proportions of characteristic chemical components are an effective method for monitoring volcanic activity; surveying variations in the intensity and extent of active areas using a remote sensing infrared radiometer; mapping magnetic anomalies using a magnetic sensor towed behind the ULA; determining, on a specific route, such meteorological parameters as air temperature or humidity to permit precise application of geodesic techniques such as laser distance measurements; and estimating wind speeds in the vicinity of a volcanic plume.

It is the intention of this project to demonstrate the feasibility of these methods of investigation at a number of Indonesian volcanoes chosen for their inaccessibility. In addition to the purely scientific and preventive aspect of the project, we have also adopted a media approach and have organized press coverage and several thousand photos. The English production house of John Gau, exclusive representative of National Geographic in Europe, will co-produce the documentaries with the BBC (Great Britain) and TF1 (France) television networks.

The ultra-light aircraft in hot air turbulence over the Kawah Idjen crater lake.

Schistosomiasis control programme on Pemba Island, Zanzibar

Lorenzo Savioli

Via I. Panattoni 74, 00189 Rome, Italy

Italian, born 25 April 1952. Studying for a degree in medical parasitology. Educated in Italy, Belgium, and United Kingdom; degree in medicine from the University of Rome in 1977.

Schistosomiasis is a disease caused by a worm of the genus *Schistosoma*. It is one of the major causes of morbidity and mortality in developing countries, affects not less than 300 million people and is second only to malaria in its incidence. The infection is linked to the use of surface water, and is the major reason for impaired agricultural and water scheme development in third world countries.

In the genus *Schistosoma*, the species *haematobium* is the most diffuse, accounting for about 80 million cases in Africa and the Middle East. *S. haematobium* lives in the venous system of the urinary bladder where the eggs, produced by the female worm and trapped in the tissues of the urinary tract, cause severe damage. About 50% of the eggs of this parasite are trapped in the tissues, the other 50% being expelled in the environment. If passed into water, they hatch and release a larva that will penetrate a suitable host snail, if present. After a certain amount of time, thousands of larvae will be shed by the snail ready to infect persons who come into contact with that water and then penetrate their intact skin. For the moment, the most accurate technique for the diagnosis of this infection is based on the identification of the eggs of this parasite in the urine of patients.

In the 1970s, a diagnostic technique was developed in which a fixed amount of urine is filtrated through a reusable filter fine enough to capture the eggs. The eggs could then be counted with the aid of a microscope, and the people with many eggs and worms and thus at higher risk of severe disease could be identified. It also became clear that disease was directly proportional to haematuria (blood in urine). The people with more lesions in their urinary bladders, ureters and kidneys also had more blood in their urine. Of those with haematuria, patients with visibly bloody urines had a very high number of eggs and worms and severe urinary tract disease.

At the end of the 1970s a new drug, praziquantel, was synthesized with the financial help of the World Health Organization. It is capable of treating the

Health workers in the team examining the filters with retained eggs of Schistosoma haematobium using a microscope. They report their findings as the number of eggs per millilitre of urine.

infection with only one treatment by mouth and with very few side effects. Soon after this discovery, some research workers began to think that maybe reagent strips for haematuria could be utilized to identify people for treatment without the aid of trained personnel, equipment and laboratory facilities. The positive subjects could then be treated, easily, with the new drug. Nobody had tried this approach on a large scale.

The idea of the control programme on Pemba Island

Having spent some time as a volunteer physician on Pemba Island, Tanzania, and having realized the enormity of the schistosomiasis problem there, I decided that the time had come to carry out a trial programme for the treatment of a large population group, on the basis of the diagnosis of haematuria. I started by selecting and training, in a few months, a team of enthusiastic young people who originally knew nothing of microscopes or schistosomiasis. We had no funds for running costs but a budget that could pay for three motorcycles, four micro- scopes, some drugs and the reagent strips. We first compared the filtration of urine for eggs with the reagent strips for blood, in a sample of 9,000 people, and demonstrated that, on the island, we could use this technique to identify nearly 90% of the people infected.

After ten months we were ready for the first campaign in schools. We decided a school campaign to examine the 26,000 children on the whole island would require about one month and that we should retreat the school population every six months. If the same team had carried out the work with the traditional microscopic diagnosis, we would have needed to calculate not less than 90 working days. The first campaign began and ended in November 1986, the second in April 1987. All this was performed by my team of five health assistants aided by teachers and students. My plan of action stated that haematuria in children had to be reduced by 60% in two years; this objective was reached in one year. The other objective of reducing visibly bloody urines by 90% in two years was also achieved in one year.

The future

Up to the present, the programme has been successful but major developments are ahead. We now know the areas of the island where the infection is more severe, where transmission is more intense, and where the water is more contaminated. It is there that our efforts have to be stronger. We also need to control the snails in the rivers and lakes.

The second main necessity is that of developing the operational capabilities of the dispensary health system on the island. The 36 dispensaries there must now take over the work in the schools and in the community. However, this is not possible at the moment. If all this is not done soon and a strong surveillance system is not organized at the school and village level, the disease will return to pre-treatment levels within about two years' time.

A larger amount of enterprise and endurance will be needed for the second part of the project. I feel that we are still at the beginning even if 26,000 children have already been examined five times and the first examination of the whole population (300,000) will soon be completed. The success of the project, with its limited resources, has been a model for all the countries where this disease is prevalent and where financial and technical resources are scarce. The work performed on Pemba is a unique example of a simplified approach for the control of a disease on a large scale. Schistosomiasis has been used as a port of entry for the whole reorganization of the island's health.

The first community campaign for schistosoma detection and eradication. The detection measures and treatment are now available for older members of the population and for pre-school children.

New and cheap dental prosthesis to increase cattle production

Jorge Raul Spinelli

Moreno, 7007 San Manuel, Argentina

Argentine, born 5 December 1957. Veterinary surgeon. Educated in Argentina; degree in Veterinary Medicine from the Faculty of Veterinary Science, Buenos Aires.

Argentina has about 54–56 million head of cattle. The average lifespan of an animal is 10–11 years, although this may vary considerably depending on activity and diet. However, if one calculates that a cow will calve for the first time at the age of 3 years it can be said that a cow's productive life is 7–8 years, during which she might have 6–7 calves or the equivalent in dairy production, i.e. 6–7 lactations. It is therefore common to leave between 15 and 20% of cows in heifers to replace those mothers that grow old and are discarded.

The process of ageing

Getting old is a general physiological process that is still not well understood. It affects the cells and systems formed by them, as well as the components of the tissue, such as the collagen. One of the many theories put forward to explain the ageing process is that mammals have a biological clock, possibly located in the hypothalamus which is responsible for body ageing.

However, in cattle, it is usually not the general overall process of ageing that heralds the end of the animal's productive life; rather, the determining factor is tooth wear. As the teeth are worn down, the animal is no longer able to chew normally and therefore it becomes less well nourished, starts to suffer from reproductive disorders and finally undergoes overall deterioration of its general condition. The economic loss here is multiplied by the fact that animals sold when in this condition bring a very low price. However, our experience indicates that animals like this still have 2–3 years of useful life before them, provided their dental problems could be solved.

A full-grown tooth consists of three substances which are structurally different: ivory, enamel and cementum: the ivory is a modified osseous tissue which has a central socket where the dental pulp is housed. The enamel is usually white, and is the strongest tissue of the tooth and the organism. The cementum is brown or yellowish, with a structure and chemical composition similar to those in the

21

The animal with its worn teeth displayed prior to veterinary dental intervention.

osseous tissue. The cementum, the enamel and the ivory are abraded and wear at the points where the teeth grind together during chewing.

Each tooth comprises a crown and a root. The crown gradually wears out but the tooth length usually remains unchanged. Due to the progressive reduction of the root, the teeth may fall out in very old animals. The speed at which teeth wear depends on the animal's diet; for example, the hard and fibrous grass of the Altiplano (in northwest of Argentina) will, in seven years, cause the same degree of wear that is found after 11 years in cattle that inhabit the humid pampa.

Dental prosthesis in cattle

Dental prostheses have been used in cattle for some time now and good results have been achieved; however, current methods and materials for prosthesis manufacture and fitting are time-consuming and expensive. To overcome the disadvantages of current techniques, we have developed a new technique using polyacrylate resin moulded *in situ* instead of the conventional chromium and cobalt alloy. Teeth moulds of standard dimensions, usually designed on the basis of the distance between the external sides of the canines, have been produced.

Once the animals have been classified by breed and mouth width, fixing is simple. First, the animal is immobilized, and the worn teeth are checked to see if it is necessary to extract any part of the gum. The mould is then put in place and checked for correct fit; the resin and catalyst are mixed correctly and poured into place, and any excess is removed. After a period of only 10 minutes, the resin forming the new tooth crown has cured completely. Thereafter, the animal can be allowed to start grazing again without any inconvenience. The total time that is needed for the whole operation is about 17 minutes; however, the fixing of the tooth itself without any surgical work being undertaken on the gums takes only about 12 minutes.

It is advisable to arrange for a check-up to be carried out on the animals some 30 days after the dentistry work has been done since we have found that 5–6% of the treated animals lose their prosthesis; this may occur either because the fixing points on the original teeth were inadequate or because the resin did not set properly. By now, some of the prostheses are two years old and the degree of wear we have encountered to date indicates that this period is about the maximum life of the denture. However, a worn prosthesis is easily and rapidly replaced. It is merely necessary to roughen the surface of the worn denture, using a file; thereafter, one selects a mould that is one size larger than the one used previously, inserts it in place and then pours in the two-part resin mix.

Results to date

The results to date are excellent, and we find that we have succeeded in significantly extending the useful life of animals which would otherwise have been discarded. We estimate that at current prices of beef in Argentina, these prostheses cost about 10 kg of live meat or US$ 4 per prosthesis; however, they allow at least one calf more per animal, which represents some 200 kg of meat and another lactation with an average yield of about 3,500 litres of milk or 1,000 kg of meat. The calculation is even more attractive in the case of high-quality cows that are used as donors in embryo-transfer programmes. Here, the result is not just one extra calf per animal but 60 extra embryos per extra year of productive life.

The same animal with its "denture" in place ready for several more years "productive" life.

Bone metabolism in black bears: potential applications to human osteoporoses

Charles Timothy Floyd

Honourable Mention
The Rolex Awards for Enterprise – 1990

145 Cielo Via, Walnut Creek, California 94598, United States

American, born 6 January 1955. Orthopaedic surgeon, Orthopaedic Associates of Aspen and Glenwood. Educated in United States and Scotland; M. D. from University of Florida in 1982.

Osteoporosis is a disease characterized by loss of bone mass and resulting fragility of the bones. Very difficult to detect until fractures occur, this disease is probably linked to many factors, of which only the main ones are known, primarily age, sex and race. It is fast becoming a major public health problem, due to the general ageing of the populations in the main Western countries. It is estimated, for example, that in the United States alone, some 20 million people already suffer from osteoporosis.

The only existing treatment, more or less efficacious, is oestrogen-based, applicable for only one particular form of the disease – post-menopausal osteoporosis. There is no specific treatment, then, for this disease. The only hope at present is in the various preventive measures. This project starts out from the hypothesis that denning black bears do not develop osteoporosis despite months of immobilization and the corollary hypothesis that denning black bears produce a substance or substances which prevent osteoporosis.

"Bear" bones

Bears survive harsh, winter conditions by "denning", a unique set of metabolic adaptations. Unlike other hibernators, the denning bear remains metabolically active. For three to five months, the animal does not consume food or water and it does not eliminate waste. Combustion of stored fat provides the daily energy requirement (4,000 kilocalories) and liberates water to balance insensible losses. Urine is not produced because urea does not accumulate. Rather, urea is rerouted through a metabolic pathway which degrades it into its constituents. The carbon dioxide is eliminated with respiration and the nitrogen is incorporated into protein metabolism. Thus, the bear remains recumbent and metabolically active throughout denning, yet does not produce urine.

The effects of immobilization on the skeleton have been studied in other animals, including man. Bone volume is in a constant state of turnover and remodel-

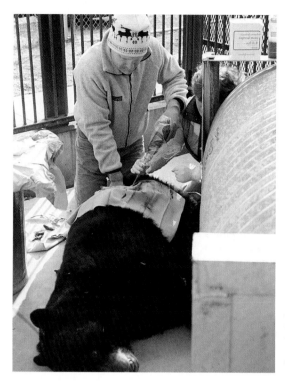

Charles Floyd performing a transilial biopsy on an anaesthetized bear in which he is studying bone metabolism in the hope of finding a substance that may prevent osteoporosis in humans.

ling. One set of cells, the osteoclasts, constantly resorbs bone. This activity is followed by co-ordinated bone formation by osteoblasts. Under normal conditions the amount of newly formed bone equals the amount resorbed, and bone volume increases. Similarly, if stress is decreased, less new bone is formed and bone volume decreases. In all studies of immobilized animals, paralyzed patients and animals in weightless conditions, marked changes are observed in bone. Bone volume decreases significantly and bone formation ceases in the face of continued resorption. The result of this process is osteoporosis. As osteoporosis develops, the resorbed bone mineral is eliminated in the urine to maintain serum calcium concentration within a narrow range. Deviations from this concentration range lead first to muscular and neurologic disturbances and, ultimately, to death. In all animals studied to date, immobilization results in osteoporosis and obligatory loss of calcium.

As discussed above, the denning bear remains recumbent in a small den for up to five months yet, during this period, it does not produce urine. Calcium, therefore, has no avenue for elimination from the body. Assuming the serum calcium concentration remains within the normal range, this set of conditions suggested to me that denning black bears maintain bone volume and produce a substance(s) which prevents disuse osteoporosis.

Research procedure

I studied three captive male black bears. Seasonal measurements of serum calcium confirmed the earlier finding that this remains constant throughout denning. In summer, winter and spring, I performed biopsies of the ilium in order to study bone metabolism. I found no difference in bone metabolic activity between the summer and winter biopsies. Bone volume remained constant during winter. That is, osteoporosis did not develop in denning bears, contrary to observations in other animals. However, bone formation also continued despite three to four months of immobilization.

Maintenance of bone volume and continuation of bone formation have not been observed in any other immobilized animal. These data support the hypothesis that denning bears maintain calcium homeostasis, conserve bone volume and maintain coupled resorption and formation of bone despite months of immobilization, anuria and starvation. These findings provide the basis to continue this study and expand its scope.

I now plan to chart fully the metabolism of every bone in the bear, in order to gain a better understanding of the overall functioning of this bone metabolism. I have permission from the proper authorities to "use" certain bears that have become dangerous and will probably be destroyed. I will proceed in the same way as for my preliminary study: recording urine levels and doing comparative biopsies in winter and summer. I think that this work could lead to isolation of the substance peculiar to the bear and which is responsible for regulating the bone metabolism and preventing the development of osteoporosis. This substance could then be tested *in vitro* to see how it works biologically. Specific tests on rats would follow, with the active substances extracted from the substance isolated. This research, in its final stage, could take place in a laboratory I plan to set up.

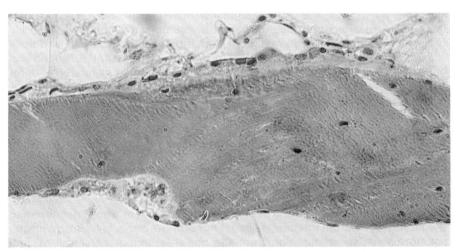

This slide illustrates the phenomenon of simultaneous resorption and formation of bone in a denning bear.

A new tracheostomy cannula

Dario de Oliveira Fauza

R. Marcondéssia, 301-Chácara Monte Alegre, 04645 São Paulo-SP, Brazil

Brazilian, born 4 October 1961. Medical residence trainee in paediatric surgery at the University of São Paulo Medical School. Educated in Brazil; M. D. from the University of São Paulo in 1985.

The first tracheostomy is said to have been performed by Asklepiades of Bythinien, who lived in Rome during the last century before the Christian era. Tracheostomies are nowadays a valuable surgical procedure and may in some cases offer the only way to save a patient's life. However, as with many other medical acts, tracheostomies may cause complications and even death.

Drawbacks of current cannula designs

Most cannulae consist of a curved tube which acts as a passage for air between the patient's trachea and the environment or an artificial respirator. Since it is often necessary to use positive inspiratory pressure by means of the above-mentioned respirators, this tube is enveloped at its caudal end by a small balloon inflatable with air or liquid, which, by adhering completely to the internal lining of the trachea by means of a cross-section of this organ, prevents the air insufflated by the respirator from escaping into the environment and/or into the larynx and pharynx; in this way, the air can be conducted to the caudal section of the trachea, the bronchi and pulmonary alveoli.

Many tracheostomy complications result from irritations caused by the tube itself and/or the cuff, although the greatest aggravating factors are the lesions to the trachea walls and/or to contiguous structures by the tube, ranging from simple ischaemia to actual perforations. Consequently, with a view to reducing irritation or injury caused by tracheostomy cannulae, lowering resistance to the air flow, and simplifying the cleaning of the cannula and the trachea, I have developed a new design of tracheostomy cannula.

New cannula design to prevent tracheostomy complications

This new design consists of a short curved tube with a circular cross-section which offers low resistance to air flow and is easy to clean. Since the caudal extremity of the tube will not reach the intersection between the trachea and the innominate

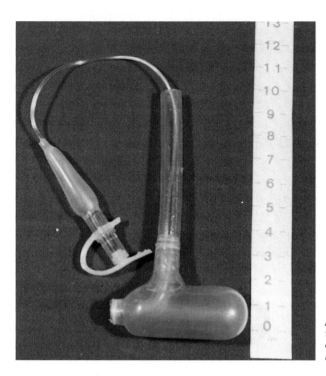

A prototype of the tracheostomy cannula made of polyvinyl, with its cuff inflated.

artery, the danger of lesions to this region is significantly reduced. The cuff is placed posteriorly to the tube, with the anterior or caudal portion closely adhering to it. Such positioning of the cuff should also help minimize the risk of tracheo-innominate fistula.

The exterior extension to the cuff forms a "collar" which prevents the escape of air insufflated under positive pressure through the tracheal stoma and may act as a "cushion" between the tube and the stoma, minimizing possible stomal lesions related to the movements, transmitted to the tube from the artificial respirator. This collar, together with the configuration of the proximal extremity of the tube, will also help to fix the cannula to the site, thereby dispensing with the uncomfortable use of tapes around the neck. Control of pressure, and also the insufflation and deflation of the cuff takes place by means of conduits. The cannula should be made from materials which are biologically inert, e. g., polytetrafluoroethylene, polyvinyl, etc.

Potential for further adaptation

This tracheostomy cannula may, starting from the basic concept described above, undergo certain changes. Its dimensions will vary according to the patient's anatomical characteristics. The tube may have two "central cavities" or, in other words, an internal removable lining for cases of acute obstruction and/or for facilitating cleaning, as is already the case with conventional models. In addition, the proximal extremity may be removable, and in such a case, it will be coupled to the tube, for instance, by means of threading. The "collar" may be produced in a number of configurations, and it may also be totally or partly fixed to the tube. Its mobility, should it not be totally fixed, should facilitate the sealing of the tracheal stoma, particularly when the dimensions of the trachea – principally the anterioposterior diameter – are extremely variable.

The cuff may be fitted with two separate compartments so that one compartment may be insufflated while the second is not, and vice-versa. This may occur alternately, which may decrease irritation to the tracheal wall without resulting in loss of function, as occurs in the case of periodic deflation of common cuffs. Also, the contour of the cuff may assume forms other than elliptical, according to the anatomical characteristics of the patient. Finally, in some cases it should be noted that it may be necessary to wear tapes around the neck if the cuff, with its "collar", and the movable proximal extremity are not enough to hold the cannula in place.

The functions of this tracheostomy cannula are thus the same as that of a "conventional" one. Its insertion into the patient is effected by means of the classic tracheostomy technique, and it is introduced into the trachea with the cuff totally deflated. Then, once it is in place, it is insufflated. As in existing models, insufflation and deflation, and also the control of pressure inside the cuff, are carried out by means of small sealable conduits that connect the interior of it to the environment.

This cannula has so far been tested only in animals. The first experimental results have already been presented at medical conferences in Brazil with good acceptance and have been reported in an article published in a medical journal.

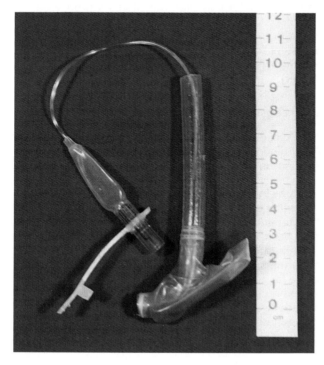

A prototype of Dario de Oliveira Fauza's cannula, with its cuff partially deflated.

A metal-plastic composite for architectural applications

Roger Questel

136 East 74 Street, New York, New York 10021, United States

American, born 30 June 1955. Conceptualizer and developer of patentable products for licensed sale. Educated in United States; B. A. (Environmental and Product Design) from Parsons School of Design in 1986.

Two years ago, in seeking to cast a number of wood carvings in bronze, I quickly learned that the cost was prohibitive. Realizing that this is the reason why sculpture alone is cast in bronze and why there were few bronze products available, I set out to find a less expensive way to solve the problem.

After six months of experimenting in a plastics factory owned by an indulgent proprietor, I managed to develop something that looked like a bronze bar of soap. I then conceived of a process which was applicable to the mass production of flat objects such as wall and floor tiles, panels, etc., at an extremely low cost. I further developed a series of steps for the polishing and finishing of the material. I found I could achieve the same effect with copper, brass and nickel silver (which looks like gun-metal or pewter).

Materials that match up to considerable demands

After an extensive patent search I discovered there was no overlapping prior-art and, in the summer of 1987, I filed for a patent. Thereafter, I subsequently filed international patent applications in 39 countries including Japan.

Interior tiles were chosen as the initial product for this material for a number of reasons. There are no metallic tiles presently available on the market. Compared to ceramic, the material is lighter and less breakable, making it easier to transport and install. It may be easily cut with a handsaw or shaped with a bench grinder. The process by which these tiles are formed does not subject them to the size limitation imposed upon ceramics (by kiln size and thickness requirements), allowing the product to have a far greater range of sizes and shapes. The range of images which can be produced is unlimited. The tiles need not be confined to a glazed two-dimensional surface design but can be cast in high relief. Each tile can be customized with a logo or exclusive design for commercial use in, for example, a restaurant or hotel.

The copper owl is a Questech reproduction of an ancient Egyptian image. The patina occurs naturally from exposure to the air and the oils on the skin of persons touching it, in the same way as with solid copper.

A wide range of potential uses

The metal-composite has a wide range of other applications in both the home and commercial construction market, for example, copper roof tiles or bronze doors. Both the copper roof and the bronze door have long been an architectural element reserved for churches, public buildings and exclusive town houses. Since my metal-composites require only a small fraction of the material used in a solid metal, they can be supplied at a price far below that of the solid metal equivalent.

Similar cast objects can be used as panels for the front of kitchen appliances, metallic mouldings, desk and coffee-table tops, bathroom and kitchen counters or decorative panelling for commercial interiors. The new material can be polished or patinated in exactly the same way as the actual metal. It can be designed as an indoor product which can meet stringent architectural fire codes or as an outdoor product which resists ultraviolet radiation in sunlight.

An expert opinion has indicated that, with proper development, this material could act as a skin for multi-storey structures. This is, I believe, the most exciting application of the material. The process itself can be successfully implemented with a variety of high-technology engineering plastics. Using technology developed largely by the aerospace industry, this material could be reinforced with a lightweight aluminium honeycomb or plastic matrix and mounted on a steel frame to form a lightweight building panel.

A modern style of ornament and surface decoration

Unfortunately, a modern style of ornament and surface decoration has been unable to evolve fully due to high labour costs and the shortage of craftsmen. An ornamented metallic facade would reflect light off its various facets, creating a warmer, more visually exciting urban landscape.

The tiles, mass-produced in moulds, can be easily imprinted with any pattern or design at no extra cost – a process which in solid metal would require the individual tooling of each tile.

The interior-design and architectural industry is currently experiencing a return to traditional values, particularly with regard to materials. A need has thus been created for interior design and architectural products that possess strong traditional qualities while solving problems that have made the large-scale specification of these traditional materials virtually prohibitive due to today's accelerated production schedules, performance, and cost-effectiveness requirements. In essence, I have taken well-known and trusted architectural materials, e.g. copper, bronze, pewter and brass – given them numerous advantages that they previously did not have (lightness of weight, dramatically reduced production time, and low cost, to name but a few) and reintroduced them to the market place at a time when these traditional materials are experiencing an unprecedented resurgence of interest.

In March 1989, Intaglio Ltd. was incorporated as a manufacturer of decorative architectural products. Intaglio's initial product offering is a distinctive collection of decorative metallic interior wall tiles and trim. Intaglio has copyrighted the name *Questech* as the name of the metal-composite material used in the manufacturing process. Our most recent installation was custom-designed bronze art-deco tiles and trim in New York's Radio City Music Hall.

This architectural tile is made of Questech, a patented composite material. The surface may be of real copper, bronze, pewter or brass. The tiles can be produced in any desired dimension or design.

The first Czechoslovak Pamir '88 – Himalaya '90 Medical Expedition

Juraj Čiernik

SNP 1445/38–11, 01701 Považská Bystrica, Czechoslovakia

Czechoslovak, born 4 April 1954. Head of the Theoretical Department of Engines Research Institute. Educated in Poland; graduated from Technical University ČVUT, Prague.

The need for adequate medical (both preventive and curative) support for very high-altitude expeditions has been demonstrated by the growing number of tragedies that have occurred. Moreover, the support system provided should be of optimal level and this presupposes exploring the problems of mountain-climbers in all their complexity. Pamir '88, the first Czechoslovak mountaineering expedition with a purely medical programme, has assessed the feasibility of biochemical laboratory work under base-camp conditions and studied the procedures for processing, preserving and transporting biological material.

In addition, it evaluated techniques of carbon dioxide inhalation during climbing, and detected a subsequent significant increase in pO_2. At altitudes of 7,000 m, most climbers displayed intraretinal bleeding and some suffered from myocardial ischaemia. The expedition studied changes of internal environment at various heights and also those during hospital testing (starvation, thirst, load). Some useful experience for doctor-climber co-operation was gained.

Monitoring the health of high-altitude climbers

The main aims of this expedition were to: verify the feasibility of operating a biochemical laboratory under high-altitude base-camp conditions; elucidate the part played by hypocapnia in high-altitude disease and investigate the prophylactic effect of carbon dioxide intake; devise new ways of assessing climbers' adaptation and efficiency; detect pathological changes in the fundus and in audiograms following high-altitude exposure; and undertake individual and group psychosocial studies among the expedition team.

The expedition team comprised 22 climbers who were accompanied by two doctors specialized in intensive care, an anaesthesiologist, an otolaryngologist, a surgeon and a technician in charge of the measuring equipment. Several firms lent the equipment for the tests, i.e., a portable Siemens electrocardiogram, a Corning blood gas analyzer and Boehringer chemical reagents. We also received

Scanning an electroencephalogram at an altitude of 4,800 m.

various equipment from Lab Systems, Baker Instruments and Konstrukta Trenčín.

One of the purposes of the expedition was to verify that, under the conditions at the base camp, i. e., at 3,600 m altitude, in the cold, with no electricity, etc., the equipment for taking the measurements worked properly and it was possible to perform reliable biochemical analyses. Another objective was to find a way to tell how well the climbers were adapted to high altitudes in order to select the best ones for the 1990 expedition.

The protective role of carbon dioxide at high altitudes

From a medical viewpoint, the purpose of the expedition was to determine precisely the role of hypocapnia (a fall in the level of arterial carbon dioxide) in the physical distress caused by high altitudes and to see if inhalation of carbon dioxide would help reduce it. We also wanted to ensure that the inhalation of carbon dioxide was not harmful to the human body and, finally, to see if any warning signs of clinical symptoms appeared in the eyes or ears after exposure to the sun.

The doctors on the the team did thorough medical and psychological tests both before, during and after the expedition. At each stage of the climb, they took blood and urine samples from the climbers and measured their pulse. These tests were performed as soon as the climbers arrived at the base camp at an altitude of 3,600 m, just before their climb to the high-altitude camp, as soon as they reached 4,800 m and, finally, 30 minutes later. A skier took the samples down to the base-camp each day.

The doctors also measured the partial pressures of carbon dioxide and oxygen in the arterial or capillary blood taken from the arteries and did biochemical tests on the venous blood to measure the concentrations of lactate, urea, creatinine and mineral elements. They also measured the pH of the urine. In order to determine cardiovascular response to physical effort, they took the climbers' pulse in each of the different circumstances.

The climbing proceeded in a systematic manner and, among other things, it was found that the climbers who had inhaled carbon dioxide did not suffer from any physical ill-being during the climb. When they arrived at the high-altitude camp, their urine was found to be more acid than that of the other climbers and partial pressures of oxygen and carbon dioxide in their arterial blood were higher. The inhalations also prevented a drop in the quantity of oxygen in the blood once they had rested from their exertion. The periodic respiration typical of hypocapnia was prevented by giving the climbers 0.25 l of carbon dioxide per minute during their sleep.

The examinations of the fundus will be repeated and trials will be made in which climbers with no medical qualifications are asked to examine the fundus of their colleagues in an attempt to detect early warnings of intraretinal bleeding before the appearance of clinical symptoms. This would mean that intraretinal bleeding should be considered an indication that the affected climber should immediately descend to a lower altitude. Finally, we will be searching for further markers of altitude acclimatization and distress.

The evaluation of the whole day's medical monitoring work is carried out at the base camp by members of the medical team.

Using the Vai language to promote literacy in Liberia

Dorith Minna Ofri-Scheps

38 rue de l'Athénée, 1206 Geneva, Switzerland

Swiss, born 3 June 1930. Secondary-school teacher, Department of Education in Geneva. Educated in Switzerland, Israel, Monrovia and Italy; attended the Universities of Rome, Ohio (Tel Aviv branch), Liberia, Geneva and Bern.

Throughout Africa, the fight against illiteracy faces much the same problems as those encountered in Liberia where: the vast majority of the population has poor common English, the national language; and the indigenous population is disinclined to acquire literacy in an African language by means of a non-endogenously developed writing, e. g., using Roman or Arabic alphabets.

If one defines literacy as the ability to read and write (in that order), then an essential prerequisite is the availability of reading-matter in the target-language. Consequently, the aim of this project is to write up a number of significant original Vai folk-texts in Vai characters, and develop the necessary software to permit the text to be typeset in Vai characters via the Liberian Government's integrated computer-system. Finally, the texts would be published and this would permit the Liberian Ministry of Education to experimentally institutionalize tuition of spoken and written Vai at primary schools throughout Vai country.

My work falls into two parts, one theoretical, one practical: the theoretical part is my doctoral thesis, and the practical part is to publish in typeset form major and original Vai folk-texts in Vai language and characters; a further aspect of the practical part is the development of the necessary tools for typesetting in Vai characters through the Liberian Government's computer. The project also has both linguistic and technological components: the linguistic task will be to select and edit the Vai folk-texts and prepare them for the reader; the technological task will be to produce software to type-set the texts.

In the study's conceptual approach, a culture is defined as the code which determines a group's way of knowing nature, both practically and symbolically. Scientific culture studies, then, articulate their description in terms of the culture's concepts, preferably in its own language, since its language identifies them best. Given that the culture's major, original folk-texts encapsulate those concepts, one cannot but embody them with a scientific study of the cultures; this

bai t. moore

9:30:86

maya i seneo
tobaa keme be
ilo keu hee
fila dende ba
nalowani dee
amu a kpemgba
kofeja gengee
amu anda i desi sa
anda i fili
fila dendee lo
amu wotoa kpafona ka
wo kea tetaa
numu kilaa kpoziani
mu temalo kpan
n mafo keima
menuu la
poo sane
1821 bulo
mua ya kule sunda dan
ke i be kila fe
n komu maya
mu koni i fele
wele tela me la
mu fa sale ba mu hee
maya i seneo
i sene maya i sene

maya hello
truly this one's
like a dream
the big sailing ship
came very slowly
and lay
along the sea
very plainly
they snatched you quickly
and put you on the ship
and you floated
to the west
and the path
between us closed
it was not til
yesterday the kwi
year in 1821
we heard from you
saying you were coming
therefore maya
if today we see you
our hearts are filled with joy
maya hello
hello maya hello

A lyric by a contemporary Vai poet Bai T. Moore (1920–1988) in Vai characters and accompanied by a phonetic transcript and English rendering.

does not occur as a matter of course, and practically never do the non-specialized descriptions follow up with texts in the language spoken by the studied culture-group's members. In other words, it took the theoretical work performed by my thesis to conceive of the necessity to prove a described culture's identity through the practical "availabilization" of its texts in their original form, for Africa too. This, in turn, led to the conception of their utility as instruments of autogenic literacy.

The linguistic component of the project

The linguistic segment will be carried out in collaboration with Vai speakers with a more-than-superficial knowledge of the script and deeply steeped in their culture. The selection of the texts will be based on three criteria: they must have been transmitted traditionally through an oral change; two or more written renderings must be available for consultation; and they must be demonstrably of Vai origin (i.e. not borrowed from non-Vai sources). Once the texts have been chosen, it will be necessary to segment them since a particularity of Vai is that it is written in such a way that even sentence identification is difficult. Consequently, they need to be segmented, not only into sentences but also into units of meaning from the logical multiplication of which they actually result.

The technological component of the project

The technological job, i.e. the creation, or adaptation, of software for the Vai language is to be carried out by a Japanese systems engineer, seconded to Liberia by Japan within the framework of the Japanese Overseas Corporation of Volunteers (JOCV) programme.

His task will be either to adapt existing Vai software to the requirements of the Liberian computer system as it exists now, or the creation of new software. Creation of new software will be envisaged only if we cannot come to terms with the authors of existing Vai software; should this be the case, it would take the engineer about four months. Otherwise, he will adapt the existing Vai software so that it will operate with the dot-matrix printer system employed by the Liberian Government computers; this will be done under an agreement with the software's current users at the Institute of Liberian Languages (TILL).

The engineer will have to learn the Vai characters, a task which JOCV Director Mr. Minoru Yoshimura and I hope I can undertake very soon. Should TILL receive authorization to share their product with us, the JOCV engineer would be taught the Vai syllabary and the Vai phonemic structure, and also be provided with the diskette/disk of Vai character software, so that he can prepare the job even while not in Liberia. Eventually, I will learn from him all that I can about the Vai software. Subsequently, he and I, and my chosen Vai collaborators on this project, will work out the texts selected for the collection, and produce the blueprint I have in view as an instrument of Vai literacy, during our work together in Vai country.

Mrs. Dorith Ofri-Scheps in a working session in the Nepeja house in Monrovia. She is shown together with Mr. M. Cole, an expert in Vai writing, and Mr. M. Davis a young collaborator.

Strategic significance of a dominant male-sterile gene in wheat breeding

Deng Jingyang
Honourable Mention
The Rolex Awards for Enterprise – 1990

Institute of Crop Breeding and Cultivation, Chinese Academy of Agricultural Sciences, 30 Bai Shi Qiao Lu, West Suburbs, 100081 Beijing, People's Republic of China

Chinese, born 5 May 1916. Senior researcher, Institute of Crop Breeding and Cultivation, Chinese Academy of Agricultural Sciences. Educated in Switzerland; M. D. from University of Geneva in 1959.

Wheat is a self-pollinating cereal: each ear has several flowers that are both male and female. The male organs (anthers), which produce the pollen, are right beside the female organs which produce the grain following fertilization. This characteristic is very useful in maintaining the quality of an already-selected pure strain, but it creates difficulties in any attempt to improve wheat by crossing one kind with another. In that case, the problem is actually to prevent self-pollination. Selective breeders have therefore long been searching for a way to produce genetic male sterility in wheat. In other words, they want to obtain plants that produce functional ovaries but no pollen, which would make large-scale selection easy.

I currently possess strains of wheat that carry just such a gene for male sterility. The first plant of this kind was discovered in 1972 during an intensive research campaign where hundreds of people went looking in the fields for a plant without pollen. Thousands were found, but only one turned out to possess a male sterility that was transmissible to its descendants. It was Gao Zhongli, a young botanist of 20, who made this discovery in the province of Taigu. But the gene proved difficult to control and impossible to stabilize in lines of wheat. By dint of research and patience, I managed to obtain a stable line in 1979, and firmly established that the reason it had no pollen was because it contained a single dominant gene for male sterility. All kinds of cross-breeding experiments were instituted.

Taigu wheat gene research and breeding strategy

In the 1970s, genic male-sterile genes were recommended for breeding programmes, because they would make it possible to build an intercrossing population with any desirable gene basis at modest expense. However, the material to implement this strategy was not available. The Taigu genic male-sterile wheat discovered in China has a number of outstanding characteristics that go to meet these requirements: the male-sterile plant, if bagged, produces no seeds; segre-

Drought resistance: planted in an experimental plot with no irrigation, the selected fertile plant grew normally whereas most of the varieties from conventional breeding withered and died.

gation for fertility begins from the F1 hybrid; if the male-sterile plant is crossed with a common wheat variety the segregation ratio will be one male-sterile to one fertile; fertility is clear cut without intermediate types; and the fertility of the progeny of the fertile plant is breeding-true fertile.

Wheat is a self-pollinated crop; and its advantages in competition for existence and breeding are that desirable genotypes can be more easily maintained, reproduced, propagated and used in production; but its defect is that it is difficult to realize crossing between individuals, so there is less chance for gene exchanges. These advantages and defects of self-pollinated crops are just opposite to those in cross-pollinated crops. The male-sterile plant of the Taigu genic male-sterile wheat produces seeds by cross-pollination, so it is favourable for gene recombinations, and the other half fertile offsprings segregate owing to the cross-pollination of the sterile plant and tend to become homozygous after selfing, so in other words, it is favourable for breeding new varieties. By using the Taigu genic male-sterile wheat as a crossing tool, breeders can combine the merits of selfing and cross-pollinated crops in breeding to make the development of wheat breeding advance more rapidly.

Male abortion of Taigu genic male-sterile wheat is thorough and stable, it shows no linkage with any undesirable genes after observations for many years. Once open-pollinated, every fertilized flower is a hybrid, so combinations are abundant and unaccountable. In breeding, this material can be used in simple crossing, multiple crossing, complex crossing, stepped crossing or back-crossing; all these would be revealed with high efficiency at a very low expense, but its most important value is the use in recurrent selection in which desirable individuals are selected in a population for mating and the elimination of undesirable offspring and therefore undesirable genes, and indistinct hybridization.

Over recent years, a wide range of cross-breeding experiments have been instituted in order to improve the lines already grown in China and transmit this gene in other crossings designed, for example, to transmit resistance to salty earth, disease, or drought. In Cangzhou, the dry region on Hebei Province, where recurrent selections have been carried out for a few years, through natural and artificial selection, we obtained a number of fertile plants which, under annual rainfall conditions of 80–150 mm, had normal functional leaves. Also in Cangzhou, Hebei Province, in a national test of salt tolerance, Taigu wheat materials were found to grow normally and produce seeds having good agronomic characteristics under 0.5% total salt content. Finally, there is some hope that some newly developed lines will be resistant to scab – the "wheat cancer". Another contribution of the Taigu wheat is using it to exploit wheat gene resources which are claimed by many wheat breeders to have been virtually fully exploited.

The prospect of international co-operation

In view of the growing demand for food, the search for innovation in agro-technology is an urgent one. The Taigu genic male-sterile wheat controlled by a dominant genic male-sterile gene is of major significance in opening up new ways for worldwide agricultural breeding. Although I have managed a research group of more than 100 members in 44 research units in China, I think that our work will advance better and quicker if we can institute co-operation with other nations. This will entail making arrangements to deal with certain problems (e.g., the ban placed by the Chinese Government on the export of this valuable germ plasm) and establishing the necessary organizational and administrative structures. However, we are sure these obstacles can be overcome and that this gene can be applied more widely for the benefit of mankind.

In an experimental plot with 0.5% total salt content, some fertile plants produced seeds, but the control variety (right) died.

Rituals and traditional medicines for "repeater children" in West Africa

Stuart J. Edelstein

Department of Biochemistry, University of Geneva, Science Building II, 30 Quai Ernest Ansermet, 1211 Geneva 4, Switzerland

American, born 6 September 1941. Professor and Director, Department of Biochemistry, Faculty of Sciences, University of Geneva. Educated in the United States and France; Ph. D. (Biochemistry) from the University of California, Berkeley, in 1967.

The dramatic transformation of human red blood cells into sickle-shaped structures was first observed early in this century; and during the 1940s, a mutant form of haemoglobin was identified as the component of sickled cells responsible for their bizarre shape. These stiff but fragile cells are now known to be the result of a genetic disease, sickle cell anaemia, occurring almost exclusively among individuals of African descent. The disease, which greatly reduces life expectancy, is present when the mutant haemoglobin is inherited from both parents; individuals who inherit the mutant from only one parent are carriers but effectively symptom-free. In Africa, the incidence is high with about 50,000 new cases being born each year. The nature of the sickling process is now understood in minute detail and has permitted the development of prenatal diagnosis, although this has had little impact; however, no treatment has been developed.

"Repeater children" in Nigeria and sickle cell anaemia

Since the disease has existed for so many thousands of years in Africa, it was thought that some useful natural products with therapeutic activities may have been discovered and could be of value throughout the world. I therefore embarked on field work in rural Africa to find children with sickle cell anaemia who were identified in African cultural terms and to study the rituals and traditional medicines applied to these children.

I commenced the project among the Igbo ethnic group of Nigeria which has a population of some 20 million that remains only modestly urbanized. Sickle carriers make up 25% of the Igbo population, which corresponds to an incidence of one sickle cell newborn out of every 64. The Igbos have a concept called *ogbanje* (loosely translated "repeater children") referring to the successive deaths of several siblings, each dying before the birth of the next – and this concept is a major preoccupation of village life. As my research progressed, the idea of a connection between *ogbanje* began to emerge as a reasonable hypothesis: as would be expected for a genetic disease, the incidence was within

42

Temporary clinic for blood testing set up in a primary school. (Stuart Edelstein is seated behind the table).

particular families; and children designated as *ogbanje* had a bossing of the skull that is among the typical symptoms of sickle cell anaemia.

In addition, among rituals of a symbolic nature, and practices involving herbal medicines, rural Igbo healers amputate the last phalanx of the left little finger of suspected *ogbanje* children. Since painful swelling of the hands and feet (dactylitis) is often one of the symptoms of sickle cell anaemia, striking infants in the age range 1–4 years, a certain logic is apparent for a society that seeks to attack the site of a bodily affliction, perhaps to eliminate some unspecified agent.

However, it became obvious that *ogbanje* is not always synonymous with sickle cell anaemia. In addition, the link between the two phenomena was found to vary from village to village according to the activity of particular healers and local traditions. Following the initial studies, it was apparent that a much wider inquiry would be needed to establish the extent of correlation between *ogbanje* and sickle cell anaemia in different localities. Contacts were established, therefore, in various parts of the Igbo territory in order to resolve this issue and will be pursued in future studies. In addition, since sickle cell anaemia is prevalent throughout the African tropics, the scope of the research was extended to determine whether similar practices occur among different ethnic groups in other parts of Nigeria and in other West African countries.

"Repeater children" theme widespread in West Africa

From this information, the concept of "repeater children" emerged as a recurrent theme of West African customs although, surprisingly, it was apparently never previously investigated on a cross-cultural scale. Among all of the ethnic groups studied, the idea of a "spirit" repeatedly plaguing the same parents is a general feature, although different ethnic groups react with different rituals. In many cases minor amputations or other body marks are utilized, but the specifics vary considerably. The common feature of marking some part of the body arises from the belief that upon death of a marked "repeater child" a corresponding mark will appear on the body of the subsequent child born in the same family. Seeing the alleged mark on the new infant, the parents would presumably be forewarned to limit their attachment to the child and to perform certain rituals. The markings may also be carried out on the corpse of a recently deceased child.

The nature and origin of the birthmarks involved are unclear. Whatever their ultimate explanation, the rituals surrounding "repeater children" merit investigation in their own right for their remarkable ethnological content and geographic expanse.

In conclusion, for areas of tropical Africa where the sickle mutation is particularly prevalent, the specific symptoms of sickling have probably not passed unnoticed and some traditional medicines may have been applied that could provide useful knowledge for new therapeutic approaches. In order to pursue this possibility, an African designation of sickle cell anaemia is needed and the widespread incidence of the "repeater children" phenomenon may provide such a concrete indication within the traditional African conceptual framework. It is not yet established from my preliminary study how closely "repeater children" correspond to sickle cell anaemia, nor the extent to which the connection may vary from one ethnic group to another and even from one region to another in the same ethnic group. On the basis of the information already collected, future investigations can now be focused more clearly and attention gradually shifted to herbal medicines applied to "repeater children" that might yield natural products of therapeutic value in the treatment of sickle cell disease.

Ogbanje *child missing last phalanx of her left little finger.*

Standards for conserving early American scientific instruments

David V. St. John

Benchmark Instruments, 317 Maple Street, Franklin, Massachusetts 02038, United States

American, born 11 June 1933. Technical Director at Berger Instruments, Massachusetts. Educated in United States; industrial training in the field supplemented by evening classes and personal study.

Restoration of ancient objects is an intrusive process. When it must be done, an opportunity presents itself to gather detailed technical information about materials, designs, precision, innovative features from the period and specific details that separate the maker from his peers. Without guidelines, established terminology and definitive procedure, little information can be secured by one practitioner for use by another. The technique should be consistent, produce maximum results, provide historical advantage, and impart no damage to the artifact. In the final analysis, the findings of one conservator should be reproducible by another. Documentation should follow in a firm format to enable those who are entrusted with the preservation of an artifact to maintain and extend the original restoration effort for many years.

The need for a standard of practice for the conservation of early American surveying instruments was something that I recognized immediately but the magnitude and details of the work developed over a period of years. The proposed standard is intended to be used by a diverse group of professionals within the conservation community, as well as collectors and historians. To facilitate communication, a thorough glossary of terms and definitions will accompany the standard. Such terms will relate to the restoration process, preservation in general, specific problems, the instruments and components. Communication is a vital aspect of the general acceptance of the standard. Terms must be clearly understood and in many cases accompanied with drawings or photographs to provide a clearer understanding of the subject. In certain cases it will be necessary to define the term in its historical context, and the modern definition.

The instruments

Although the intent is to restrict my work to surveying instruments, other types have been accepted for restoration from the same period of interest. These include: surveyors' compasses; microscopes; plane table alidades; transits;

LA Buff & Buff transit manufactured in 1900. David V. St. John restored the instrument, which is owned by the State of Massachusetts, in an effort to bring more public attention to the legacy of the instrument maker and surveyor.

planimeters, etc. Among the above instruments there is a mix of materials and the processing of these materials must often be constrained to the period of the instrument maker. One does not use 20th century technique on an early 19th century artifact.

Characteristics that differentiate one maker from another are important from a historical perspective. For the most part these details are easily captured for reference. The collection of more intimate detail provides historical advantage and a sensitive exposure to the work of the maker throughout his life.

Studies which add this type of historical advantage essentially are never complete. The details take years to accumulate but eventually a substantial fund of knowledge will exist for others to study. The present characteristics being collected include tabulations of: spindle tapers used between 1800 and 1900; thread classification of different makers; spirit level vial configurations, glass type and condition, etc.

Documentation

The use of appropriate camera equipment and lighting provides an important record of the artifact, its details and condition before, during and after treatment. The use of colour and orthochromatic film captures intimate characteristics which define, in part, the mind of the maker and his execution of thought. Such information provides sensitive historical advantage.

Having been trained as an instrument maker, I have personal insight into the type of details which should be collected to fully characterize an instrument and provide data to gain understanding of the thoughts and abilities of the maker. A

Final collimation of optical system for functional restoration of artifact.

systematic examination enables the conservator to retrieve sensitive information which often proves valuable in the determination of provenance. Selected features help greatly to identify the maker and the period in which the instrument was fabricated. In addition to securing information of historical advantage, an appropriate examination provides the necessary information on the state of condition or the deterioration of an artifact. Each restoration is, in a real sense, a design task in reverse.

One of the objectives of establishing a standard of practice is to secure detailed technical and physical information from each artifact for future reference. Aside from routine written and photographic documentation, detailed drawings are made of components and assemblies of each instrument. This fund of knowledge provides the advantage for component replacement as a service to institutions and collectors.

Apprenticeship programme for the future

Early in the development of the standard of practice, it was clearly recognized that a definitive training programme would be necessary to continue the work for future years. Meetings were held with the Massachusetts Department of Labor and it was agreed in principle that the training provided through Benchmark Instruments, an organization which I have founded, would qualify as a state-approved apprentice programme. Efforts were initiated to generate the necessary elements for training which would entail a study of subjects related to the maintenance, repair and calibration of sophisticated modern surveying instruments. Included would be the requirements of the standard of practice for the conservation of early scientific instruments.

Dolphin-assisted therapy of the neurologically disabled

Betsy Smith

67 NW 21 Street, Homestead, Florida 33030, United States

American, born 24 February 1945. Associate Professor, Social Work Department, Florida International University. Educated in United States; B. A. from State University of New York, Buffalo, in 1969.

A project on dolphins and autism entitled "Dolphins Plus Autism" which began in 1981, has been designed from research conducted at the Wometco Seaquarium to verify observed unique responses between Atlantic bottlenose dolphins and neurologically impaired individuals. It established the feasibility of using this dolphin as a facilitator in eliciting communicative responses from autistic persons.

Interaction between autistic children and dolphins

The first phase of the Dolphins Plus Autism project was a case study intended to: use dolphins to establish an environment in which the autistic person could act in a spontaneous manner; use dolphin and human facilitators to expand the display of appropriate communicatory behaviour; and demonstrate that this behaviour can be retained and repeated. Phase two of the project worked with other autistic children and conducted exploratory swims for blind and blind-deaf children and adolescents with a variety of learning disabilities.

Simultaneously, a survey gathered data on experience of the public of aquatic contact with these dolphins to provide so called "normal response" information.

In summer 1987, the Dolphins Plus Autism Camp was held to explore in a more scientific manner the effects of dolphin-assisted therapy on seven non-verbal, severely autistic adolescent males. The goals of the camp were to increase appropriate social responses and initiate spontaneous behaviour. Although the project produced little statistically significant data, it did provide some startling therapeutic responses and laid ground for the development of a comprehensive theory on the subject. During summer 1989, dolphin contact sessions will be held with a control group, and follow-up sessions for the Dolphin group at the Dolphins Plus location in Key Largo, Florida, will also be held.

Autistic children often have an aversion to touch. Dr. Betsy A. Smith and Bobby introduce David to touching by letting him wear gloves (Photo: Gloria Leigh O'Connell).

Developing dolphin projects in other countries

During the months of July and August 1990, a pilot therapeutic programme for students of the Perkins School for the Blind in Massachusetts will be held at Dolphins Plus in Key Largo, Florida, to explore the effects of ultrasound on the blind and deaf children and to develop a therapeutic protocol for this disabled group. In May-September 1991, under the auspices of the International Society for the Preservation of the Tropical Rainforest (ISPTR), Dolphins Plus Autism and Dolphins Plus the Blind projects will be established in Lagoa da Prata, Brazil, a lake containing dolphins rescued from life-threatening situations.

The Society for the Preservation of the Amazon River Dolphin (SPARD) and a small staff will set up therapy and research programmes, and Brazilian professionals will be trained to continue the therapy year-round whilst the staff of SPARD will oversee the continuing collection of research data.

In May-August 1992, a Dolphins Plus Autism programme will be organized jointly by my team and some Australian colleagues in Nambucca Heads, Australia, under the auspices of the International Cetacean Education Research Centre (ICERC), in which a group of autistic children, prepared by adapted aquatic specialists from Vic Swim of Melbourne, will be put in contact with wild dolphins off the coast of New South Wales. It is expected that after this initial contact with friendly pods of wild dolphins, the Australians will be able to run an ongoing programme at the Centre and continue to amass data. Facilities and on-site resources have already been committed by the ICERC.

Potential for effective therapeutic results

We believe that the results of these programmes will: provide concrete methodologies to be used with dolphins and disabled children; compile initial data about the possible involvement of electrical, magnetic and acoustic energy interactions and exchanges between the children, therapists and dolphins; enhance our understanding of the role of aquatic environment in the therapy; and expand our understanding of man's connection with the other beings on the planet by exploring the many faceted relationship with the only "wild" animal that seeks out the companionship of man.

Dr. Betsy A. Smith places Roger in the water with the dolphins for his first aquatic interaction (Photo: Gloria Leigh O'Connell).

Anabiosis. Success in a simple experimental model

León Herszage

Honourable Mention
The Rolex Awards for Enterprise – 1990
Viamonte 1620 2' C, 1055 Buenos Aires, Argentina

Argentine, born 19 December 1931. Head, Department of Abdominal Wall
Surgery, Hospital I. Pirovano. Educated in Argentina; M. D. from University of
Buenos Aires in 1968.

We have been researching the use of the healing properties of sugar (saccharose)
in the treatment of infected wounds in humans since 1986 and have demonstrated the effectiveness of sugar as an antiseptic treatment. The findings also
clarified host immune-system response and allowed us to develop a clinical test to
measure immune reaction.

In 1982, we began applying our sugar treatment method on agricultural and
domestic warm and cold-blooded animals, and obtained the same type of
response as in human beings. Our conclusion was that all injured live tissue
should respond in the same way to an aqueous saccharose system: moreover,
lesions in plants also reacted in a manner similar to those in animals.

Our analysis of the phenomenon was that: sugar dehydrates cells with which it
is in contact in a close relation with the water in the solution. This increases
osmotic pressure and the cell is plasmolysed. The limit of liquid loss from the cell is
determined by the physical properties of the saccharose solution and when this
limit is reached, the plasmolysed cell status may be maintained indefinitely.

The next step was to determine whether the "dead" cell then lost its essential
vitality or whether it was only dormant; was this in fact a case of anabiosis –
resuscitation after apparent death. Our experiments with experimental models
of skin, heart and kidney proved problematic and consequently we turned to the
cornea which is easy to manipulate and re-implant without rehydration and
which readily rehabilitates *in situ*; it is easy to determine its functionality macro-
scopically, and it can readily be removed in order to test microscopically.

Experimental procedures

Experiments were carried out at the Buenos Aires City Zoo Laboratory using
receptor and donor rabbits (2–4 kg) and pigs (6–10 kg) immediately prior to
their being slaughtered for food. Eyes were kept in non-sterilized jars full of over-

51

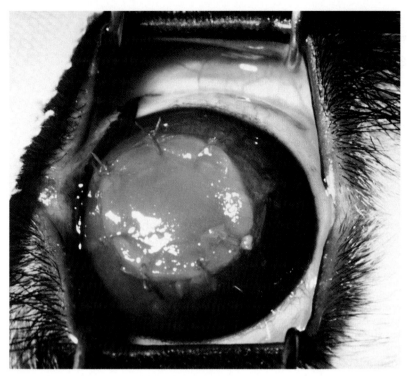

A homologous cornea transplant showing the whole dehydrated cornea, hyper-hydrated and opaque.

saturated saccharose-water solution (250g/100cm^3), hermetically closed and stored at room temperature. All samples were kept for 90 to 210 days, before being implanted.

Implants were made in 12 animals: eight of which were rabbit-to-rabbit total homologous implants, two were rabbit-to-rabbit lamellar homologous implants, two were rabbit-to-pig lamellar heterologous implants. No medication was administered. Autopsy was carried out on one homologous case after 48 hours. In one lamellar homologous case, autopsy was performed after 360 days. In both heterologous cases, the eyes were removed after 80 and 90 days respectively.

Results

The preserved corneas were placed over the receptor surface, clearly showing their transparency. As the operation progressed, increasing opacity of the cornea indicated over-hydration. However, a progressive renewed transparency finally appeared; and was total and stable at the end of the second month. Vision was recovered. The scar was noticeable after six months, but one year after it was almost invisible. Since we had proved that the tissues kept in our solution, were losing a great part of their antigenicity, we decided to implant donor rabbit corneas in pigs. The grafts began to become transparent again at the start of the second month and recovered their function at about eight weeks, showing no evidence of surgical scarring in either case.

Further research

It is of considerable importance that this project should be continued until completion in 1993. It is difficult to raise funds in Argentina, and it is necessary to begin research in cellular biology, biochemistry and immunology to understand this amazing property of sugar. The fact that these grafts (skin, embryo, etc.) are practically never rejected leads me to believe that the graft tissue loses its antigenicity after immersion for long periods of time in a saturated sugar solution – a factor which could be of considerable significance for organ grafts.

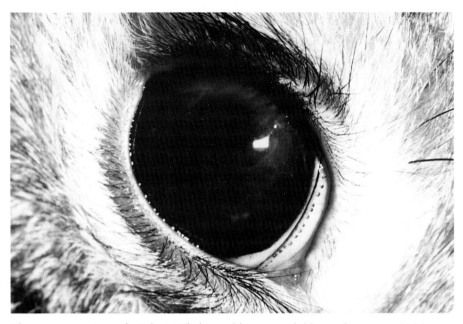

The same cornea transplant six months later with recovered vision and a cornea which is once again transparent.

Visceral leishmaniasis on a Colombian Indian reservation

Darvin Scott Smith

Centro Internacional de Entrenamiento e Investigaciones Médicas "CIDEIM", Avenida 1 Norte No. 3–03, 5390 Cali, Colombia

American, born 4 January 1963. Investigator at the Centro Internacional de Entrenamiento e Investigaciones Médicas. Educated in United States and Colombia; M. S. (Tropical Public Health) from School of Public Health, Harvard University, in 1987.

Leishmania are protozoan parasites which have a life cycle that involves both insect and vertebrate hosts, and man is an accidental part of the cycle, particularly in the New World. The pathology caused by this parasite in man ranges from self-healing cutaneous lesions and disfiguring mucocutaneous ulcers to a visceral form of the disease that is fatal if left untreated. The disease is worldwide, found in jungle and arid regions of Central and South America, desert regions of the Middle East and on the alluvial plains of China. The worldwide prevalence has been estimated to be from 12 million to 20 million.

The public health problem that leishmaniasis poses is significant, and this disease has been singled out by the World Health Organization for special research and control efforts. However, general public health measures are particularly difficult to formulate because the disease involves reservoirs and vectors whose characteristics and interactions with man vary greatly. Furthermore, demonstrating the parasite for clinical diagnosis and characterizing its ecology in the interest of implementing public health measures has proved a difficult task; the parasite has to be cultured in a special medium for a considerable period of time, or it must be grown in animals and then identified definitively. These methods are slow, time-consuming and not very sensitive.

Application of DNA probe technologies

High technology and molecular biology techniques may offer solutions to many of these parasitic diseases; but much remains to be done in applying proven methods and developing protocols that enable progress in the field and actually alter behaviours that will control disease. Use of a DNA probe in this type of enquiry will address many of the difficulties encountered using classical techniques. On the public health programme and clinical level, accurate differential diagnosis is important because the drug to treat this disease is expensive, toxic and not readily available; it cannot be given presumptively. Therefore, more sensitive and less invasive detection methods attainable through the use of

Emaciated dogs with long nails and general unhealthy appearance are identified in the village centre. When the most suspect dogs are culled, the owners are interviewed and samples are taken from the dogs.

DNA probes would be useful. Application and adaptation of molecular biology techniques (such as DNA probes) in *Leishmania,* to the actual problems presented in the field would result in more appropriate control and prevention, with fewer side effects to the victims and to the environment.

The principle of *Leishmania* identification using DNA techniques and possibilities for its application in epidemiology is well described. I propose to apply these techniques in an Indian reservation near Córdoba, Colombia, and develop a methodology for their specific application in defining the ecology of *Leishmania* involved, including insects, dogs and patients.

Because patient samples for visceral leishmaniasis are difficult to obtain, the utility of the probe as a diagnostic tool in these circumstances will largely centre around the incrimination of reservoir hosts, and the detection of infected vectors. These probes may subsequently prove useful for the confirmation of diagnosis in patients.

Other closely related endeavours to the application of DNA probes in the field will include: improving the design of a dot blot applicator suitable for field use in the detection of *Leishmania* in samples; testing different filter membranes to improve the sensitivity of the test for each phase of the parasite's cycle; and a specific protocol for the characterization of this parasite.

Expected results and further application

A clearer picture of the ecology of *Leishmania donovani chagasi* will emerge once a sensitive and specific method of probing DNA is established. The availability of this information will enable public health measures for the control of disease to be implemented. Thus, definite options can be considered for this particular focus, like eradication of infected reservoirs where appropriate, and control of vectors. Also, concrete plans for a dot blot applicator will be worked out so that the apparatus is field-tested, modified, standardized and available for routine epidemiological studies.

Probes will not be appropriate in all situations, for example in a clinical setting for diagnostics. Because it is a relatively new technique, its application may be initially more costly than classical methods and require more training and sophistication in the laboratory than is routinely available. However, the benefit from the epidemiological and ecological questions that can potentially be addressed justifies their application in this setting.

Results obtained from the analysis of the ecology of this infectious disease possibly will be applicable to foci of the same disease in other parts of the world. Furthermore, some of the tools and methods developed may prove useful in elucidating other infectious diseases, since the principle of DNA probes and their application in diagnosis is the same. Thus it is a worthy investment with possible far-reaching implications for the betterment of public health in tropical zones.

Examining a highly suspect case of visceral leishmaniasis. This seven-year old girl lives in an endemic zone, near lush vegetation where the Lutzomyia *vectors are found. She has severe ascites.*

A video-collar to study aquatic fauna: A view from the animal's back

Greg Marshall

Marine Sciences Research Center, State University of New York at Stony Brook,
Stony Brook, New York 11794, United States

American, born 14 October 1958. Manager of a research project in Belize.
Educated in United States; M. Sc. (Marine Environmental Sciences-Ecology) from
State University of New York, Stony Brook, in 1988.

The inspiration for this project came to me from a close diving encounter with a shark. I saw how, housed in a streamlined package attached to an animal's back, a video camcorder would record images from the animal's perspective. This "video-collar" would, for the first time, enable scientists to know an animal's location and activity, finally relieving us of the need to infer behaviour from blips on a radio-telemetry grid. A visual record of the animal's responses to its physical environment, and its interactions with other organisms would accompany maps of its movements. It was at that moment that I felt the promise of a whole new world of ecologies to explore. To virtually swim with sharks, whales, sea turtles, pinnipeds, and even alligators and crocodiles seemed a profoundly compelling objective. It still is.

A vision takes shape

In an effort to facilitate development of the video-collar method, I chose to begin this work not with sharks but with the larger sea turtle species and the American alligator. These animals are relatively easily handled, can be pulled from the water and are stalwart. Additionally, all seven species of sea turtles are endangered or threatened and therefore demand immediate research attention. Alligator populations, on the other hand, have begun to make a resurgence and are now labeled as "nuisances" in many populated areas. This has brought about management policies focused on wild alligator harvests, despite limited baseline research to identify the species' minimal ecological requirements.

The behavioural ecology of these species under water, beyond observable nests, nesting beaches and basking sites, is still mostly inferred from radio and satellite tracking data, gut content analysis and some few fortuitous *in situ* observations. In order to develop and implement appropriate management strategies for these species, an urgent need exists to assess behaviour and ecology under conditions in which these animals spend the vast majority of their time... in and under the water.

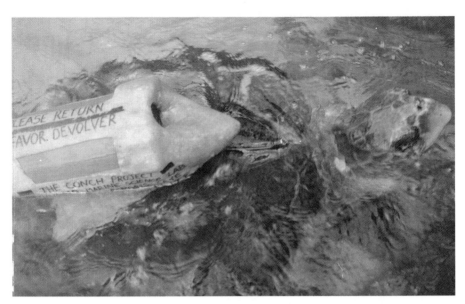

Early prototype video-collar on a loggerhead sea turtle in Belize, Central America (1987).

The video-collar as I conceived it is an imaging video-system which, when harnessed to animals, records behavioural responses to factors in their visual field; the term was derived from its conceptual precursor, the radio-collar.

Over the past two years I have developed a video-collar system based on a very simple 8-mm video camcorder which, being small in size and in a streamlined underwater housing, has little adverse effect on animal behaviour. There are three basic components: the video camcorder and housing; the harness and release mechanisms and the retrieval system. The video camcorder has been reduced to its barest components and reconfigured to fit a streamlined profile. The epoxy-fibreglass housing is designed to withstand hydrodynamic pressure to some 1,000 m of depth and, for example, its lens port is an optically clear Lexan plate 2.5 cm thick and 5 cm in diameter. Video recording is initiated at any specified time using a simple electronic timing circuit. Once activated, the unit records animal activity for two hours, either consecutively or on a time-lapse.

A new view of the marine world

Animals to be harnessed with the videocollar are captured and handled by the least disturbing means possible. For example, female sea turtles can be harnessed as they return to the water after nesting, when released from accidental entrapment in fishing gear or when caught swimming. Alligators can be cage trapped, snared or lassoed.

Video-collar harnesses were designed for both sea turtles and alligators in preliminary experiments. For alligators, 5 cm wide, rubberized-nylon webbing straps wrap across the chest, shoulder and forelimbs in a simple dorso-ventral cross pattern. The video housing system rests atop the animal's shoulders. On sea turtles, the system is attached to the shell apex by light stainless steel cable secured between forward and aft hooks at the shell margin. Both harnesses are adjustable to fit animals of a variety of sizes and can be secured within approximately one minute.

In order to assess behavioural patterns with respect to animal age, size and sex, basic morphological data will be gathered from video-collared animals. Following release, the animals will be visually tracked at a discrete distance for as long as possible and, thereafter, they will be tracked by the radio transmitter housed in the unit's tail section until the experiment is terminated. This occurs when, after the predetermined recording period, the harness releases from the animals by mechanical detachment. Automatic release is mediated by the degradation of galvanic elements at critical points on the harness. Dissolving magnesium elements serve this purpose in sea water, as does cellophane in fresh water. Once detached, the slightly buoyant video-collar floats to the water surface and is retrieved by radio triangulation.

This project will assess the utility of the video-collar method in providing new insights into the *in situ* behaviour of large marine and aquatic fauna. The method may afford us an opportunity to significantly increase our knowledge of these animals in a time when such knowledge may be critical to their survival.

Video-collar being deployed on an American alligator in central Florida (March 1989).

Human-powered helicopter

Andrew Zsolnay

Box 7554, Burbank, California 91510, United States

American, born 2 November 1941. Manufacturing Research Specialist Senior at the Composite Development Centre of Lockheed Aeronautical Systems, Burbank, California. Educated in United States; Degree in Chemistry from University of California, Los Angeles, in 1970 and Registered Professional Engineer in 1977.

The goal of this project is to build a human-powered helicopter to be flown by a single pilot. Flight demonstration is planned for late 1991. The project is undertaken by engineering students at California Polytechnic State University at San Luis Obispo, United States, applying the latest aerodynamic design principles and advanced structural materials. I am donating my time and expertise in fabricating light-weight aircraft structures to assure the success of the programme.

A five-century challenge

Humans have dreamed of taking to the skies under the power of their own muscles for thousands of years. While the feasibility of human-powered fixed-wing aircraft has been successfully demonstrated in recent years, including the historic flight in 1987 from Crete to mainland Greece by *Daedalus*, the challenge of human-powered helicopter flight still beckons. Leonardo da Vinci was the first person to conceive a human-powered helicopter in his sketch books. Over five centuries have passed and only now has technology caught up with da Vinci's dream by the development of advanced helicopter theory and the advent of strong, light-weight structural materials. In 1980, recognizing the feasibility of human-powered helicopter flight, the American Helicopter Society (AHS) made this offer: a US$ 25,000 prize for the first rotary-wing aircraft that can climb to a height of 3 m and hover there for 60 seconds without drifting more than 5 m in any direction. The prize has never been claimed.

Students of the California Polytechnic State University (Cal Poly) desire to pioneer a new realm of flight: the human-powered helicopter. They have designed an aircraft that is a showcase of modern aerodynamic theory and features light-weight structural materials to achieve vertical flight with approximately 0.5 horse power from the pilot. The aircraft is named da *Vinci III* to honour the great renaissance artist and engineer. The first flight is planned for late 1991, marking a decade of building and testing human-powered helicopters at Cal Poly.

Prototype main rotor blade of the human-powered helicopter is being constructed from a graphite/epoxy composite spar tube, with polyvinylchloride (PVC) foam ribs and polystyrene foam leading edge supporting a lightweight film covering.

An evolutionary project

This is an evolutionary project, with the first attempt to build *da Vinci I* dating back to 1981. The technical approach that has been adopted is: to generate lift by spinning long rotor blades at low speed rather than spinning relatively short rotor blades at high speeds; to minimize aircraft weight by using strong, light-weight structural materials; and to use a single pilot. To evaluate these concepts the *da Vinci I* prototype was built and tested and the lessons learnt from the first aircraft were incorporated into *da Vinci II* featuring two 23 m long rotor blades powered by propellers located at the tip and driven by the pilot.

This aircraft was tested in March 1988 and demonstrated the feasibility of human-powered vertical flight by briefly lifting off before encountering control problems, causing it to lurch forward and crash. Although the helicopter was damaged beyond repair when it crashed, it served as a test bed of ideas that have been incorporated into the current version of the aircraft, *da Vinci III*. The redesigned human-powered helicopter has a more efficient main rotor blade and will weigh less than 77 kg. The take-off weight including the pilot is 135 kg, and it is estimated that between 0.5 and 0.7 horse power will be required for vertical flight. In preparation of flight testing, the pilot has been tested on a stationary bicycle, generating a sustained power output of 0.8 horse power for over one minute. This will be sufficient to meet the requirements of the 60 second flight stipulated by the American Helicopter Society's contest for human-powered helicopter flight.

Technical highlights of *da Vinci III*

The helicopter features two 17 m long main rotor blades, driven through two propellers located at the tips. The drive train consists of a power cord wound around the propeller shafts and is connected to an elliptical spool equipped with foot pedals. The structure is a showpiece for the utilization of light-weight aerospace materials, from the graphite/epoxy spar tubes of the main rotor blades to the Kevlar-covered foam propellers. With an estimated weight of 75 kg for the helicopter and 55 kg for the pilot, the combined take-off weight is less than 135 kg. The airfoil shape of the main rotor blades has been designed with the help of computers and has undergone further refinements through wind tunnel testing.

The pilot is suspended in a semi-reclining position below the main rotor blades in a triangular frame and pedals the drive train spool at 85 to 100 rpm, causing the blade-tip propellers to turn at 500–600 rpm. The force generated by the propellers moves the rotor blades forward at 8.5 to 9.0 rpm, providing the necessary lifting force to become airborne. Directional control of the aircraft is accomplished by the pilot shifting his weight.

The present schedule calls for completion of *da Vinci III* by late 1991. If success-ful, human-powered helicopter flight consisting of vertical climb to a height of 3 m and remaining airborne for 60 seconds without drifting more than 5 m in any direction will be demonstrated to an observer of the American Helicopter Society.

The significance of the present endeavour goes beyond the potential of a first flight for a human-powered helicopter. The technologies developed will serve to foster research into the development of alternate means of transportation, especially those suited for the needs of third world and developing countries without an efficient network of roads, while helping to conserve energy and preserving the environment of this planet.

The human-powered helicopter will be flown by a single pilot suspended below the main rotorblade in a semi-reclining position and generating the lifting force by pedalling.

Transferring the Edward Lowe "Cell System" to entrepreneurial ventures in Latin America

Edward Lowe

Honourable Mention
The Rolex Awards for Enterprise – 1990

Edward Lowe Industries, Inc., Big Rock Valley, 21725 Allegheny Street, Cassopolis, Michigan 49031, United States

American, born 10 July 1920. Chief Executive Officer, Edward Lowe Industries, Inc. Educated in USA; graduated from high school in 1939, no further formal education.

While creating the cat-box-filler industry and inventing and patenting more than 20 tools and procedures for the mining industry, I conceived and refined a management philosophy called the "Cell System"; this system nurtures the entrepreneurial spirit and encourages its continued growth within the corporate culture. The philosophy was cultivated in what I call the school of "hard knocks" and was guided by gut instinct and refined through personal trial and error. This philosophy and management system, which helped create an almost $200 million company, can be understood and applied by entrepreneurs in many types of political, economic and corporate cultures.

The Cell System is a scientifically designed, corporate structure based on natural, organic principles. Its primary purpose is to nurture and enhance an entrepreneurial cell which I identify as a "growth cell". The Cell System concept evolved from a general theory I call "nuclear economics", the basic premise of which is that business organizations are, or should be, living entities. They are not built – they are grown. When business organizations stop growing, the general economy atrophies. The system alleviates the isolation which traditionally hampers the entrepreneurial owner-manager. It also reinforces the entrepreneur by bringing into the growth cell the type of people who thrive in an entrepreneurial culture.

Additionally, the Cell System encourages continual innovation and growth by ensuring the growth cell will be open to and infused with ideas from the outside and from within. The system also encourages the growth cell to reinvest in newly emerging cells (new, independent businesses) in the economy. Doing so stimulates the entire economic system of the country. Thus, the original cell is forever reproducing itself. The effectiveness of the Cell System has been proven in my own life and in my company. It has enabled me to create a foundation which supports entrepreneurial spirit, and to invest in and personally mentor emerging companies.

*Edward Lowe who
conceived the Cell System
and is now promoting its
adoption in Latin America.*

Seminars on entrepreneurship

My goal for this project is to make the Cell System available to entrepreneurs in the developing countries of Latin America in view of this area's potential role in an expanding global marketplace, its willingness to embrace Cell System principles and its high marks in an area risk analysis. I propose to sponsor a seminar which will explore the unique principles of my Cell System and focus on these underlying ideas: real wealth and the importance of the free-enterprise company in its creation; giant conglomerates are not the foundation of the American economy; America's "riches" were cultivated by small, independent innovative enterprises; the performance record of the Cell System companies demonstrates that the Cell System can stimulate the development of emerging Latin American economies. The seminar will be designed jointly by faculty from the American Graduate School of International Management (Thunderbird), which has major experience in management training in Latin America, and faculty from my own American Academy of Entrepreneurs, which has expertise in the application of the Cell System.

The contents of the seminar will combine theory with the wisdom of practical experience, and we will trace the hazards of the lone entrepreneurial trail: lack of counsel, absence of checks and balances, and inaccessible sympathetic financial sources. Our seminars will graphically diagram the bureaucratic, pyramidal structure of conventional, publicly-owned companies and demonstrate how the top-down weight of the typical corporate structure paralyzes its original spirit of enterprise. We will show how coercive command in these companies freezes the creative initiative in their operating divisions. We will explore the innovative Cell System structure and demonstrate how it keeps the incentives of self-initiative and self-fulfillment activated in operating cells – and how that keeps the business economy growing. Our seminar will show how the "dinosaur syndrome", which fuels big business take-overs, conglomeration and monopoly, can be effectively remedied by a renaissance of entrepreneurialism nurtured by a thriving Cell System.

Bringing the Cell System to Latin America

Implementation of the Cell System does not require financing, underwriting or special legislation. All that is required is a will to succeed through use of new,

64

dramatic techniques and procedures. I intend to prove to seminar participants that the small business economy of Latin America can unify itself through my Cell System. Our seminar will use prime examples of theory and practice, both past and present, to formulate the Cell System for our audience. I will be supported by the most capable proponents of nuclear economics available, including prominent Latin American advocates of free enterprise.

There are at least seven original, innovative principles in my Cell System that will be outlined and demonstrated during the seminar. These are: free market philosophy; protected autonomy; decentralized structures; creative self-initiative; para-managerial network; built-in appetite for growth; and co-investment mutualism.

My resources, while considerable, are committed to many domestic undertakings such as the development of a Big Rock Valley curriculum and the American Academy of Entrepreneurs. In my zeal to "give back" some of the fruits I have garnered in my life as an entrepreneur, this plan of mine may be the most meaningful contribution I can make to posterity. I believe that much of the world is unaware of the real roots of economic growth in the United States. The real economic history of the United States will be presented in the Cell System seminar. It is the often-ignored story of how it became one of the richest countries of the world, not through giant trusts, but through the ingenious efforts of entrepreneurial-spirited individuals and their small, independent companies.

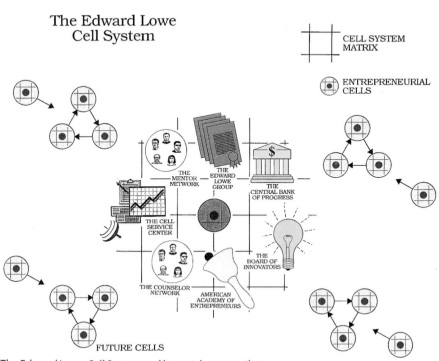

The Edward Lowe Cell System and its matrix conception.

A belt buckle incorporating basic survival needs

John J. Poluhowich

Department of Biology and Geosciences, West Texas State University, WT Station Box 808, Canyon, Texas 79016, United States

American, born 25 March 1939. Assistant Professor of Biology. Educated in United States; Ph. D. (Physiology/Cell Biology) from University of Connecticut, Storrs, in 1969.

Over recent years, a wide range of outdoor activities such as hiking, backpacking, cross-country skiing, etc., have become increasingly popular. However, as the number of inexperienced people who begin to undertake this type of endeavour activity augments, many of them become exposed to the danger of being stranded or lost in remote wilderness areas.

For the most part, these individuals are in no way prepared to survive any length of time in an inhospitable environment and, according to numerous news reports, they soon find themselves in dire straits. Additionally, there are other groups of people such as aircraft crews and passengers who are the victims of a crash, or automobile drivers who have a vehicle breakdown in sparsely populated areas, and find themselves involuntarily thrust into similar precarious situations.

Survival knives are of limited value

Numerous different types of survival knives have been developed and marketed to provide a degree of safety for those who venture into the out-of-doors. These knives are fitted with hollow handles which contain a limited number of items designed to provide the user with the wherewithal for wilderness survival.

However, one of the major drawbacks of such survival knives is that they are relatively large and clumsy and, therefore, they are inconvenient to carry. What is more, the legalities involved with carrying knives often defeats their purpose. The chances are that, when an individual really needs this tool, he will not have it with him. Additionally, the inexperienced person would probably not be familiar with the proper techniques for utilizing a survival knife, and this consequently greatly diminishes the device's effectiveness and usefulness in a true emergency situation.

The "Survival" buckle opened with its contents spread out ready for use.

Incorporating a survival kit into a buckle

The present invention was designed to overcome the above-mentioned limitations of the survival knife. In addition to providing the necessary means for survival under most wilderness survival situations, this patented belt buckle contains a brief outline of survival strategies and techniques. The latter was incorporated into the device for the purpose of combating the adverse psychological aspects of survival, i.e. to alleviate the fear and panic which are the major causes of loss of life in survival situations.

The starting point for the device was a standard (7.5×5.0 cm) brass belt buckle. Attached to this by means of two lateral channels is the brass cover (measuring 6.25×4.75×2.0 cm) which slides in the channels and is held in position by a locking top latch. The rear of the buckle has a narrow, spring-loaded latching device to hold the knife blade which is contained inside the cover when not in use. Inscribed on the sides of the cover are various pieces of survival information (e.g., international distress signals, Morse code, etc.)

The contents of the buckle include four plastic laminated cards providing the user with basic survival information (e.g., for obtaining water and starting fires, basic survival strategies, how to construct shelters, obtain food, etc.). Also included is a whistle, a magnesium "match" and fire starter, a fishing line, hooks and split shot, a compass, snare wire, Fresnel lens (for reading the cards and also starting fires), signal mirror, salt and halazone tablets and a condom (for use as a water container).

Marketing

The buckle has been successfully used in survival training programmes that have been organized for people who venture into the outdoors such as field biologists, sportsmen and scouts. The directions provided and the materials contained within the buckle have provided a marked degree of comfort in the wilderness during three to five day excursions of survival training.

It is envisaged that the concept of the survival belt buckle will be offered to a corporation specializing in the manufacture of survival and/or carrying equipment, and efforts are currently being made in this direction.

The "Survival" belt buckle assembled ready to be worn on a mundane outing or an adventure trail.

Infusion of joy in the disabled.
An effort in the Third World

Mahendra Kumar Goel

B 2/2, River Bank Colony, Lucknow 226018, India

Indian, born 26 June 1924. Orthopaedic surgeon, K. G.'s Medical College, Lucknow. Educated in India; M. S. (Orthopaedics) from K. G. Medical College, Lucknow University in 1954.

It was in the 1960s when I was tremendously moved by the deformities I saw in lepers that it became my ardent desire to infuse new life and joy into the disabled. I would visit the lepers in their colonies and take them to the hospital for reconstructive surgery to allow them to become independent and do some useful work. Ultimately this desire took a more definite shape in the 1970s when I became Professor and Head of a department of orthopaedic surgery and Director of a large rehabilitation and artificial limb centre.

On many occasions, I visited the leper village at the invitation of various voluntary organizations to examine disabled children. To my horror, I found hundreds of grossly neglected patients who, if proper facilities were provided, could be rehabilitated and lead an independent life; what is more, patients and their parents were quite ignorant of these facilities. They were frightened to venture out of the village and enter a rehabilitation centre and did not have the funds to cover the cost of hospital treatment and the necessary appliances. It was then I decided that some constructive steps should be taken to achieve com-prehensive rehabilitation.

Treatment for the disabled

Since 1970, I have been devoting at least two days a month to visiting these areas to provide rehabilitation services to the disabled on their home-ground. With the collaboration of the Rampur Rotary Club and funding from various philanthropic organizations, I examine the disabled children at a central point near their home where I educate and motivate them to carry out the rehabilitation programme. Subsequently, I started working in other areas such as Bareilly, Moradabad, Shahjahanpur and Hardwar.

In 1975, I discovered that there were many thousands of this type of disabled patient for whom a larger camp was essential. Simultaneously, I was also working on patients with paraplegia due to spinal tuberculosis, spinal fracture and on the

Grossly disabled patients have in many cases been provided with three-wheeler chairs to restore their mobility.

surgical correction of severe spinal deformities. I developed simple and safe operations for these fractures and deformities which could also be performed by other orthopaedic surgeons at district hospitals, and these techniques were subsequently published.

A strategic plan for future action

I have now drawn up a general plan for the establishment of camps for the orthopaedically disabled covering such items as: voluntary organization; availability of funds; expertise and availability of appliances; location of camps; follow-up research; and future action strategy.

It is essential to contact voluntary organizations and seek the participation of willing social workers and philanthropists, and obtain support for patients in such areas as transport, food and funds to cover the expenses and appliance costs. In the same way, medical and paramedical care at the camp, and the correct documentation of patients' records including socio-economic status and details of the disability and its treatment are essential factors for the smooth functioning of such camps. Suitable follow-up of patients treated in the camp is a vital factor not only for the patients but also for our further education and research on the type of handicap aids and appliances that are needed in relation to the patients' customs, culture and socio-economic status.

Surgery in the camps became an essential item since the majority of the children were late, neglected cases of polio and their contractives required correction. Patients were afraid to go to a city hospital and were beset with financial problems; consequently, with the help of a team of nurses, doctors and surgeons, we set up our operating theatre in some rooms in a nearby building and were able to operate about 50 cases in a day. Having been given the necessary care the patients were able to return home after three days with their walking abilities much improved.

A life closer to normality

I found that many of the poor disabled could only lead a wheelchair life and were transported from place to place on the back of their spouse. Wheelchairs were provided free and they were taught to participate in various sports such as table tennis, archery, basket ball, etc., from their wheelchairs; efforts were made to organize intercity, national and international matches. I took the severely disabled paraplegic and bilateral lower-limb amputees to participate in the para-Olympic Games in Japan, Australia, Hong Kong, etc., where they won several gold, silver and bronze medals. The Prime Minister of India, the late Indira Gandhi, received them at the airport, and one could see the joy in their eyes and hearts.

The various camps organized over the last 18 years have brought to light some important findings. Long-neglected poliomyelitis of both the lower limbs is very common in the Third World as are also cerebral palsy and congenital talipes. Some 70% these polio cases were neglected and had developed contracture at the hips, knees and ankles. Until these contractures were corrected it was not possible to fit calipers.

Much still needs to be done but it is clear that with adapted technology, a committed team and, above all, tenacity, enormous achievements can be made to infuse joy into the lives of the disabled in the Third World.

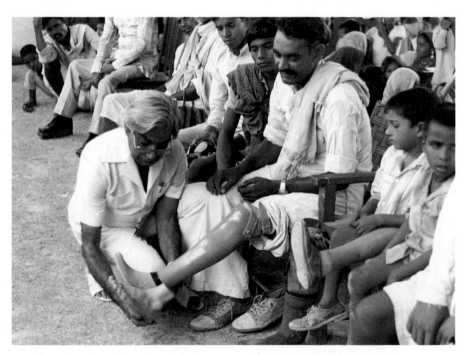

Dr. Mahendra Kumar Goel examining a disabled patient who has been fitted with a prosthesis to replace his amputated leg.

Rolex Laureate – The Rolex Awards for Enterprise – 1990

John Fredrich Asmus

John Fredrich Asmus, a research physicist from the United States with long experience with lasers, offers hope of recovering the colours originally decorating the terracotta warriors in the Chinese Qin Dynasty treasure trove. He plans to treat the warriors with a pulsed laser under the protection of a special atmosphere in order to restore the polychrome to something of its original splendour.

Laser recovery of the Qin Dynasty treasure trove polychrome

John Fredrich Asmus

Rolex Laureate
The Rolex Awards for Enterprise – 1990

Scripps Institution of Oceanography A-025, University of California – San Diego, La Jolla, California 92093, United States

American, born 20 January 1937. Research Physicist, University of California. Educated in USA and Denmark; Ph. D. (Electrical Engineering) from California Institute of Technology in 1965.

Much of the world was startled in 1974 when a grand army of at least 6,000 terracotta warriors was unearthed near the Mount Li tomb of China's first emperor, Qin Shih Huang Ti. This 22-century-old site astonished observers first by the realism and artistic quality of each piece. Later, it became clear that no two figures were alike, but that each was a unique likeness of a person living in that era. Finally, investigators were stunned by the sheer enormity of the site. Not only had Emperor Qin's regime erected much of the Great Wall, but perhaps 700,000 souls had toiled for 36 years to build this funerary complex that rivals those of ancient Egypt.

Many estimates suggest that 100–200 years will be required to complete the bulk of the excavation of this archaeological site. Nevertheless, the probative beginning has turned the site into a major scholastic centre as well as a tourism focus with the attendant influx of foreign currency for the local economy. Yet, it seems that the major impact of these uncovered guardians at one corner of this immense site is psychological. Most tourists, local residents, archaeologists, writers, and art historians shed a tear upon first gazing on these ossified figures.

Faded ghosts of the past

The Qin terracotta figures are most impressive technically, artistically, aesthetically and quantitatively. Yet these pieces are hardly more than faded ghosts of their appearance at conception since they initially were clad in realistic polychrome. Today, after divestment from clay incrustations as well as cleaning they emerge in a grey-brown monotone. The contrast may be sensed by comparing a well-conserved della Robbia ceramic with another that, through defoliation, is merely a pottery core.

Fortunately, there is some hope for the recovery of the colours originally decorating these artworks. The conservators and technicians at the site have noted that, when many of the warriors and horses are first cleaned, some of the

Photographs of two Qin treasure-trove warriors showing the monotone brown cast without any evidence of colour.

polychrome is visible. However, after a few weeks these traces of colour generally disappear. Subsequent inspection indicated that the offending phenomenon is not one of an efflorescent film covering and hiding the glaze. It is probable that a chemical reaction is taking place with the air and, in particular, with oxygen. It is well known that the colours of many minerals are highly dependent upon oxidation and hydration states. Thus, it may be possible to recover the poly-chromatic glory of the treasure trove if *in situ* chemical reduction can be accomplished on the surface without damaging the fragile terracotta. We believe that pulsed laser irradiation in a reducing atmosphere may accomplish this best.

Using lasers to bring the colours back to life

If one accepts the desirability of conserving the Qin collection with authentic polychrome for aesthetic and scholarly reasons, then it is inappropriate to repaint them as was so frequently done in past art restoration practice. The only viable option is to chemically reduce the glaze pigment minerals to their original valence states although not in a high-temperature furnace as would normally be done, since the objects are too fragile and too diverse in coloration.

It has long been known that laser-induced chemical catalysis can promote photochemical and photothermal reactions without recourse to bulk heating; it should therefore be possible to exploit this technology to return the Qin pieces to their polychromatic state by placing the objects in an airtight transparent box that is flushed by a reducing fluid. A pulsed laser beam would then be directed through the transparent wall to the specific area being chemically reduced in a high-temperature rapid-quench reaction. The significant parameters such as

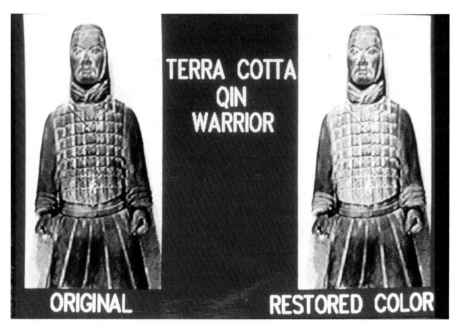

Computer image enhancement simulation of the polychrome recovery of some of the pigments of a terracotta Qin warrior.

cover-fluid composition, laser wavelength, energy density, pulse length and repetition rate would be selected to achieve an optimum result. Past studies have shown that laser-induced surface damage can be avoided.

At the present time I have several ruby and other pulsed lasers in Northern Italy for the divestment of sulphation from friable marble statues in Cremona, Vicenza and Venice. I have offered one of these as a gift to the Xi'an Electromechanical Information Institute for field evaluation of *in situ* recovery of the treasure trove polychrome. This token of friendship has been accepted and my associate Giancarlo Calcagno and I have been invited to collaborate in establishing a polychrome conservation programme. This was scheduled to begin in 1988; however, a budget cut at the Institute has caused an indefinite delay. We now hope to proceed during April-October 1990.

The first step will be to ship the laser to Xi'an in China. Giancarlo Calcagno and I will next provide instruction in pigment chemistry and laser technology, respectively. When an appropriate transparent enclosure is fabricated and gas handling equipment is installed, laser-reduction tests will begin on expendable shards to determine optimum laser and cover-fluid parameters for each pigment type. Laser-triggered combustion in reducing and oxidizing gases is not a problem as a millisecond is too short for convective mixing to take place. Surface chemical changes will be monitored via real-time spectroscopy of the back-scattered light.

When the feasibility and training phases are completed, the Institute's engineers and site conservators will be in a position to fabricate and operate additional lasers and incorporate the polychrome recovery technology into the routine conservation activities at Mount Li, and dramatically improve the results.

Transference of NASA robotic technology to prosthetics

Mark Elling Rosheim

Ross-Hime Designs, Inc., 1313 5th Street S. E., Suite 221, Minneapolis, Minnesota 55414, United States

American, born 28 February 1960. President of Ross-Hime Designs, Inc. Educated in United States; attended the Department of Mechanical Engineering at the University of Minnesota.

Of all the actuators in the human body, the hand stands out as the most complex and, because of this, it is the most dependent on the human body's ability to lubricate and repair itself. It is indeed a great challenge for designers who have to work with inorganic materials to achieve the hand's functionality. Hand joints, and tendons in particular, present challenges in wear resistance and flexibility. Typically, robot hands consist of a number of pivoting hinge-like joints making up the finger joints. The wrist is usually a Cardan universal joint.

My project is to carry out a study to apply the technology of robotic hands to prosthetics. Amputees would benefit from transference of NASA technology by acquiring improved functionality. My anthropomorphic robot hand, originally designed for use in telerobotics, improves on the state of the art in both robotics and prosthetics by reproducing the motions of the fingers and wrist in a more lifelike and dextrous manner. The simple, modular head knuckle joints have a common axes centre, simplifying control computations. This is very important when multiple joints are used.

Articulated, multi-jointed robot hands can be traced back to "Handyman", a two-armed electrohydraulic robot developed by Ralph Mosher at the General Electric Corporation in 1960. These hands had two fingers with five pivoting movements. Each finger effectively had three degrees of freedom and was controlled by the operator "wearing" the slave apparatus. Since then work has progressed primarily in the United States and Japan. Typically, present-day robot hands have three fingers and a thumb. The head knuckle consists of two separate rotary joints, thereby complicating the design and computer control. The state-of-the-art design in prosthetic hands is the Otto-Bock myo-electric hand and wrist which consists of a two-part open-close end effector, mounted on a simple wrist joint, which receives electric signals from muscles in the arm stump. Areas in which this design could be surpassed by the successful application of my robotic hand technology, include improved flexion of the finger joints and the addition of a third, thumb-like digit.

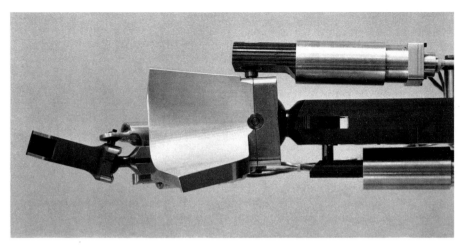

Partial NASA robot hand.

Our current work on robotic hand technology

My present hand design was developed under contract to NASA and relates to a multi-jointed flexible end-effector design for robotic technology in space. Basically a hybrid, it features ruggedness, dexterity, high power, durable design and anthropomorphic kinematics which are important for robot as well as prosthetic control. A wrist, palm and one-finger head knuckle were constructed. Closed loop servo-control activated by a personal computer was achieved for each joint.

Applied as a wrist and knuckle, the head knuckle features circumduction identical to the human hand and vital for creating an opposable thumb. This increases dexterity and simplifies computer control which is not found in other robotic hands. In particular, the head knuckle cup is biased to allow a greater range of motion in one direction, as in the fingers of the human hand. The other joints also have built-in stops to prevent backward hyperextension. Modular in design, all other fingers operate in this same way and are interchangeable plug-in units. Two motors with magnetic encoders are mounted on the back of the palm by a bracket. The motors drive standard miniature ball screws through a sliding spline for a linear output. Actuation of the head knuckle is comparable in range to the human finger's head knuckle. Future work on this design includes plans for a motor in the fingers to drive the upper finger joints and, with gearing, the joint above it.

For the head knuckle, the motor actuates the miniature ball screw that rotates a sector spur gear which, in turn, drives a ring sector connected to the cup. This sector is held in the ball groove by two pivotal pins, the ball sliding across the sector. The ball is two halves mated together; contained in the ball is a second ball with a pin press fitted into it. The purpose of this ball is to retain the finger socket on the head knuckle ball without restricting its two-axis motion. Yaw motion of the head knuckle is produced simply by an arm protruding out of the finger socket connected to a ball-and-socket joint. The ball-and-socket joint is necessary to decouple the two-axis motion of the arm so that it may be driven by a linear drive.

77

The wrist is simply an enlarged version of the head knuckle with its actuators mounted on the forearm through pivotal bearings. Note that wrist roll may be added by simply interposing a motor between the elbow and the forearm section.

Development of a three-finger system

We are now concentrating on detailing and applying the robot hand joint to a complete three-finger telerobot hand/wrist system. Design and construction of two three-fingered robot hands with wrists using the present components for one hand is being carried out to test design enhancements. The first hand joint is being used as a test bed design. The second incorporates the improvements proven on the test bed hand. All of the features and test procedures used in the initial robot hand joints will be retained in the subsequent designs and will be explored for their applicability to prosthetic technology.

Space-age technology for amputees

We now plan to study the feasibility of transferring the NASA-funded robotics technology to prosthetics. The design will be based on a three-fingered hand developed for NASA. Use of plastics for weight reduction in addition to alternative power sources such as air-servo will be studied. The following areas of research will be covered: weight reduction; the mechanical stump interface; the electronic stump interface; miniaturization of the electronics, power supply and battery requirements; a literature research on prosthetic hand electronics; system reliability; cost; and cosmetic appearance.

A report will be produced, as well as an end initial design incorporating the modifications required by the application. When commercialized, this design will give amputees a new level of dexterity, closer to their missing limb than any device currently available.

The robot hand system layout.

Mineral accretion technology to preserve Isla de Aves

Carlos Henrique Hernandez Merchan

IDEC – Facultad de Arquitectura y Urbanismo – U. C.V., Avenida Las Acacias, Ciudad Universitaria, Los Chaguaramos, Caracas 1041-A, Venezuela

Venezuelan, born 16 December 1958. Researcher for the Institute of Experimental Development of Construction. Educated in Venezuela and United States; M. Sc. (Architectural Studies) from the Massachusetts Institute of Technology, Cambridge, in 1987.

Mineral accretion technology uses the minerals dissolved in the seawater as building materials for the construction of structures in a process similar to the one exhibited by living marine organisms in the construction of their protective carapaces. First developed by Wolf H. Hilbertz at the University of Texas, accretion technology is based on the fact that electrolytic processes can selectively precipitate materials over conducting surfaces in an electrical field created between an anode and a cathode in an ionic solution (in this case, seawater); positive-charge ions (Ca, Mg, Na, etc.) will migrate to the cathode and negative-charge ions will move toward the anode.

If the potential between anode and cathode is kept low enough to avoid water electrolysis being the main reaction, an over-saturation of positively charged ions will happen on the cathode and deposition will occur. Brucite, argonite (calcium carbonate) and calcite are the main products of this deposition; the percentage relationship between these products will change according to the density of current applied to the system, but brucite is the main component of new deposited material. With time, calcium will replace the magnesium in the brucite and the material will slowly become richer in argonite and also stronger.

Using an iron mesh as a cathode, structures of any shape and size can be built in the sea. By shaping the mesh to the desired form and placing it in the water, where calcium carbonate and brucite will precipitate, a material with a high compression strength will be formed in a period of around eight months. If the current is maintained, the structure will continue to grow indefinitely; moreover, it can be repaired or reinforced merely by connecting it back to the power supply.

This technology provides a non-contaminating method of using local resources to build structures, with very little labour, no heavy machinery, and with parts that are easy to handle and transport. The structures soon become integrated into the environment and colonized by sea animals and coral, which contributes to the strength of the whole.

Placing a framework to commence an accretion test in La Guaira port.

Making an island grow

Isla Aves is a very small island which has been dangerously reduced in size since its discovery; its current size is approximately of only 3 hectares, and its highest point is only 3 m above sea level. The island is built mainly of coral sand and phosphate-consolidated sand which makes it very susceptible to hurricanes. It is a very important breeding site for many sea birds and green turtles.

We propose to use mineral accretion technology to build barriers to protect the island and to create land by using sediments generated in the area; subsequent sediment will ensure more stable ground. This method will have a less traumatic impact on the island's ecosystem than would extensive conventional earthworks and would be less expensive. The island will grow slowly in a natural way, using local resources and sandy areas for the turtles will be constantly available and gradually expand in size. Since the mainland is nearly 500 km away, our techno-logy will ensure lower transport costs since all the materials except the wire mesh, etc., are available on site.

We intend to start the preservation of the island by repairing the protecting reef to the north and east of the island since we can grow structures to form barriers faster than can coral. Galvanized mesh forms placed in the water at the places where the natural barrier has been damaged will take some eight months time to be accreted. This will allow us to work between hurricane seasons and to have structures heavy enough to stand the strong winds that will subsequently strike the island. After the eight month period, accretion will be continued to reinforce the structures so that, by the beginning of the next season, the island will already be colonized by coral. This will transform the initially artificial structure into a natural growing organism. Barriers will then be placed to the south-west of the island, in order to slow down the currents and create larger areas of sediment deposition.

The estimated yearly production of sediment from calcareous organisms in the island is about 500 tonnes which can be used to create land. On these areas a mesh will be placed horizontally so that it will be embedded inside the new sediment. Thereafter, the mesh will be electrified and the sediment will start to cement around it. By placing consecutive layers, a solid soil resistant to erosion will be obtained.

A three phase growth project

The project is divided into three phases for its completion and it is hoped to finish it in a period of three or four years. The first phase includes the elaboration and finishing of some essential studies and the construction of a prototype. In the second phase, the superstructure will be designed (support structures, electrical system, power generation, fixing methods, etc.), and the building process will be planned. The third phase will be the actual construction process and also includes the evaluation of physical and ecological results.

The electricity will be supplied by wind generators. A current of 1 A dc per square metre of surface to be accreted will be applied at 6–24 V. Wind generators will be placed on deployable aluminium towers, located near the island, and also on the coral reef. The level of current used is harmless to humans and animals. Preceding experiences have shown that fishes seem to be attracted by the electric field created around the structure.

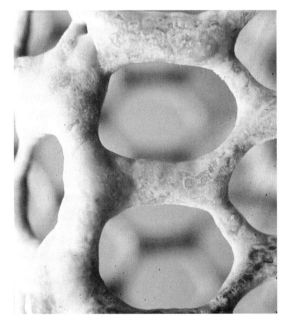

The material that accretes on the trellis work soon begins to form a hard wall.

81

Innovative animal breeding for protein production in arid lands

Reuven Yagil

14 Bar-Kochba Street, 84231 Beersheva, Israel

Israeli, born 6 September 1935. Associate Professor at the Ben Gurion University of the Negev (Faculty of Health Sciences). Educated in Israel and the Netherlands; Degree in Veterinary Medicine (Hons.) at Rijksuniversiteit te Utrecht in 1969.

The reason for the endemic famine in many parts of Africa is aridity. The lack of, and unpredictability of, rainfall leads to sparse and unpalatable fodder for animals and no food for man. In addition, overstocking and overgrazing have destroyed the remaining vegetation. The end result is a barren landscape and an encroaching desert. The outcome has been the lack of local food supplies leading to widespread malnutrition.

To tackle these arid land problems, we have set up a research station in an area southeast of Beersheva, which is topographically similar to the drought-stricken areas of Africa. Three animals which can provide food for man (the camel, the ostrich and the goat) but which can flourish under such inhospitable conditions are kept in closed areas and not allowed to graze freely in order to protect the environment from overgrazing and destruction of vegetation. The research station attached to the farm offers trainees from developing countries the opportunity for training in innovative state-of-the-art farming methods. In this way we are developing and spreading suitable technology to enable the farmers in arid lands to gain self-sufficiency in animal protein production.

Desert camels

Since 1969, we have been carrying out research on the one-humped Bedouin camel as a source of food for man in arid lands. To start with, the basic physiology of the animal was established while keeping in mind the necessity to confirm the animal's ability to survive and produce in drought areas. We were then asked to help increase the number of high-yielding camels (i.e. those producing over 20 litres of milk per day) without culling the poorer producers of the herd, and we set about establishing simple techniques for utilizing the poor producers as surrogate mothers for large numbers of embryos produced by selected, hormonally treated mothers.

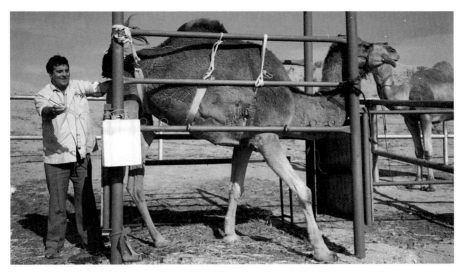

One of the camels at the experimental farm held in a restraining frame ready for gynaecological flushing.

This aspect of the project entails: selecting the most suitable hormone for producing numerous follicles; choosing the optimal time for mating in order to cause ovulation (in the non-spontaneous ovulating camels) and to create embryos; finding the optimal time and procedure for flushing the uterus for embryos; examining the feasibility of freezing camel embryos; and discovering an artificial method to cause ovulation in the recipient females to allow embryo transfers.

A method for harvesting embryos has now been perfected; however, the project must be continued for another few years to obtain further data on ovule transfer and embryo freezing and to bring in selected persons from African and Asian countries for training before introducing the techniques in breeding stations in their home countries.

Ostriches

Although the basic idea of the farm is to establish a model for raising animals for food, one of the needs of modern man is a source of income that will allow him not only to survive but also to improve himself. The ostrich, which can be used for food in times of need, also has great potential as a source of income from such things as: feathers, skin (for leather producers), meat, and egg shells (which can be decorated and sold as gifts).

Intensive farming of ostriches is a new practice and its success depends primarily on selecting the best male and female breeding stock. Experiments are therefore being carried out to determine whether: sex hormones are excreted in faeces, urine or both; and whether levels of hormones in the excreta are a true indication of blood levels. If the excreta of the ostriches are a true indication of blood levels, the ostrich farmer can easily collect samples for determinations in a laboratory and so select the appropriate birds for breeding. This will save the time spent on trial and error matings and the loss of chicks due to infertile males and females.

Goats

Goats are much maligned animals and have even been accused of desert formation. Nevertheless, they are well adjusted to desert conditions and an inseparable part of livestock farming in arid lands. Therefore, suitable and innovative methods of goat management must be found. Suitable and improved goat breeds must be developed to guarantee food for man with as little as possible negative effect on the environment.

The recurring droughts have depleted the flocks of high-yielding animals, both meat and milk, and have left as "survivors" goats that are hardy but not necessarily good producers. "New breeds" like the Kalahari and the Cypriot Damascus goat are suitable new breeds for arid lands. However, the introduction of goats to these areas using anachronistic husbandry will result in the same destruction of the local vegetation and the eventual deaths of the animals themselves.

Our studies show that these new husbandry methods should include the planting of suitable vegetation for the animals and should be based mainly on keeping the goats in closed-off areas. Goats do not suffer any ill-effects if they are restricted to one area and hand fed. In the coming years, the growth rate of various breeds of hardy goat species will be examined. Nutrition studies will be initiated to determine the quality of the diet necessary for maximal growth, and the possible effects of restraining the movement of the animals will also be examined. Other breeds of goats from other desert areas in Africa, Asia and the Americas will also be introduced into the project.

A group of the young
ostriches being raised on
Reuven Yagil's experimental
arid-lands farm.

Establishing laser diffraction imaging as a visual art form

Lawrence Martin Weissmann

99 Gilmour Street, Ottawa, Ontario, Canada K2P ON5

Canadian, born 6 April 1943. Clerk, Regional Municipality of Ottawa-Carleton. Educated in Canada and United States; Degree in Mechanical Engineering from City University of New York in 1964.

Diffraction takes place when, e.g. a light or water wave bends, when passing close to the edge of an obstacle. If a set of waves are initially in random relationship with each other (incoherent), the effects of diffraction are for practical purposes not observable. If, however, all of the waves in a set are initially in definite phase relationship with each other, crest matching crest, wave trough matching wave trough, as in the case of laser light, diffraction results in a "shadow" composed of many distinct parallel lines. Such phase-related light is referred to as coherent, and the resulting set of lines termed an interference pattern (interference fringes). The size, spacing and contrast of these fringes may be carefully controlled, with the process forming the basis for production of diffraction images.

In simplest form, a diffraction image may be formed using a lens to diverge a laser beam, which is then projected through a photographic negative or other transparency, and recorded on film. The film does not record a sharply focused image of the transparency itself. The diffracted image exists at all points in space after the transparency, and it is various aspects of this which are recorded onto the film. For monochrome imaging, a single colour of laser is used; standard black and white film for recording the diffracted image, and a final print from this made by normal photographic technique.

The development of laser imaging in colour

The resulting black and white prints have been the major production·of my imagery to date. Colour work has been done by copying the diffracted negative on to colour film. While the colour so generated has been derived to complement the basic fringe image, the major refinement yet to be developed is that in which the fringes themselves are given their own distinct coloration. It is the development of several methods for achieving this effect which forms the subject of my project. The two processes comprise: synthesized colour using black-and-white diffracted separation negatives; and direct colour using multiple laser beams.

*Visions in a different dawn.
One of a series of ten
diffracted images by
Lawrence Weissmann.*

Synthesized colour using black-and-white diffracted separation negatives starts with an original transparency in either black and white or in colour and passes through the production of multiple negatives which are then exposed on to colour film. Although apparently straightforward, the approach is somewhat cumbersome, while an additional difficulty is created by the requirement for accurate registration of the three separations onto the final recording film. Nevertheless, the requirement for only one laser, a relatively inexpensive one at that, dictates that the above methods be the first to be developed for practical application.

Ability to fully visualize the appearance of the final image before recording it on film is essential if complete control over the process is to be achieved. The necessity for this becomes manifest when it is understood that the final colour image is composed of overlapping, but not geometrically identical, sets of fringes. If the range of subtleties available is to be fully used by the artist, it is necessary that the supplementation of the three differently coloured diffraction images occur at the same stage of the process in which the fringes themselves are generated. Each of the diffracted separations (red, green, blue) should be capable of variation independently of the other two. The requirement is thus for three differently coloured laser beams to simultaneously generate diffracted images, which are optically recombined before the final film exposure is made.

Where the original transparency is in black and white the beams from separate green, red and blue lasers (or one laser operating simultaneously at three wavelengths) are simultaneously projected through the original transparency. Selective colour beam-splitters are then used to separate the three beams, each into its own diffracting lens. The three projected images are then recombined using a further set of beam-splitters, and this recombined image recorded directly on to one frame of colour film. Additional optics are required in each beam, to compensate for the fact that the total distance of transparency to film is not independently variable for each beam.

Where the original transparency is in colour, the same optical technique is used, with results similar to, but more refined than, those attainable using the technique of synthesized colour with an original colour transparency. Large areas will approximate the colours of the original transparency, while small forms and the boundaries of larger forms will be composed of fringe "rainbows", with the dominant colours of adjacent areas appearing to mutate into each other through successively finer colour variations.

High cost of multiple-beam refraction

In practice, the multiple-beam technique is substantially simpler than the synthesized colour method, as the need for separation negatives, and the concomitant difficulties of registration of the distinct colour images, are dispensed with. The main obstacle to multiple beam diffraction lies with the cost of lasers and additional optics required. When a helium-neon laser is utilized for red, the blue and green beams would be provided by an argon ion laser. Alternatively, all three colours can be generated by a single laser, either krypton ion, or multiple wavelength helium-cadmium. Of these, the only one which is of proven reliability and long life is the argon laser. System optics as well, most significantly for the requisite selective colour beam splitters, further add to the costs. While such a system is beyond my present means, general system prototyping using my currently owned helium-neon lasers, is planned as part of the proposed project. In addition, although laser manufacturers cater to an almost exclusively technological/commercial market, my plan is to negotiate with manufacturers for loan or low priced rental, in exchange for graphics done with this technique, and associated public relations.

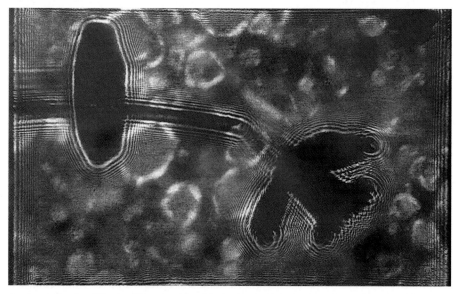

An example of a diffracted image with added colour produced experimentally by Lawrence Weissmann.

87

IDQ test kit for detecting fake drugs

Oleka Kelechi Udeala

Honourable Mention
The Rolex Awards for Enterprise – 1990

Faculty of Pharmaceutical Sciences, Department of Pharmaceutical Technology and Industrial Pharmacy, University of Nigeria, Nsukka, Nigeria

Nigerian, born 28 September 1940. Professor, Department of Pharmaceutical Technology and Industrial Pharmacy, University of Nigeria. Educated in Nigeria, USA, and UK; Ph. D. (Physical Pharmaceutics) from Victoria University of Manchester in 1975.

The importation and distribution of substandard, poorly formulated or expired drugs (antibiotics, analgesics, antimalarials, antihypertensives, etc.) in Nigeria and other West African countries have reached crisis levels. The administration of substandard drugs may have undesirable or even fatal effects on the patient, call the medical profession into disrepute and even aid the development and dissemination of resistant strains of bacteria worldwide. The importation and distribution of fake drugs thus constitutes an intractable problem facing various arms of the Nigerian Government such as the Ministry of Health, Food and Drug Administration and the Nigerian custom control. The establishment of quality control laboratories in each of Nigeria's 21 States would scarcely be feasible since most States do not have the necessary trained personnel and equipment is not generally accessible to rural clinics or small drug stores.

Producing a low-cost, easy-to-use drug test kit

The objective of the project is to evolve an "alarm system" which warns that a drug is either fake or expired. Such a system should be available to teaching, specialist and general hospitals, rural clinics, retail pharmacies and pharmacists, nurses, doctors in rural and city clinics and pharmaceutical inspectors at entry ports and elsewhere. The "alarm system" envisaged is a kit for on-the-spot testing of a given drug. The tests are based on pharmacopoeial and/or reliable analytical test reactions. No electronic or other sophisticated modern laboratory equipment is involved. Indeed, two or three 12×16 mm test tubes are the only laboratory wares used in the kit. The test solutions are contained in plastic dropper or screw-up bottles with capacities ranging from 10 to 30 ml. The solutions are coded. For instance, in the IDQ test kit for ampicillin, cloxacillin and ampiclox, there are three test solutions coded Ampisol 1, 2 and 3. The required volumetric measurements are invariably calibrated into drops for small volumes such as 1 ml or even 2 ml since most working environments may not have accurate small measures. Powders for tests, which have been accurately weighed, are

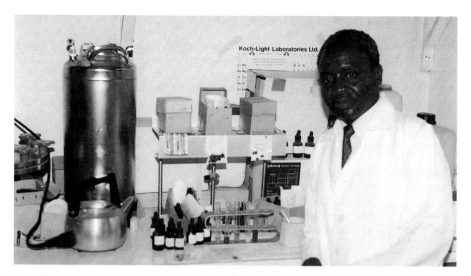

Prof. Oleka Udeala in his laboratory where he has carried out the development work for his IDQ test kit for detecting fake drugs.

packaged in small sachets. Where moderate heating in a water bath is required, the use of boiled water stored in a Thermos flask has been found adequate. The average time required for most of the tests is 10–20 minutes. Each kit contains an insert on which the instructions for carrying out the tests are provided.

The tests have been designed to provide answers for the following questions. Is there the named drug in this capsule or tablet? Has a good deal of the capsule or tablet been made up with excipients such as chalk, lactose or starch? Although these tests are not quantitative, the result of the second test is capable of indicating that there is a high amount of excipients by the appearance of a visible layer or a colour reaction uncharacteristic of the drug but characteristic of known pharmaceutical excipients. It would be impossible to establish an IDQ test kit for each and every class of drug and formulation. Consequently, kits have been prepared for only very commonly used but expensive antibiotics: ampicillin/cloxacillin/ampiclox, erythromycin and chloramphenicol. The other drugs for which IDQ test kits are contemplated are paracetamol, aspirin, chloroquine and an antihypertensive drug containing reserpine.

So far, demonstration IDQ test kits for ampicillin, cloxacillin, ampiclox, chloramphenicol and erythromycin are being assembled. Although the instructions contained on the insert in the IDQ test kits are written in simple clear English, there is the need to have the use of these kits demonstrated. Improper use and cross-contamination of test solutions may lead to results that cannot be correctly interpreted. There are therefore two main areas that require a lot of work for the successful execution of the project. These are: massive production of the kits so that they can enjoy country-wide distribution; demonstration of the use of test kits through seminars and a country-wide tour to clinics in cities and villages.

Procedures for introducing the IDQ test kits

In order to discourage fakers, massive quantities of these kits should be made available. No appeal has been made to the Government since one is never sure of the result of such an appeal. Indeed, such an appeal may fall on deaf ears, especially if by chance the functionary required to take a decision is remotely connected with the drug business. Besides, even in a state of emergency such as drug faking, government bureaucracy can often abort a worthy project. Above all, the IDQ test kits should be put into circulation without fanfare; fakers should be taken unawares.

In order to successfully launch the IDQ test kits, the tests should be demonstrated to people in the field. It is hoped that these kits can save lives and reduce the possibility of bacterial resistance. It is also hoped that this project can help to restore confidence in imported and locally manufactured authentic drugs and in local doctors and pharmacists.

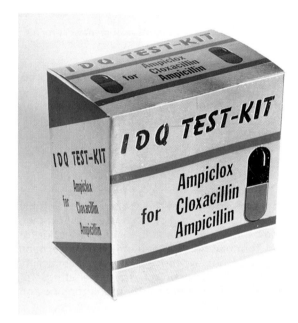

The packaging for the first IDQ test kit for detecting fake drugs, developed by Prof. Oleka Udeala.

World's first supersonic, propeller-driven piston-engine airplane

William Jeffrey Montagne

9794 Davona Drive, San Ramon, California 96583, United States

American, born 25 June 1953. President of Performance Engineering. Educated in United States; attended Diablo Valley College from 1972 to 1974.

This project aims to develop and produce the world's first supersonic piston-engined, prop-driven aircraft using state-of-the-art carbon fibre composites, honeycomb aluminium and steel structures. The engine is state-of-the-art, except for the pumps which are axial flow and a new type of supercharger that increases engine efficiency by approximately 15%. The prop operates at speeds of 1.2 to 1.5 mach.

Compromises in basic design

Several problems had to be overcome in the overall aerodynamic concept. The prop has been placed at the rear as a pusher to gain thrust efficiency; however, this required a 3.5 m drive shaft transmitting over 2,000 horse power and damping the power strokes. It was necessary to install a support bearing every 75 cm, so the drive shaft diameter is restricted because the bearing speeds would be too high if too large a diameter were used. Alignment of all the support bearings will be very time consuming but not impossible. The farther to the rear the prop is placed, the longer the drive shaft and the smaller the tail surfaces. Moreover, the farther back the prop, the higher the plane must be for the prop to rotate for takeoff and landing.

The tail surfaces will be optimized for flight in the transonic and supersonic ranges. Control surfaces are designed so that control stick forces are such that one cannot overstress the plane in the supersonic mode. This is done because the controls are all manual (no hydraulics). The wing was designed for optimum performance at supersonic speeds, only compromising slightly its size for improved flight quality at lower speeds. A full-span flaperon (aileron that can be drooped as flaps) system was added since the wing is so small that, if normal ailerons and flaps were used, the take off and landing speeds would be in the 310 km/h range, compared with 265 km/h in the system I chose to use.

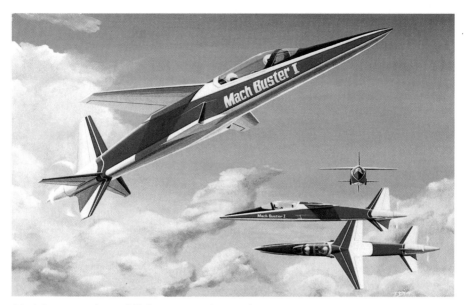

Mach Buster 1 – the world's first supersonic prop-fan, piston-engine aircraft. Designed and built by William J. Montagne.

Air induction requirements vary with speed, altitude, power and cooling needs, and it was decided to optimize for supersonic speed at 650 m elevation and higher. This type of compromise sacrificed about 40 km/h at lower altitudes, and lowered engine operating temperatures. Speed brakes (hydraulically controlled panels that can be deployed after touchdown) were placed under the wing to shorten landing distances because landing speeds will be in the neighbourhood of 240 km/h. The plane is so light that at these speeds the brakes would be very inefficient. There is not enough traction on the tyres until speed is reduced and the entire weight of the plane is placed on the tyres.

The front half of the fuselage was sized as a function of weight and balance and streamlined to a supersonic shape. The nose cone had to be quite long in order to accommodate the long nose wheel.

Structural design

Centrifugal loads on the prop of 2,200 to 3,000 times the force of gravity are very difficult to deal with when the blade is so thin; the prop will therefore be made from carbon or boron fibre and the section thickness ratio will be kept between 1.5% and 5% in order to maintain supersonic flow with minimum drag.

The tail surfaces are all made of carbon fibre and honeycomb composite, and are aerodynamically more accurate than if they were aluminum and a little lighter. The wing was built in the same way as the tail surfaces with the addition of a very complex spar arrangement. This was needed because the wing carries very high loads and needs to be very thin to be able to go supersonic. The rear fuselage has to carry side loads, thrust loads, down loads from the horizontal, and turning loads and gyroscopic loads from the prop. After designing the rear fuselage with a double-wall structure, these loads were easy to accommodate.

The centre section of the fuselage ties the wing, front and rear fuselage halves and the main landing gear and the engine together. This is a trussed tubular structure because it was the easiest way to tie the points together, and its structural properties do not change with the heat of the engine. The front fuselage was built as a double-wall structure, again for its lightness and stiffness.

The main landing gear retracts hydraulically and has gear doors. The upper part of the gear leg is steel tubing while the lower part is a carbon fibre lay-up that acts as the spring. The unusual design of the gear is that it had to fold in half before it retracts. This keeps the fuselage narrow by moving the tyres forward. The nose gear also folds in half, but has the additional complication of having steering that must uncouple when retracting and recouple when extended.

All the engine components had to be custom built and are of my own design. They include, crankshaft, connecting rods, pistons and pins, camshaft, valves, block modifications to the lubrication system, fuel injection and plenum chamber, axial flow supercharger, axial flow water pump, axial flow oil scavenging, and gear drive. All the pumps and the supercharger were built as axial flow units to gain as much efficiency as possible; they added over 400 horsepower and raised the total to over 2,000 horsepower.

We believe that the efforts we have made will establish the validity of new prop technology that will improve performance and fuel economy and lower the cost of air travel. This technology can improve fuel economy by 15% to 30%, performance by 80–320 km/h and cut engine costs in general aviation by as much as US$ 25,000. The general aviation industry which has been in financial trouble for ten years will benefit the most by having a high speed prop that will allow engines to operate at higher speeds and make more power, more economically.

William J. Montagne with his Mach Buster I *in an advanced staye of construction.*

Hyperbaric aquarium

Minoru Yamada

309 Yamanouchi, Kamakura-shi, Kanagawa, 247 Japan

Japanese, born 14 November 1943. Researcher on diving technology and operations at the Japan Marine Science and Technology Centre. Educated in Japan; graduated from School of Fisheries, Nihon University, Tokyo, in 1966.

Many fish that are placed in aquaria come from low depths of the sea and it was consequently hypothesized that their comfort could be increased if they were held in a hyperbaric aquarium at a pressure similar to that in which they live in their natural environment. The hyperbaric aquarium was therefore developed with the objective of culturing fish, etc., under a high pressure (up to 5 kg/cm^2) for a long period.

Various requirements were stipulated: without reducing the pressure, it should be possible to filter and aerate the water and feed the fish; by using either air, oxygen or helium to pressurize the water, it should be possible to modify the level of dissolved oxygen and thus initiate hyperoxic and hypoxic conditions for the aquarium inmates; finally, the water should operate in a closed circuit so that there is no evaporation of the sea water and container transport is simplified.

Culturing fish under hyperbaric condition

When fish are placed in the hyperbaric aquarium and compressed, the fish's air bladder, which is filled with gas, shrinks due to compression, and the fish sinks to the bottom due to loss of buoyancy. Since carp, for example, can supply gas from the oesophagus to the air bladder, they may rise to the surface to breathe air; others swallow bubbles in the water, thereby supplying gas to the air bladder. Ordinary sea water fish can exchange gas only via the blood and gills, and thus it takes them one to three days to regain sufficient buoyancy. Fish with no air bladder show no changes in their behaviour after compression.

If fish living under hyperbaric conditions are exposed to a lower water pressure, their air bladders expand. In this case, as well, fish capable of exchanging gas between the air bladder and the oesophagus can release gas from the air bladder by belching. However, in other fish incapable of exchanging gas between the air bladder and the oesophagus, reduction in the water pressure causes expansion of the air bladder, increases buoyancy, and thus the fish finally

A general view of the hyperbaric aquarium designed and built by Minoru Yamada.

floats to the surface. We can estimate a fish's buoyancy on the basis of its swimming style, i.e. the degree of head lowering (fish with normal buoyancy swim while keeping their heads parallel with the body, but fish with too much buoyancy swim while keeping their heads downward in order to overcome the buoyancy).

In the hyperbaric aquarium system, the water pressure can be reduced in accordance with the rate of discharge of gas from the air bladder of fish, which can be estimated by the above described method. When we employed this approach for bream, 43 hours were required to reduce pressure from that at a depth of 30 m to that at the surface.

With this type of experiment, we can evaluate the ability of each fish species to discharge gas from the floating bladder. In fish with poor discharge of gas from the air bladder, no diver's sickness has been observed, but in fish with good discharge of gas from the air bladder, pressure must be reduced in a way that prevents occurrence of diver's sickness. We plan to conduct experiments to obtain data from which to compile a suitable decompression table.

Using the hyperbaric aquarium, it may now be possible to culture deep-sea fish that could not previously be maintained under atmospheric pressure. Deep-sea fish which go down to a depth of about 30 m are surmized to be incapable of living at a lesser depth due to their physiological characteristics. Therefore, although deep-sea fish are exposed to normal atmospheric pressure when they are caught, if we place them in the hyperbaric aquarium and increase pressure again to the necessary level, it may be possible to culture them.

Future plans for the study of marine biology

It is important to develop an aquarium which can reproduce a suitable water-pressure environment on land for marine organisms. If the aquarium can reproduce an environment ranging from shallow sea to deep sea, we can obtain new scientific information regarding many marine organisms. The present hyperbaric aquarium model can reproduce a water-pressure environment equivalent to that at a depth of 50 m or less.

In the future, we plan to collect marine organisms and transfer them to the hyperbaric aquarium without exposing them to a lower pressure so that they are maintained under the same high-water pressure and thus prove that they can be cultured for a long period. Also, it is thought that various technical problems relating to development of aquaria for deep-sea organisms will be solved step by step by conducting experiments using our hyperbaric device. Such efforts will eventually lead to the development of more advanced aquaria for deep-sea organisms.

Lastly, in order to elucidate the meaning of "pressure" for organisms, we would like to construct a hyperbaric laboratory which can be maintained at an absolute pressure of about three atmospheres and be capable of accommodating investigators. Marine organisms would be cultured in the laboratory and various experiments would be performed. In addition, plants, which grow under an absolute pressure of only 0.5–1 atmospheres, would be cultured under an absolute pressure of 3 atmospheres for a long period. In this experiment, the intention is to investigate the effect of "pressure" on organisms by studying morphological and other changes which may occur in the root, stem, flower, etc.

A detailed view of the compressor unit, valves and controls of Minoru Yamada's hyperbaric aquarium.

Robotic system for cementless total hip replacement surgery in dogs

Howard Paul

Orthopaedic Research Laboratories, TB 150, University of California-Davis, Davis, California 95616, United States

American, born 24 January 1949. Chief of Surgery, Sacramento Animal Medical Group. Educated in France and United States; D.V.M. from L'Ecole Nationale Vétérinaire d'Alfort in 1979.

About 196,000 hip replacement operations are performed each year in the United States, and over 300,000 worldwide. In the 1970s, acrylic bone cement was used to attach essentially all hip implants. Although this fixation method has been found to be successful for the first five to ten years after surgery, it is prone to failure after that, especially in active individuals. Consequently, considerable research over the past decade has focused on cementless devices that rely on a press fit and/or bone in-growth for fixation, and by 1985 approximately half of all hip replacements used cementless devices.

Critical factors affecting the efficacy of cementless implants include biocompatibility, stability of the implant, uniform stress transfer from the implant to the bone, and restoration of the proper biomechanics. The latter three factors, in turn, are signficantly affected by the proper placement of the implant relative to the bone and by the accuracy with which the femoral canal can be prepared to match the implant shape. Traditionally, the selection of the correct size of implant, and (to some extent) placement planning have been done by superimposing acetate templates of implant designs over X-rays of the hip. More recently, the development of computed tomography (CT) imaging and modelling has made it possible to design custom implants for individual patients. One somewhat paradoxical consequence is that the precision of design and planning now greatly exceeds the precision of surgical execution which is traditionally carried out using a hand-held, mallet-driven broach matching the implant shape.

A robot to extend the surgeon's skills

These considerations have led us to explore the possibility of using a robot to mill out the desired bone-cavity shape, rather than to rely on broaching. The positional accuracy of present-day industrial robots is more than sufficient for this task, and (indeed) robots are frequently used in low-precision material removal tasks. However, successful application of a robot to bone shaping nevertheless presents some challenges. These include determination of appropriate material

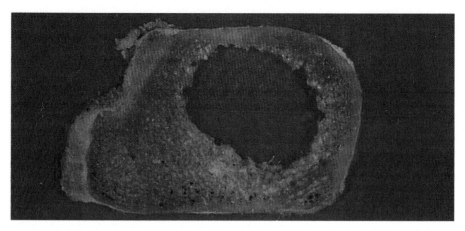

The proximal femur ready for hip replacement surgery showing the femoral canal that has been prepared using a hand-held broach.

removal process parameters (cutter design, speed, feed rate, etc.) for cutting both cortical and trabecular bone, development and verification of reliable means to relate the image-based surgical plan to physical reality (e. g., location of the bone relative to the robot), solution of a host of "clinical" and practical problems (sterilization, safety, etc.), and gaining actual clinical experience.

Our earlier studies have demonstrated successful machining of shapes in cadaver bones and have also illustrated the feasibility of using pre-operatively implanted calibration pins to accurately define a bone co-ordinate system both in the CT images and in the robot's workspace.

We are now developing a second-generation system suitable for use in an actual operating room, targeted at clinical trials on dogs needing hip implants. This system will provide the clinical experience necessary for eventual application to human surgery and (we believe) should also help a number of dogs with severe arthritis. In developing this system, we must also consider (at least by example) a number of issues that seem more generally applicable to robotic surgery. These include the man-machine interaction in a surgical situation since it is unlikely that the surgeon will push the "go" button and go out for coffee while the femoral cavity is being cut. He requires means of carefully monitoring the progress of the operation and intervening where appropriate.

One challenge here is that, to some extent, the surgeon must rely on the precision of the robot and sensing systems, which greatly exceed his own, to cut the right shape. On the other hand, the surgeon's comprehension of (and responsibility for) the total situation is clearly much greater than the machine's. Suitable interfaces must be provided to allow him to pause the application at any time, modify plan parameters, initiate error recovery actions, and provide positional guidance to the robot.

Status and plans

In March 1989, we began integration of our surgical system. However, before beginning clinical trials, we must repeat a number of our earlier experiments using the new system on dog bones to verify system integrity. We must also rehearse the procedure repeatedly both on plastic and cadaver bones and (in "dress rehearsals") on cadaver dogs.

We have also begun to consider future extensions of our work. As mentioned earlier, clinical experience with dogs is clearly very useful in considering whether and how to apply similar methods to people, although it would be premature to speculate on what a human-oriented system would look like or how long it might take to develop. We have begun to consider what would be required to modify the hip replacement system for use in other procedures. One obvious candidate is knee replacement, although we have begun to speculate about other applications as well, including femoral rodding, other trauma repair, hip implant revision, etc.

Other important areas are better pre-surgical planning and modelling (including such topics as optimal placement and design of implants, bone remodelling simulation, etc.), incorporation of better sensing methods of locating and tracing bone positions relative to the robot end-effector, incorporation of better force feedback and adaptive control for bone machining, identification and removal of acrylic bone cement, and more advanced man-machine interfaces.

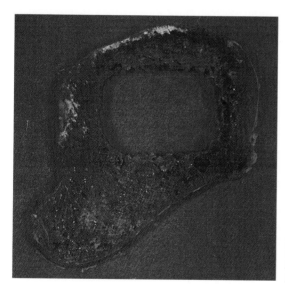

The proximal femur ready for hip replacement surgery showing the femoral canal prepared using a robot.

99

Low-cost coiled metal strip tubular structures for building construction

Alejandro L. Stein

Honourable Mention
The Rolex Awards for Enterprise – 1990

C. C. C. T. Torre B/Piso 4/OF. B-408, Avenida La Estancia, Caracas 10709, Chuao, Venezuela

Venezuelan, born 31 January 1948. Architect and Teacher, Central University of Venezuela. Educated in Venezuela, Canada, and Switzerland; B. A. (Mathematics) from University of Montreal in 1967.

The word *tronco* means "log" in Spanish and Tronco is a new technology which brings together various fast and efficient metal-working techniques for the production of uniquely versatile structures. The central idea of this technology involves the easy, local processing of coiled strip metal into strong structural components to be used in a multiplicity of applications. Tronco technology is being developed by a Venezuelan professional team under the aegis of a small firm called Organización Tronco S.A. as a part of an ongoing programme of research and implementation.

To date, the principal applications of Tronco structural systems have been in the field of building construction. In the short span of seven years, substantial results have been obtained in the design and erection of low-rise building structures (e. g., government housing and schools, mainly at remote sites). These significant achievements strongly confirm the inherent potential of what may be considered a breakthrough in this field. Further research is planned to extend Tronco technology to various other fields, including mass-produced furniture, agricultural structures, floating structures and even structures for outer space.

A significant factor is that the Tronco system can exploit the coiled metal production capacities of many developing countries, and is aimed at creating new markets for coiled steel output, while providing innovative solutions for local needs.

Tronco Building Structure System

The Tronco Building Structure System is an amalgam of old and new concepts in construction technology, combining the time-proven principles of the log cabin with the most advanced techniques of mechanized metal-working. With Tronco, a wide variety of dwellings and other low-rise buildings can be built at very low cost and with great speed. The result is affordable shelter which equals or surpasses other methods of construction, both old and new, in terms of sturdi-

A typical Tronco superstructure completed from start to finish in three hours by one skilled supervisor and six locally hired unskilled men.

ness, durability, flexibility of design and environmental efficiency.

Unlike many innovations in the construction field, Tronco's technology is of an open type, for its structures may be combined with a wide variety of secondary structures and finishing techniques in accordance with local conditions of labour, materials, building codes and environment. The structures themselves are indeed habitable shells, allowing users or local contractors to finish the buildings on their own, if needed.

General characteristics

The system draws its inspiration from the heavy wood structures used in the past in northern Europe and subsequently introduced to North America. The simplicity of assembly and the robust structures accomplished in log cabin construction are obvious advantages. In place of timber logs, the Tronco Building Structure System uses lightweight, hollow tubes of galvanized steel or aluminium. These are manufactured on the construction site with compact tube-forming machines, employing coiled strip metal. These tubes are then assembled, much as in the original log houses, forming the walls, upper floors and roofs of the buildings, creating a structurally and architecturally integrated unit. The construction is then finished in the manner best suited to its end use and available resources, with the tube structure either showing or completely hidden from view.

The system brings together numerous advantages: it is rapidly erected, is low in cost and versatile; it can be optimized for both mass-produced developments and custom-designed units; suitable for construction in the most remote sites; the finished structures are easily disassembled, transported and reused; they have durability and high strength and are impervious to fire, rust, rot and termites; production and assembly are easy; it entails minimal use of specialized labour; there is built-in thermal insulation in the structure itself, due to the airspace within the tubes; it is well adapted to both tropical and cold climates; and the technology is environmentally sound.

Future development

The Tronco technology is therefore flexible enough to be suitable for all sorts of buildings, as long as they are low, and these can be "tailored" to people's needs or wishes: the buildings can be covered with any kind of decorative material, such as paint or roughcast – in which case, wire netting is first placed over the tubes to give them a rough surface. The finishing can be easily done by the building owners or occupants. What is more, Tronco construction costs 20 per cent less than ordinary systems.

The objective now is to improve the Tronco system, which should be fully tested and proven by summer 1992. It will then be possible to expand from Venezuela and Florida, where most of the buildings have been constructed, to other parts of the world. There may also be an opportunity to spread the technology even further, and find other possible applications in mass-produced furniture, and even the space industry.

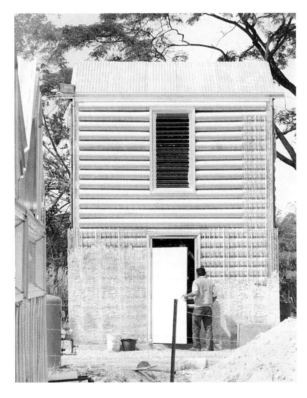

Tronco – the ideal structure for self-help housing: the habitable shell being finished by the owner.

Universal all-crop thresher for developing countries

Amir U. Khan

28 C. Mohamed Mazhar Street, Zamalek-Cairo, Egypt

American, born 15 June 1927. Agricultural Mechanization Adviser at Agricultural Research Centre, Egypt. Educated in India and United States; Ph. D. (Agricultural Engineering) from Michigan State University in 1967.

Wheat and rice are the two most important cereal crops in the world. In most semi-arid and arid developing countries, wheat is popularly grown in rotation with paddy. Because of the special requirement of hay-making from wheat straw, these two major cereal crops cannot be threshed with any one of the available threshing machines. Most developing country farmers do not have the resources to purchase separate machines for threshing wheat and paddy.

No single machine suitable for rice and wheat

Since wheat is comparatively more difficult to thresh due to the hay-making requirement, only mechanical threshing of wheat has gained popularity in such countries. Special beater-type threshers which can thresh wheat and simultaneously chop and bruise straw to produce fodder are widely used for threshing wheat. Such threshers are popular in India, Pakistan, Egypt, Turkey, Bangladesh, Iran and other Middle-Eastern and African countries. Because the beater-type threshers cannot be used for threshing rice, in these countries, paddy continues to be threshed either manually or by treading under animals or tractors. Such inefficient threshing methods require much labour and result in delayed threshing and excessive grain losses.

In the wet tropical Asian countries, where paddy rice is the major cereal crop, special axial flow threshers have gained rapid popularity. The Asian axial flow threshers were originally developed by the author at the International Rice Research Institute in the Philippines and are now locally produced in many tropical Asian countries. The axial flow threshers are versatile machines which can thresh all the major cereal grain crops. These machines, however, cannot make hay from wheat straw while threshing. For this reason such machines have failed to gain wide popularity in those developing countries where wheat and rice are grown in rotation.

The universal all-crop thresher being tested for the threshing of wheat.

If a thresher could be developed which could thresh all the major cereal grain crops and could also make hay from straw while threshing wheat, it could find a huge market in almost every developing country. The development of such a universal threshing machine is perhaps the most significant challenge that machinery designers and agricultural engineers are facing today in the developing countries.

Many attempts have been made in India and Pakistan to develop such a universal all-crop thresher. However, so far no machine has been developed which could satisfy the above requirements. Almost all attempts to develop a thresher of this type have involved the mounting of straw chopping knives or other cutting devices on axial flow threshers for chopping straw into small pieces for hay-making. The hay produced by these machines, however, is not sufficiently tenderized to be fodder.

I am now taking a different approach by developing a threshing machine which could be quickly converted in the field from a beater-type mode for threshing wheat while hay-making to an axial-flow mode for threshing paddy and all other crops. Thus the machine will offer a wheat-threshing performance which would be fully comparable to that of existing beater-type threshers. With a flip of a few levers, the machine could also be used as an axial flow machine for threshing paddy and all other cereal grain crops which today cannot be threshed by beater-type threshers.

The universal all-crop thresher

The machine has the following main innovations: dual concaves, one of perforated sheet metal for wheat threshing and a bar-type concave for paddy threshing; a door on the paddy concave to block it when threshing wheat; an adjustable set of axial flow louvres which can be set at 90 degrees to the drum axis for beater-type operation when threshing wheat and at 70 degrees for axial flow operation when threshing paddy or other crops; a hinged partial cover in the feed opening to permit full width feeding of wheat when in beater-type threshing mode, and feeding at one end of the threshing drum when in axial-flow threshing mode with paddy and other crops.

With the above-mentioned design features, the machines can be quickly converted from a conventional beater-type threshing mode to an axial-flow threshing mode by the four following steps: opening the paddy concave door; opening the straw thrower door; setting the axial flow louvres at a 70 degree angle to the crop movement; and closing the partial feed door to permit feeding at one end of the threshing drum for axial-flow operation.

Prototype machine built and tested in 1988

A conventional beater-type thresher which is popular for threshing wheat in Egypt was modified by incorporating the above-mentioned innovations during early 1988. Since the original beater-type threshing machine did not have a grain cleaning system, an air screen cleaner was added to the machine. This prototype machine was tested in 1988 from May to June during the wheat threshing and from September to October during the paddy threshing season.

The machine proved to be capable of threshing wheat well and of making fine quality hay since no basic changes had been made which would affect the beater-type threshing mechanisms. A wheat threshing output of 500–800 kg/h was obtained with the machine. Later the machine was also tested for threshing rice. A threshing output ranging from 840 to 1,230 kg/h was obtained with paddy. The machine was also tried in the axial flow mode for threshing sunflowers and beans with good results.

Further improvements are now being incorporated in the prototype machine and it will be tested again more extensively on all the major cereal crops grown in Egypt during 1989. On successful completion of the testing and improvement phase, the machine will be introduced to local manufacturers.

The first prototype unit of the universal all-crop thresher being tested for threshing paddy. Note the straw ejecting from the straw outlet.

A dream telescope for serious amateur astronomers

James Delwin Burr

1960 County Road 23, Evergreen, Colorado 80439, United States

American, born 17 December 1937. Proprietor of Tim's Mobile Industries. Educated in United States; attended Electronics School at Coyne Institute, Chicago, from 1959 to 1960.

Amateur astronomers and educational institutions who contribute greatly to the field of astronomy are often restricted to mediocre 8-inch and l0-inch commercially made telescopes that sell for a few thousand dollars, since research-grade telescopes may cost US$ 50,000 and more. To fill this gap, I have developed, built and tested an 18-inch telescope, baptized the Next Generation Telescope (NGT 18-D), that is unsurpassed for stability and accuracy whilst still being very light in weight. I would now like to build a 20-inch and a 24-inch telescope employing the same design concepts.

Overcoming drawbacks of conventional amateur telescopes

Telescope manufacturers seem to be locked into a mind-set of look-alike, mass-produced instruments which are susceptible to the slightest vibration, are difficult to control with any precision, are very heavy, and are scarcely portable. The telescope that I have developed has been designed to overcome all these defects; it is now complete and working, although we are making some minor changes so that it can be produced in volume.

For example, the NGT places the mirror close to the ground suspended in a 36-inch diameter drive ring which gives a pathway directly to ground for vibration. In this way, all of the weight is on-axis for minimum vibration and low centre of gravity. Rather than use a 3-inch or 6-inch gear, our telescope uses a 36-inch diameter ring with friction drive, which gives a degree of accuracy that is over ten times greater that that of a 3-inch gear. The NGT is made mostly of aluminum and is incredibly light for its size and stability. Although it has been said that a properly mounted 20-inch telescope requires a sturdy equatorial support weighing 2 tonnes, the NGT weighs a total of only approximately 70 kg, including the mirror.

The NG telescope assembled for use (left) and dismantled for transportation (right).

For astronomers who live in urban areas and travel to the country for observing, portability is a key factor. We have designed the NGT so that it can be assembled/disassembled in one to two minutes, and easily loaded into a compact station wagon. By extracting four bolts at the focal point adjustment, the nose assembly is removed and the serrurier truss rods snap from their spring steel bracket. For permanent observatory installation, these spring brackets can be replaced with a permanent fixture. Once removed, the nose assembly is secured inside the tub for transport.

Outstanding optics

The NGT is designed for comfortable viewing in any part of the sky due to the rotation of the eyepiece/diagonal holder. Without this feature, an astronomer can get into a very uncomfortable position viewing parts of the sky. I spent about a year in developing this idea because it requires very accurate surfaces to keep the optics in alignment. The nose assembly rests on nylon pads and is guided by spring-loaded nylon rollers. These nose assembly rings were made of aluminum and required special tooling. Both rings were made from one tool.

I have chosen to have the mirrors supplied to us by an outside company, Galaxy Optics of Buena Vista, Colorado, which has acquired a reputation for excellent quality and very consistent and dependable products. The mirror is 18 inches in diameter, f4.5, and made of 2-inch annealed Pyrex. It is located at the rear of the telescope where it rests on an 18-point flotation which is recognized as being the finest way to support a mirror. Other telescopes generally use 9-point flotation, but our telescope has 18 evenly balanced pads which support the mirror while preventing any unnecessary pressure areas.

When an astronomer tries to photograph through his equipment, he often finds that the camera is right up against the telescope with little or no room for adjustment. This is because the eyepiece used for visual work has a focal point which is different from that of the camera. Since the focal point is a factor of distance from the primary mirror, by moving the nose assembly closer to the mirror, this problem is overcome.

There are approximately 10,000 17.5-inch f4.5 telescopes currently in use; they have very simple but heavy wooden structures which do not track the stars. With our adjustable focal length, these astronomers can purchase the NGT without mirrors and adjust the focal length to match their mirrors (a 17.5 inch f4.5 has a focal length 2.25 inches shorter than that of an 18 inch mirror of the same f-ratio). This obviously makes the NGT more versatile. The telescope is driven by a very accurate, crystal-controlled quartz oscillator circuit that in turn feeds a stepper motor which rotates the drive roller and the 36-inch drive ring. The NGT is, in fact, three telescopes in one. F-stop capabilities located in the mirror dust cover give the telescope three different apertures: 3 inch, f27; 6 inch, f13.5; 18 inch, f4.5.

The fruit of five years of development work

The project is near completion after five years of development. People in the telescope industry are waiting with bated breath, sensing that the industry has not yet achieved the ultimate telescope. However, the 18-inch model need only be a start since our plan is to build both 20-inch and 24-inch models using the same sophisticated design principles.

Astronomers who have seen the NGT can hardly believe it. It is like a dream come true. I believe this is the telescope of the future, and plan to market it in the summer of 1989. I have developed a reputation in the industry for honesty, quality products, and innovation. I have had many years to watch the industry and I think I have a reasonable idea of what the people are looking for in a telescope. The tooling is almost all completed and paid for. There are a few minor items yet to modify and there are three other companies which will make parts for us as we need them. There is no question in my mind that the future could be ours with careful planning and some additional financial help. Then the astronomers around the world could have a dream come true.

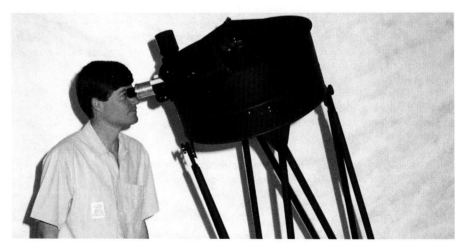

By using the rotating nose assembly of the NG telescope, even a relatively short person can view all the required parts of the sky.

Ethanol from sweet sorghum for use as cooking and lighting fuel

Anil Kumar Rajvanshi

Nimbkar Agricultural Research Institute, P. O. Box 23, Phaltan-Lonand Road, Phaltan 415523, Satara-Maharashtra, India

Indian, born 1 September 1950. Director of Nimbkar Agricultural Research Institute. Educated in India and United States; Ph. D. (Mechanical Engineering) from University of Florida, Gainesville, in 1979.

Cooking and lighting in rural India accounts for about 57% of the country's total energy consumption. There is already a major cooking energy crisis in certain rural areas, and reports talk of women in some parts of the country having to walk as much as 5–10 km every day to collect firewood. At the same time, sudden shortages of kerosene in rural areas darken the houses of thousands of people. The major fuel used for cooking in rural areas is wood. However, studies have shown that with the increased income level of the rural population, there is a perceptible shift towards liquid fuels like kerosene which has to be imported. Forecasts indicate that liquid cooking and lighting fuel consumption will continue to increase and, consequently, there is an urgent need to find a replacement for kerosene.

Ethanol as a kerosene substitute

Ethanol (ethyl alcohol) is one such alternative fuel since studies have shown that it can easily be used for cooking and lighting in new stoves and lamps, and can be produced from locally available renewable sources like biomass. Traditionally, alcohol has been produced from sugar cane, molasses, etc. However, the search for a multipurpose biomass source for alcohol production has highlighted the attractions of sweet sorghum (*Sorghum bicolor (L.) Moench*). It provides grain from its ear head, sugar from its stalk, and the bagasse is an excellent fodder for animals. Besides being a multipurpose crop, sweet sorghum has a great tolerance to a wide range of climatic and soil conditions. It is a short-duration crop, is cheaper to grow than sugar cane and requires less water.

Exploiting sweet sorghum for fuel production

Our institute, the Nimbkar Agricultural Research Institute (NARI), has launched an integrated programme to develop the cultivation of sweet sorghum and its use for production of cooking and lighting fuel. The programme entails: the breeding of high-yielding sweet sorghum varieties for alcohol production;

Alcohol distillation plant running on solar energy capable of producing 30–150 litres/day 95% (v/v) ethanol. On the right is shown the solar hot-water storage tank.

studies on sorghum distillation and fermentation, in particular using solar energy; and the development of stoves and lanterns running on alcohol.

Breeding work at NARI since the 1970s has resulted in sweet sorghum varieties which yield in one year, from one hectare, about 2–4 tonnes of excellent quality grain, 2,000–4,000 litres of 95% (v/v) alcohol, and sufficient bagasse for all the yearly fodder requirements for 3–5 cattle.

Fermentation studies have been conducted on the juice of our sweet sorghum varieties using strains of *Saccharomyces cerevisiae*, and the strain best suited for fermentation has a fermentation efficiency of 90%; fermentation was completed in 48–72 hours.

Distillation accounts for about 70–85% of the total energy consumed in alcohol production and the existing alcohol distillation facilities in India and other developing countries are usually fuelled by biomass such as bagasse, wood, etc., or by steam from sugar factories (which again is bagasse based). However, bagasse is an excellent raw material for paper and its use as boiler fuel wastes a precious resource. We have therefore installed a pilot solar distillation plant at NARI campus.

To date, the system has logged about 4,000 hours of operation and 70% of total yearly distillation load comes from solar energy while the rest is provided by fossil fuels (presently electric heaters) but fossil fuels can be replaced by bagasse. Development of devices like stoves and improved lanterns running on alcohol was essential as a part of an overall rural alcohol economy.

A wickless alcohol stove has been developed which runs on alcohol and has a thermal efficiency of 30–35%. Efforts are also under way to modify the existing wick stoves to run on alcohol. Two types of lanterns have been developed –

pressurized and non-pressurized. Efforts are under way to raise funding for the manufacture of a few hundred lamps for field trials.

Plans for the future

Much work needs to be done to spread this technology widely. Sweet sorghum is a relatively new crop in India and hence efforts are required to popularize it. We therefore propose to: breed better sweet sorghum varieties to increase the yields of alcohol per hectare; improve the effluent treatment of distillery waste; set up one mini-distillery producing 5,000 litres/day based on the above technology, hopefully in the next 2–3 years; and manufacture 100–200 lanterns and make them available to a small section of local population for field trials.

A major administrative problem is the reticence of the Government, which levies a heavy duty on alcohol for human consumption, to accept the usefulness of sweet sorghum alcohol for cooking and lighting and considerable public pressure will be required to change this attitude.

Alcohol lanterns which produce light equivalent to that from a 100-W electric bulb.

Hydrogen: a new breathing gas for deep diving

Henri-Germain Delauze

Honourable Mention
The Rolex Awards for Enterprise – 1990

Comex S. A., 36 boulevard des Océans, 13275 Marseilles Cédex 9, France

French, born 17 September 1929. Chairman, Comex Group. Educated in France; graduated from "Ecole Supérieure des Arts et Métiers", Aix-en-Provence in 1949.

Man's penetration to ever greater depths of the sea has become a major challenge and a great human adventure. Like man's conquest of space, man's presence in the depths of the sea is essential for certain specific or unprogrammed tasks.

Man is not an aquatic animal, so when he dives in this inhospitable environment what happens? The diver's physiological balance is modified by the pressure exerted on him. We must understand these modifications to be able to live and work safely at great depths. This aspect of our research programme could bring a fundamental scientific breakthrough. So, a better understanding of the pressurized-gas effects on the central nervous system will provide a better knowledge of how this system functions.

Nitrogen narcosis which occurs when divers breath normal air at depths of greater than 50 m underwater means that underwater work below this depth is carried out on a helium-oxygen "Heliox" mixture. The aim of this project being carried out by COMEX is to find a substitute for Heliox for deeper dives.

Helium is also a gas which has to be extracted from material that has been mined, whereas hydrogen can easily be produced from water electrolysis. Consequently, deep hydrogen-oxygen "Hydrox" dives could be performed in the future from an autonomous underwater habitat-like submarine.

When Heliox breathing gas mixtures are used below 250 m, two factors limit the diver's efficiency and induce fatigue and insecurity. First, there are the neurological effects of the pressure – high pressure nervous syndrome (HPNS) – caused by excitation of the central nervous system. Second, there are ventilation problems due to the density of the gas mix at high pressure. To overcome these two obstacles, COMEX launched the Hydra research programme on the use of Hydrox (hydrogen-oxygen) and Hydreliox (hydrogen-helium-oxygen) breathing mixtures.

Diver inside the wet chamber, equipped with an X-Lite helmet and a bail-out system (Photo: Alain Tocco).

An enthralling programme of development

In 1789, the French chemist, Lavoisier, placed guinea pigs in a mixture of "vital air" and "pure hydrogen gas" and observed that the animals could remain in this environment "for a long time without appearing to suffer from it". The first man who tested hydrogen on himself was Ane Zetterström, a Swedish engineer, who dived in the sea breathing Hydrox to depths of 40, 70, 110 and 160 m for several tens of minutes each time, without any effects.

In 1968, during the Hydra I programme, COMEX tried to place one of its top divers, René Veyrunes, in the open sea at a depth of 250 m. The diver's equipment was then inadequate to protect him against cold, and immediately after getting out of the diving bell, he had to return inside after changing his breathing circuit from helium to hydrogen. During Hydra II, simulation experiments on monkeys were carried out at depths of 300–700 m. COMEX then postponed its hydrogen project and started its major helium programme leading to the Physalie VI programme in 1972, in which two divers lived at a depth of 610 m and Janus IV, in 1977 in which six divers worked offshore from a drillship at 460 m.

Aware of the helium diving limits, COMEX decided in 1982 to reinstitute its hydrogen programme again to exploit the progress in deep diving equipment and technology and establish the practical methods for the use of hydrogen-containing mixtures and their advantages. During Hydra III, Henri Delauze, President of the COMEX group, and 16 divers made offshore dives to 70–91 m. The same year, in Hydra IV, six divers breathed hydrogen for the first time in a chamber, pressurized at 31 bar i.e., the equivalent of 300 m. Two years later, in 1985, COMEX achieved, with Hydra V, the first saturation dive in a Hydreliox mixture at a depth of 450 m with six divers.

113

To prove the industrial feasibility of hydrogen diving, a live demonstration of man's working capacities at sea was carried out at a record depth of 520 m. Two practice and selection dives were carried out in our research centre – Hydra VI (1986) at 520 m in Hydreliox and Hydra VII (1987) at 260 m in Hydrox. Subsequently, Hydra VIII confirmed that laboratory experience could be transferred to operational conditions in the open sea when, in early 1988, at depths of 520–534 m, divers demonstrated the type of operational efficiency normally observed with Heliox at a depth of 200–250 m. These human dives gave encouragement for the future use of hydrogen in operational diving at 300–600 m.

Future scope

Nevertheless, numerous questions remain to be answered and the aim of Hydra IX is to determine the useful range of Hydrox, minimum and maximum depths and the long stay effects on man. The shallowest depth at which Hydrox can be used is related to maximum oxygen concentration in relation to flammability and with a large margin of safety, it is possible to start a hydrogen oxygen saturation at a depth of 70 m. Hydrox use at relatively great depths is limited by the "hydrogen narcosis effect". Research has allowed us to consider the use of Hydrox beyond 260 m and Hydra IX will research maximum depths experimentally between 70–300 m. The third objective of the Hydra IX will be to research long Hydrox saturation times (50 days) with a total chamber time of over 70 days and this has the possibility of simulating life in an isolated confined space, like astronauts' space missions, which has attracted the participation of the European Space Agency.

The Hydra IX results could open up new horizons for human deep diving since, once certain technical problems have been overcome, hydrogen will offer new solutions to life under pressure and make it possible to open up the 300–600 m depth range to manned viable industrial diving operations.

The hyperbaric chamber complex at the Hyperbaric Research Centre operated by Henri Delauze's company COMEX (Photo: Alain Tocco).

The robotic laboratory of the future

Lane Yago

Intellibotics, Inc., 1617 Pacific Avenue, Suite 118, Oxnard, California 93033, United States

American, born 23 July 1953. President of Intellibotics. Educated in United States; B.S. (Chemistry and Biochemistry) from University of Maryland in 1976.

Throughout the realm of health and ecology, progress is to a large extent dependent on massive amounts of testing. Most of this testing work is still done manually: test tubes are labelled, samples are pipetted from test tubes, dilutions made, filtrations performed, sample tubes shaken – all by hand. There is now widespread agreement that sample preparation is a limiting factor in the speed of analytical processing. It may consequently be deduced that by automating and speeding up sample preparation, by being able to analyze a quantum leap more samples than we can currently, the answers to many of today's health and ecology problems may be found much, much sooner.

Many types of sample preparation devices are available and fall into two categories: inflexible devices such as test tube shakers which do nothing but shake tubes; and flexible devices such as stand-alone pedestal-type robots that require extensive computer programming, months of training and high capital outlay. I therefore came to the conclusion that there was an urgent need for a system of focused but flexible laboratory automation, and have elaborated a project to develop a robotic system which will perform the key laboratory sample-preparation activities and which is fast, affordable and intuitively easy to operate.

The workcell of the laboratory of the future

The laboratory of the future will comprise a central work station where well-trained staff control the entire activity through their computers: the handling of toxic solvents and contagious samples will be performed by robotic systems, precision and accuracy will be excellent and the results of laboratory work – data – will be of the highest quality. The drudgery of doing thousands of the same test over and over will be completely eliminated, giving scientists the opportunity to turn their attention to more creative work and produce solutions at an earlier date.

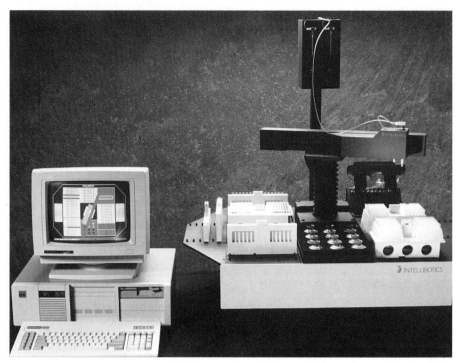

The Intellibot robotic laboratory workcell.

The Intellibot (which we are developing) is designed to be the first node in the hardware/software network for the laboratory of the future that we are designing. Everything about the Intellibot, its flexibility, its intelligence, its ease of operation and its speed and accuracy reflect what has been dictated by the needs of scientists.

The system is a "workcell", i.e. a fully automated factory area. The Intellibot is the first fully integrated workcell for the scientific community and consists of a robotic arm attached to the centre of a work platform designed to sit on existing laboratory benches and take up only 0.9 m^2 of space. The work platform comprises metal plates with conical pegs, each of which represents a discrete location, and all of these locations are resident in computer memory. The entire work platform is therefore computer-mapped and it is possible to give an order "Move a test tube rack to position 17"; the Intellibot will immediately and accurately respond to the command. Consequently, it can move test tube racks onto and off the work platform; in this way it has a unique ability to reach out past "itself".

There are the normal reservoirs for reagents and disposable tips for pipetting; however, the Intellibot has a unique system which gives it the ability to sense whether there is any liquid at all inside a test tube through the plastic disposable pipette tip it uses. In addition to liquid level sensing we have also built in feedback systems for pressure and torque sensing which give the Intellibot the reliability to run unattended by laboratory personnel.

116

A robot with built-in flexibility

We have built the Intellibot prototype to be truly flexible and, for example, one prototype is designed to perform solid-phase extraction, used for example for isolating a drug from blood. By building flexibility into the Intellibot it meets the needs of the majority of scientists.

We have created a very high-level robot computer language which completely eliminates any need to train the robot. The Intellibot already understands normal words used in experiments and sample preparations such as "move", "pipette", "mix" and "dispense", among others. The scientist enters an experiment into the "Design Experiment" screen using normal chemistry language, and in typical laboratory notebook style. When the experiment has been completely entered and all the necessary items for the experiment are on the work platform, the Intellibot can immediately run the procedure.

Finally, we plan to integrate expert systems into the Intellibot. This will allow the system to diagnose problems and try various solutions to alleviate them. It will also give scientists the opportunity to use the expert system to develop methods automatically – overnight – testing and re-testing various approaches to find the optimum way to perform a particular method. The scientist would evaluate the data the next morning and decide if the results are satisfactory. The Intellibot would truly then become the "automated technician".

To summarize, it may be said that the Intellibot is an easy-to-use, highly flexible, intelligent scientific robotic workcell which has been developed to the engineering prototype level, and we are poised to begin production engineering.

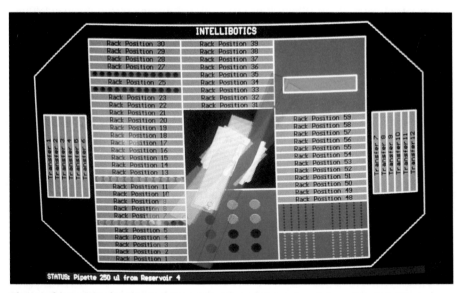

The graphics screen showing real-time animation of an overhead view of the Intellibot while it is operating.

Eye control and the severely disabled

Peter Albert Griffiths

Medical Physics Department, St George's Hospital, Long Leys Road, Lincoln, Lincs LN1 1EF, United Kingdom

British, born 27 December 1940. Director of Medical Physics. Educated in United Kingdom; Ph. D. from Nottingham University in 1964.

Communication has been described as the very essence of society, playing a central role in everyone's life. Those who cannot communicate are forced to live in a world of their own, the ultimate desolate existence. Throughout the world, there are thousands of people who, because of their severe disabilities, are in this situation – unable to take any part in society. What can be done for such individuals? How can their mental energies be released for them to communicate, to partake in the world around them, to have a degree of independence so as to preserve their dignity?

This is a challenging problem that has occupied a small group of professional staff at St. George's Hospital, Lincoln, United Kingdom, over the last five years. Their work has resulted in an innovative yet extremely simple method of harnessing eye movement to allow people with no other means of control full access to modern technology.

Harnessing the movement of the eye

During 1982, the Medical Physics Department at St. George's Hospital became involved in a programme to introduce microcomputers into the teaching environment of physically handicapped children, and encountered the problem of children who could not use even simple mechanical switches. Yet, despite their physical disabilities, these children had good control of their eyes and this led to the idea of using eye movement to activate the switches.

Under a research grant from the United Kingdom Department of Trade and Industry, a technique was developed to use a natural signal from the cornea retinal potential, to indicate eye movement. A potential difference of at least 1 mV exists between the cornea and the retina and, when the eyes move, this electrical field changes in orientation and this can be detected by simple skin electrodes. Horizontal movements of the eyes are detected by electrodes placed either side of the eyes, the electrical signal generated being amplified and

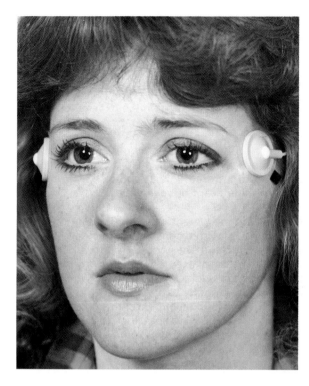

*The eye switch designed by
Peter Griffiths being worn.*

processed to provide a switch-closure effect. The user therefore has available a switch which can be activated by a simple horizontal glance of the eyes.

The outcome of this work – the Twinkle Eye-Controlled Switch – has proven to be an extremely adaptable and efficient device for harnessing eye movement. It is so simple that anyone can learn to use it within minutes, and it can control virtually anything from microprocessor devices to simple toys. It is very reproducible, independent of head position, and has been designed to comply with stringent safety standards for medical equipment. In addition the system is unobtrusive, does not interfere with normal vision and can be worn with spectacles.

The initial assessment was carried out by a girl suffering from cerebral palsy with severe athetoid movements and no speech. Due to her uncontrolled movements she had been unable to use any other aid and had very limited communication. With the eye switch coupled to a microcomputer she made rapid progress and within weeks became sufficiently proficient to communicate with other people and, for the first time in her life, she was able to write home. It has also allowed her academic ability to be assessed.

The technique has now been assessed in a great many environments by different users. At Lincoln, considerable experience has been accumulated in school, hospital and – most importantly – in a daily living context. The system has been used by children with congenital diseases and by adults who have acquired disability as a result of, for example, a stroke, motor neurone disease or muscular

119

dystrophy. One young mother who suffered a cerebral vascular accident, which left her paralyzed and without speech, has – against all odds – been reunited with her family at home and is able to make a contribution to domestic affairs.

Building on the work done at St. George's Hospital

Consequently, there is now urgent need to capitalize on the experience gained by the researchers at St. George's. During recent years two alternative approaches have been taken to automate the registration of eye movement. One, using a remotely positioned television camera to monitor the position of the eye, works well so long as the eye remains in the field of view. The other approach involves the use of reflected infrared light to indicate eye position. However, both new approaches have significant disadvantages.

The vision of the future is of an eye-movement detector, barely noticeable when worn, linked to a unit which serves as an extension of the individual. This will be the interface between the user and the world around, and will be permanently and continuously available no matter what the environment, i.e. indoors or outdoors, wheelchair or bed. In addition to being a powerful stand-alone communication unit, it will have the ability to interface the user with any other facility required. In order to generate independence, this linkage will be achieved entirely at the command of the user without the need of cables or another person. In order to keep costs to a minimum commercially available hardware must be used whenever possible. The work to date completely supports this concept and demonstrates its feasibility.

Three main areas of investigation and development need to occur: miniaturization of the eye switch; remote control; and eye control of mobility. With this work completed a practical and affordable system will be available to meet the needs of severely disabled people throughout the world.

The eye switch in use in a school.

120

Deep-ocean camera, video and lighting systems to explore RMS *Titanic*

Ralph Bradshaw White

2628 Corralitas Drive, Los Angeles, California 90039, United States

American, born 28 August 1941. Director of Photography for a National Geographic project. Educated in United States; Associate Arts Degree (Communications-Cinema) from Los Angeles City College in 1964.

Ralph White and Emory Kristof selected the task of developing deep-ocean camera, video and lighting systems since it posed significant photographic and exploration challenges; challenges that would have to be overcome before high-quality imaging could capture new, bizarre, intriguing and unknown images of the deep-sea realm. Significant effort was focused on the technical challenges. The achievements have provided vivid images of deep-sea discoveries and enlightened the public on the intriguing nature of the deep-water regions of the world. The results of their efforts and field explorations began in 1976 and continue to interest and impress both the layman and professional in equal measure.

Their joint contributions, along with the network team they have built, established them as world leaders in underwater photography-equipment design, development and application. Their investigations into the depths of Loch Ness did not reveal the monster, but did reveal evidence that the floor of the Loch Ness was once above lake level and occupied by earlier man. The discovery of the RMS *Titanic* was validated by their dramatic photo documentation, both video and still.

The history making find of the *Titanic*, and White's later dives to the wreck, have been aired on worldwide television, have received universal attention in publications, magazines, newspapers and have supplied spectacular graphic illustrations for numerous lectures. The contributions of White and Kristof have opened new vistas to the abyss, and it is expected that new discoveries and knowledge about the last earthbound frontier will follow as they continue the spirit of enterprise.

Approach to underwater exploration and discovery

To photograph the inhabitants, relics and features of the deep sea with a significant increase in picture quality and area coverage posed a number of

The camera and lighting array of the DVS Nautile prior to a dive. The 35 mm Benthos still camera is mated with a targeting colour video camera with two high intensity strobe lights. Above the viewing ports is the modified Benthos wide-angle still camera, the Sony colour video camera, and two fill lights. On the port side can be seen the vertically mounted "Super S.I.T." camera. Above the cameras is the full lighting complement (Photo by Ralph White).

challenges to underwater exploration and discovery. The achievements in which they have been involved include: development of the first acoustically triggered "Creature camera" and the illumination system for the Loch Ness "Monster" search; development of a new high-resolution lens system that could be installed on a deep-sea still camera; creation of an underwater stroboscopic illumination system with twice the normal light output; construction of the first mega-intensity lighting system to produce 24,000 joules of illumination – enough artificial light to photograph an entire shipwreck resting on the sea floor; integration of the first computer, wide-angle still camera, stroboscopic illumination and super flash; implementation of the first charged couple device video camera fitted with a servo-controlled micro-zoom lens system and lighting system suitable for photographing the hydrothermal vent dynamics and unique ecosystem inhabitants at depths of 3,000 m; design and construction of the first acoustically controlled motion picture and still off-load platforms for photographing a submersible at work on the bottom; construction of a computer-controlled "boomerang" camera system and its first deployment in the area of the *Titanic*.

A combination of inventiveness and feasibility

The conceptual design, development and fabrication of novel photographic techniques and specialized equipment for deep-sea applications has become a reality as a result of the creativity, technical competence, and ingenuity of these two men. White's and Kristof's span of inventiveness and creation of new

122

capabilities has included among others: acoustic controls, cameras, electronics, illumination systems, computer technology, optics, film material and processing, manned submersible technology, remotely operated vehicle technology, baiting techniques, remote control of cameras and lights. Their original ideas may have been transformed by others into hardware for the general use of the scientific community, but what is important is that they provided the requirement and selected the ways to go.

The feasibility of the early systems proposed by White and Kristof are now proven tools. They demonstrated extraordinary energy and ability to uncover sources for technical solutions to their unique requirements. Therefore, the technical and economic feasibility risk is reduced by their thorough knowledge of present and future trends in photographic technology. The feasibility of additional innovative breakthroughs in underwater photography by White and Kristof is virtually assured as their pattern of success is strongly allied to projected trends in the field.

The activities of White and Kristof have grown to represent a continuing series of deep-water projects spanning the globe. The project teams include scientists, engineers and technicians representing nations that desire to participate in deep-sea exploration organized by them. Funds are derived from a variety of sources, and monetary awards will be dedicated to exploration and discovery projects planned for the world's oceans and Lake Baikal.

In 1989–1991 the energy, dedication and commitment demonstrated on completed projects and advancements in technology will be applied to new quests planned for the underwater world of the giant squid, submarine canyons and submarine mountain ranges, large and deep lakes like Lake Baikal, the habitat of the coelacanth, and other poorly understood areas of the world.

The eerie bow of the Titanic four kilometres below the surface of the Atlantic (Photo courtesy of the Titanic Trust).

Fluoride glass optical fibres

Marcel Poulain

Honourable Mention
The Rolex Awards for Enterprise – 1990

17 square André Desbois, 35700 Rennes, France

French, born 11 April 1945. Professor, Department of Solid State Chemistry, Rennes University. Educated in France; Doctorat d'Etat from Rennes University in 1973.

The adventure of fluoride glass began in March 1974, by an accident that occurred when I had been working for several years on fluoride complexes of zirconium, and one of our experiments unexpectedly produced pieces of glass instead of crystals; these were the first fluorozirconate glasses (or heavy metal fluoride glasses) and their occurrence was unpredictable by current glass formation theory. Their structure seemed to be quite different from that of classical glasses and I predicted that they would have unusual properties and behaviour. They do in fact show good chemical resistance to fluorinating reagents, are transparent in the ultraviolet and infrared spectra up to 8 mm, are promising as a laser host for rare earths, have a relatively high fluorine anion conductivity, and have lower optical losses than oxide glasses.

Since no company or research centre was willing to fund application development, I decided to set up "*Le Verre Fluoré*" – a company which would develop and manufacture these new fluoride glasses, and we commenced operation in 1980; by this time Japanese and American researchers were already showing increased interest in fluoride glasses, mainly for ultra-low-loss optical fibres. With limited funding, manufacturing experience and management and marketing know-how, the task has been a challenging one. Nevertheless, our problem-solving skills in fluoride glass technology are high and, for example – although it took us a year – we were, by 1982, able to understand the glass surface phenomena and draw fluoride glass preforms into fibres without surface defects.

We have now developed a range of specialized technologies and have manufactured fluoride glass fibres for various customers in most developed countries. In particular, a special infrared fibre has been produced for the NASA Jet Propulsion Laboratory. This has been backed up by extensive research on additives, fluoride chemistry, interferences between chemical factors, and devitrification problems, etc., derived from close collaboration between ourselves and the University of Rennes.

Marcel Poulain (left) and Michel Poulain (right) co-inventors of fluoride glasses.

Fluoride optical glass fibres for telecommunications, medicine and industry

If it were possible to reduce the level of optical losses in optical fibres, it would be possible to increase the spacing between signal repeaters (in such things as optical submarine telecommunications) in fibre cables, from the current figure of under 100 km to over 1,000 km. The potential for improvement on this count with current single-mode silica fibres is limited and hope for development rests with fluoride glass.

An impediment to progress here lies in certain defects which induce wavelength-independent scattering. The origin of these defects is still a matter of research and discussion, but the defects themselves result in variable and significant losses which drastically limit the practical length of a fibre to less than 100 m. However, our team has identified the responsible mechanism and has developed a method of reducing losses and increasing fibre length, making a significant step toward the achievement of fluoride glass optical fibres with losses lower than those of silica fibres. Our development programme will target: a reduction of defects in bulk glass; control of the quality of the core/cladding interface in preforms; low-loss multimode fibres; low-loss single mode fibres; large-size preforms for multi-kilometre fibres; and chemically resistant compositions and protective coatings.

It is foreseen that optical losses lower than 1 dB/km over 1 km will be obtained within two years, and losses lower than silica within five years. The real schedule will depend partly on funding – which is limited – and also on the unpredictable aspects of research.

The use of fluoride glass fibres in medicine derives directly from the transparency of the fibres in the infrared spectrum. They have multiple applications such as: the monitoring of patients under anaesthesia; the measurement of carbon dioxide concentrations directly in the blood; the analysis of molecular species in blood and tissues; thermal imaging through endoscopes; and laser surgery, including the burning and volatilization of tumours. Special fibres have to be developed for each application, and we have extensive exchange programmes with companies and/or research centres working at system development.

Furthermore, there are several fields in which fluoride glass fibres open new and attractive possibilities including: remote chemical analysis; thermometry; power delivery; infrared instrumentation, etc. Optical fibres are actively being studied as next-generation sensors, and fluoride glass fibres will open new possibilities because of their transmission range and specific optical properties.

Further developments in perspective

For these various applications, current fibres have to be optimized. Strength will be increased, protective coatings and cables will be improved. A major research and development effort will need to be devoted to the extension of the infrared transmission range in order to increase accuracy of thermal measurements and to ensure transparency at CO laser wavelength. Meanwhile, the expected decrease in optical losses will allow longer operating lengths.

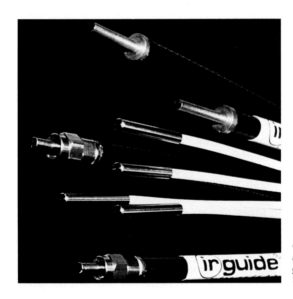

Optical fibres and cables manufactured from fluoride glasses and transparent in the infrared spectrum.

A folding bicycle in a handbag

Miguel Angel Martinez Echenique

Lavalle 1537–1. piso "G", 1048 Buenos Aires, Argentina

Argentine, born 26 October 1949. Chief of Head Office Register No. 443, Civil and Commercial Public Instruments of Buenos Aires. Educated in Argentina; graduated from University of Buenos Aires as Notary Public in 1974.

I was building a house on the outskirts of Buenos Aires and each day I had to travel there to supervise the work being carried out on the construction site. The route to the site was notorious for its traffic congestion. I, therefore, wanted to avoid using my car and, instead, use the express bus service which would drop me some 1,200 m from my ultimate destination; from there I could walk to the building site.

It was during these daily journeys that I began to conceive the idea of a bicycle that could be folded up to be taken onto a bus or other form of public or private transport and then unfolded to travel from the bus stop to the final destination and vice versa. The machine would obviously have to be light in weight, small in dimensions when folded so that it could fit under a bus or train seat, not constitute a danger to other passengers, and be fully functional and safe when unfolded and ridden on the highway.

A fold-up design

I started by putting my ideas down on paper, commencing with the bicycle chassis which I saw would be the key component. I wanted to retain the conventional chassis shape and decided that the approach would be to divide the frame just forward of the main upright tube so that one part would hold the front wheel and handlebars and the other part the back wheel and chain mechanism. This provided virtual symmetry of shape between the two separate units so that they would overlay each other in the carrying bag. A plate was welded to the extremity of each unit so that the two sections can be accurately aligned and positively locked together; the screw that passes through the two plates does not in fact exert any pressure and the join would work perfectly safely without it.

It was also necessary to design a way of removing the pedals and pedal levers without the use of tools and of making sure that, when the final pedal levers are removed, the drive chain wheel stays in place. I decided to use the existing system

127

Miguel Martinez Echenique's bicycle, folded in its cover ready for transportation.

of cotter pins but improved their fit so that they can be easily removed by hand; a ring was attached to one end to provide a grip to facilitate removal and the normal hexagonal retaining nut was replaced by a wing nut. The drive chain wheel was welded to the bottom bracket axle to ensure that the pedals can be removed without the chain wheel being disturbed.

The length of the axle on the front wheel has been shortened by 2–3 cm to reduce dimensions and the same approach could be applied to the back wheel if necessary.

Transportable and easy to assemble

The carrying bag has been designed with side pockets to hold the pedals and levers and various straps are provided inside to hold the frame securely in position. Protective pads are fitted at various critical locations to stop the metal parts from snagging the fabric. Straps on the outside will allow the bicycle to be suspended from the shoulder for easy transportation.

Assembly and dismantling entail merely joining together (or taking apart) the two halves of the frame, fitting or removing the pedals and pedal levers, locating the handle bars in position and fitting (or removing) the saddle. Once this has been done the bicycle is ready to ride (or carry away). No tools at all are required either for assembly or dismantling. Once the bicycle has been taken to pieces and placed inside its carrying bag it takes up a minimum of space – no more than a few centimetres more than the diameter of its wheels.

Improvements possible for the future

A number of improvements are under consideration and relate to the braking system, the fitting of a gear-change mechanism and perhaps the inclusion of a speedometer. However, the main objective will remain that of having something which is highly portable and which can be packed easily into the boot of a car, etc.

The folding bicycle, assembled ready for the road.

Groupers in love: Filming grouper mating aggregations in Honduras

John Christopher Fine

150 Puritan Drive, Scarsdale, New York 10583, United States

American, born 12 October 1948. Attorney, author and marine scientist.
Educated in United States; LL. B.-J. D. from Notre Dame Law School in 1967.

Fishermen call it the grouper moon. It brings them fortune, for these tasty fish can then be caught in great numbers and sold to processing plants and exported. Once each year, after the shortest day of the year in December, members of the species *Epinephelus striatus* (the Nassau grouper) leave their territorial homes in caves and crevices in the reefs of the Caribbean and begin a voyage to spawn. What triggers this phenomenon is little understood and only rarely witnessed. They have never been observed before in an undisturbed environment without heavy fishing pressure that often wipes out the spawning population of fish.

Working with friends who accidentally observed the groupers aggregating in this place where the banks rise up to shallower depths from 230 m of water, I have spent two years diving in this shark-infested, current-riddled area of Honduras, to observe and document the aggregations. To date no commercial fishing interests have exploited or disturbed the mating fish, either catching them coming from or leaving the site in shallower water. The reason for this is that the site is far off land, to the north and east of Guanaja, with frequent squalls and high seas. Commercial spearfishing is pursued in these islands but the indigenous fishermen are afraid of the many sharks that frequent these waters. Undersea currents are also dangerous. They are one of the natural phenomena that I have been studying to determine just how thousands upon thousands of groupers get to this one spot for a few days, once each year.

The mystery of the grouper

In 1988 and 1989, I traveled to Guanaja and, for the period of time before and after the full moon in January, I dived as often as my decompression limits would allow. Our little team of diving instructors, whom I have now certified as licensed scuba instructors, have made observations, measured fish and participated in dissections to study their anatomy and the maturity of the gonads of selected individuals. Our photographs and information are being shared with a handful of scientists who have an interest in this most important food fish.

John Christopher Fine (second from left with tape) measuring Nassau groupers taken by spear fishermen during the mating aggregations off Guanaja, Honduras.

This project will continue to examine the scientific aspects of what is really "the great grouper mystery"and will attempt to provide answers to a number of puzzling questions. How do the groupers get to this place? How do they find it? What makes them go? How do they get back home? Where and how far do they come from? What triggers the sex change in these fish? Nevertheless, it also forms part of a larger picture in the world's developing countries: ecology versus economy.

Fishing, the habits of fishermen as well as the dependence of villages on fishing are all part of the human interest situation that I have been studying as well. Interviews with elder fishermen and residents of little villages and settlements have provided me with a wealth of information about the habits of these fish over time. The economy of fishing is also important, and is likewise an aspect of this project. Fish processing and exporting plants have just expanded operations on Guanaja to export lobster, conch and fish to the voracious United States markets. With flash-freezing and air shipment (as well as refrigerated container ship despatching) to the American markets, fishing pressure will now increase.

Today, spearfishermen and commercial lobster fishermen go out in dilapidated and unsafe vessels, put in at the Mosquito Coast of Honduras, take on 40 to 60 Indian divers, and set off for a month of fishing. These overloaded ships ravage the reefs, taking a toll of human and marine life. The Indian divers are not trained. They dive six to 12 tanks of air a day on the most primitive scuba equipment. They dive repeatedly to depths of 40 m and more. These fishermen often suffer the dreaded diver's disease, the bends (decompression sickness) which cripples and maims 250 Indians each year. There are upwards of 15 deaths from decompression accidents each year.

More than just a nature film

This project will not only study the natural history of the fish, but will film and photograph the anthropology and human interaction of fishermen with their environment. We have already "in water recompressed" a native diver who was paralyzed from the waist down, resulting from a decompression accident, while diving his fifth tank of air to 40 m. The diver had no knowledge of even how to clear his mask underwater. He told me he would simply swim fast up to the surface to empty the water from his mask, then swim back down to resume his underwater fishing with prog or spear. One example of the inherent danger of greed and exploitation of fisheries resources by indigenous populations when outside interests offer new methods of refrigeration is the way native fishermen preserve their catch with chemicals, some of which are restricted by many nations as food adulterations.

The project will continue my work previously undertaken, where nature only reveals her secrets a little at a time and then only over years of research. By filming and photographing the aggregations of Nassau Groupers, we will be able to preserve a natural phenomenon and share the knowledge with others. I intend to make a documentary film for international television and publish the information in subsequent books and articles.

Nassau grouper sporting a colour change. Changes in colour are being studied and compared with the sex of these fish.

Dexterous hand-master technology for human hand rehabilitation

Beth A. Marcus

Exos, Inc., 78 Woburn Street, Lexington, Massachusetts 02173, United States

American, born 11 May 1958. President of EXOS Inc. Educated in United States and United Kingdom; Ph. D. (Biomechanics) from Imperial College of Science and Technology (University of London) in 1983.

Over 110,000 people in the United States alone annually have hand problems requiring post-surgical rehabilitation. When the injury is sustained or the disease manifests itself, a method of determining the level of impairment and providing a diagnosis is required. After the treatment is performed, rehabilitation is often required and may take anywhere from a few days to many months. Monitoring the patient's progress is currently an inaccurate and time-consuming process. Today, there is no precise, widely accepted technique for evaluating human hand function and little objective data on the relationship between measured parameters and diagnoses.

Range of motion (ROM) measurement is an accepted part of clinical assessment of the hand, and the current methodology (manual goniometer reading) has a relatively low accuracy and is time consuming. Therefore a system which could rapidly, accurately, reliably and repeatably collect ROM data, track patient progress, and produce patient records and insurance reports would be of extremely high value.

Improved hand-ROM measurement

We have begun the process of developing such a system based upon the Dexterous Hand Master (DHM) technology designed to convert 16 human hand joint motions into control signals for a robot hand with 16 joints. This is accomplished with a mechanical linkage or exoskeleton which attaches to the back of the human fingers and follows their motions comfortably and accurately. The linkage carries sensors which produce a near linear signal output which varies with angular retention. The sensors connect to a specially designed analogue board which plugs into a microcomputer and connects to an analogue-to-digital converter.

We wish to undertake a two-phase clinical research programme to develop effective hand rehabilitation protocols using DHM-derived devices. In the first

133

The Dexterous Hand Master, a high-precision exoskeleton, which measures human hand joint motions.

phase, the DHM measurement technology will be used to develop a data base on human hand function in health and disease. In the second phase, the data base will be analyzed and the results used in the development of rehabilitation protocols and DHM-derived devices for specific conditions.

The benefit of developing these protocols and devices is that they will be used to help patients recover faster or more fully. Although having impaired hand function may not in itself be life-threatening, this impairment affects a person's ability to earn a living and take care of himself or herself. Therefore the utility of the hands has a profound effect on every aspect of a person's life.

Building a data base of hand function

The first portion of the project is the collection of data on human hands. A preliminary scan of the literature indicates that there is information available about hand grip and pinch strength, but little on range of motion (ROM). To function in daily living, both dexterity and strength are required. Therefore the measurements will be taken primarily on range of motion and, to the extent necessary to confirm the existing data, on strength. A sampling of the healthy American male and female adult populations will be made. Both active and passive ROM data for each of the joints will be collected for all fingers. In addition radial/ulnar deviation will be measured for each finger (though not routinely evaluated in clinical practice, it is important in task performance), and anatomic measurements will be taken. Then similar measurements will be made on a sampling of injured and diseased hands. The results will be integrated into a computerized data base which can be used to evaluate the level of impairment that a patient has with respect to a particular attribute, and to track progress over time.

Developing new rehabilitation protocols

In the second task, we will develop rehabilitation protocols based upon an analysis of the data base developed in the first task. There are two types of protocols for rehabilitation to which the DHM technology and its natural extensions may be applied: feedback goniometers; and hand-specific isokinetic exercisers.

Feedback goniometers have been used for hand and wrist rehabilitation in a limited number of experiments with some success. The utility of these devices would be greatly enhanced by providing a more adaptable and comfortable sensing mode, such as the DHM linkage. In addition, automated data harvesting and a real-time feedback display capability would also improve their utility. Once these tools are configured for rehabilitation, a study of the effect of this type of training on the time required to achieve functionality and on the final level of impairment will be conducted on several injured patients.

In recent years, a number of large and expensive devices, which are used in rehabilitation to perform isokinetic exercises, have been developed. In some instances, these devices have helped patients to recover, but none specifically allows a patient to work on the portion of the hand affected by the injury. Therefore, although patients may improve functionality, they may never know whether they have improved the injured portion of the hand. By developing a resistance element which can be applied selectively to a joint of interest, the results will be entirely joint specific. Thus an experiment which compares joint-specific rehabilitation to generic rehabilitation (whole body, or limb) will be conducted.

The results of these two tasks will be rehabilitation tools and protocols which will provide clinicians and patients with scientifically derived and proven approaches to rehabilitating the hand.

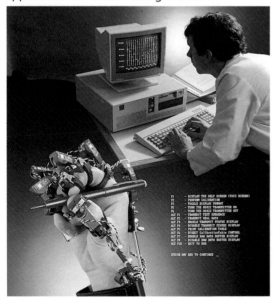

The applications of the Dextrous Hand Master include controlling robots and computer simulations, medical diagnosis and measurement of human factors.

135

Perseus: A vehicle for Antarctic ozone chemistry research

John S. Langford

Honourable Mention
The Rolex Awards for Enterprise – 1990

2509 St. John Place, Alexandria, Virginia 22311, United States

American, born 20 May 1957. Independent Consultant. Educated in USA; Ph.D. from Massachusetts Institute of Technology.

The discovery of the hole in the ozone layer over Antarctica in 1986 has added new urgency to our concerns about the impact of chlorofluorocarbons on the ozone layer. Similarly, the effects of "the greenhouse gases", carbon dioxide and methane, have also reached public prominence. A limiting factor in research here is the availability of data needed to fully understand the complicated chemical processes at work, etc.; to gain the necessary resolution, *in-situ* measurements remain necessary. Data up to altitudes of about 22 km can be obtained with ER-2 aircraft or up to 40 km with large balloons, but the ER-2s can stay aloft for only eight hours at a time at a cost of about $8,500/hour; balloons provide only vertical profiles and damage their payloads upon landing, limiting the flight rate.

The launch by NASA in 1991 of the 16-month Upper Atmosphere Research Satellite and its planned follow-on, the Earth Observing System (EOS), will increase the need for atmospheric comparison data. In addition, NASA's proposed "Mission to Planet Earth", costing $15-$30 billion, will also require expanded use of aircraft for instrument development, instrument calibration and measurements of a higher-resolution than those attainable from satellites. Furthermore, the development of low-cost aircraft could provide an accessible, highly localized platform for use by universities, and produce major improvements in the training of atmospheric research scientists.

Exploiting the successes of *Daedalus* and *Voyager*.

The immense progress made in low-speed aerodynamics and lightweight composite aviation structures that made possible the 126 km human-powered flight of *Daedalus* between Crete and Santorini in 1988 and the round-the-world flight of *Voyager* in 1986 is directly transferable to the type of high-altitude aircraft we are proposing. Further, energy-conversion technologies such as solar cells and fuel cells continue to mature and will, during the 1990s, reach commercial status. Thin-film solar cells made from amorphous silicon offer sufficiently high power-to-weight ratios that propulsion of lightweight airframes is now a possibility.

The Monarch *human-powered aircraft during testing in 1983. With a wingspan of 19 m, the* Monarch*'s size closely approximates that of the unmanned* Perseus *ozone probe. The aerodynamics and electric propulsion system of the* Monarch *led directly to the* Perseus.

Fuel cells have reached the point where they too may be considered as primary propulsion for aircraft.

Finally, lightweight, low-power electronics will soon allow "intelligent" or autonomous operation, and one of the first places where advanced electronic technologies will literally replace humans is as a pilot in aircraft. The possibility exists for "satellite-type" operations, where a central ground facility monitors aircraft operation and gives overall guidance but leaves specific local decisions to on-board systems. This will allow development of very long-duration platforms.

Perseus – a remotely piloted vehicle

These factors combine to make a new generation of aircraft both viable and useful. Traditionally, research aircraft have been developed only with direct government sponsorship. The goal of this project is to use private grants as a stimulus to development, thereby accelerating the availability of these important international tools.

Perseus is a small, battery-powered remotely piloted vehicle (RPV) designed to support ozone chemistry research. Intended to undergo a series of flight experiments in Antarctica beginning in 1990 or 1991, the aircraft is designed for low development cost and short development time. This dictates the use of commercial lithium batteries for electric propulsion and the use of a remote control system developed for existing RPVs.

With its 18 m wing-span and a weight of 316 kg, the *Perseus* could reach an altitude of at least 25,000 m and carry 50 kg of equipment. It could hold that altitude for about 30 minutes at a speed of 320 km/h. This aircraft would cost much less (for construction) than the ER-2. Of course it would have a much shorter independent flying time, but since it would be launched from a base in the Antarctic, it could fly more often. Its advantage over balloons is that it can be controlled, can take off even in a 60 km/h wind and can make a soft landing. Finally, unlike satellites and laser radars, it could take localized readings.

The *Perseus* has a much broader scope of application than just taking measurements in the ozone layer: it could help in atmospheric research all over the globe. Its comparatively low cost (estimated at US$200,000 for the first prototype) and the small number of personnel required (only three persons) would make it a very handy tool for scientists who study the atmosphere, beginning with meteorologists. Based at the American station MacMurdo, the *Perseus* should be able to fly in total darkness at a rate of at least once a week.

Like its implementation, the *Perseus'* operation is original: it will have a tail-mounted propeller driven by an electric motor powered by the latest generation lithium thionyl chloride battery. Electric power was chosen because the conventional internal combustion engine does not work at very high altitudes due to the lack of oxygen. The use of batteries restricts the aircraft to fairly short missions however, because even the best batteries still have a very limited capacity. The batteries we are planning to use will have to be changed after each flight and cost US$15,000 a piece. Given the total budget of this type of mission, and the low cost of developing the *Perseus* as well as the small number of flights to be made, this still gives the operation an acceptable rate of return.

We plan to develop the *Perseus* in four phases: a feasibility study, construction of a prototype aircraft, validation of design through extensive testing (with construction of one or more aircraft) and then flight operations in the Antarctic. It is our intention to undertake an aggressive development effort with critical attention to minimum costs, and use the operational capability of the platform to develop larger fuel-cell-powered vehicles. Our plan is to initiate the project with private grants, demonstrate viability of concept and then seek government support for actual operations in Antarctica.

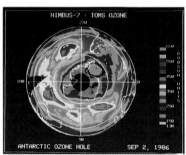

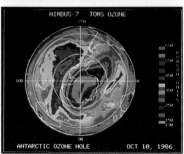

The ozone hole above the Antartic as shown by pictures produced using data from a total Ozone Mapping Spectrometer instrument which monitors the ozone over the entire Earth every day with a 50-km spatial resolution. On 2 September 1986 (above), the Arctic ozone hole is deepening and expanding. On 10 October 1986 (below), the Antarctic ozone hole is near to maximum depth. The dark violet region at 90E longitude, 75–85S latitude within the light violet area contains ozone values less than 175 Dobson Units (DU). The lowest value is 163 DU, approximately 20 DU greater than the lowest observed in 1985, and very similar to the values observed in 1984.

Technology for village manufacture of a nutritionally improved cookie

Mario R. J. Molina-Aguirre

Division of Agricultural and Food Science, INCAP, Carretera Roosevelt, Zona 11, 01011 Guatemala City, Guatemala

Guatemalan, born 1 December 1940. Co-ordinator of Technical Co-operation and Scientist at the Institute of Nutrition of Central America and Panama. Educated in Guatemala, United Kingdom and United States; Ph. D. (Food Science) from Rutgers State University, New Jersey, in 1971.

It has been shown that, in the Central American area as well as in other parts of the world, substantial numbers of the population are suffering from protein-calorie malnutrition, as well as iron and vitamin-A deficiencies. Moreover, problems such as these are more evident in the rural than in the urban population groups. It has also been found that a high correlation exists between poverty and the degree of malnutrition. It would seem that the most pressing and most difficult to overcome of the various macro-nutrient problems is the calorific deficiency in the diet.

The need for nutritional supplements

On the other hand, from the agricultural point of view, it has been found that it is possible to produce nutritionally desirable commodities (such as for example soybeans) even in the more nutritionally vulnerable rural communities of Central America. Nevertheless, soybeans do not form part of the dietetic habits of the population groups in question and, consequently, their cultivation is not a common practice. It was therefore decided that it would be of interest to attempt to develop an appropriate village-type of technology to introduce the use of these grains (e.g. soybean, velvet bean, and the like) – which are desirable from a nutritional point of view – into highly acceptable, stable and safe food products, suitable for feeding to infants (of six months of age and older), and to pre-school and school children. In addition, under ideal conditions, the food product(s) chosen for nutritional improvement with the grains mentioned above, would also represent a good vehicle for incorporating calories into the diet in a high caloric density form.

Preparation of the nutritionally improved dough for the cookie manufactured by rural bakers.

Development of an appropriate technology

Based on previous knowledge of the protein complementation between cereals and legumes and on the acceptability of a high-calorie cookie-type product, it was decided to explore the possibility of developing a cookie based on a vegetable (cereal and legume) mixture. This alternative was supported by the fact that Central American rural populations consume preferentially a local, typical cookie-like "sweet"-type of bread and by previous experience that had been obtained on the degree of gelatinization needed in maize either for the manufacture of a typical "tortilla" or for pasta products production. Several limitations on the acceptability of nutritionally improved typical "tortillas" have been reported, and this is the reason why this alternative was dropped when intended for a village level. Also, most rural populations have an oven, and the technology for the wood-heated oven is widely known and practised.

After several trials, an adequate process was developed, tested and adopted. The process proved to be valid for use of either common maize, opaque-2 maize or sweet sorghum as cereals, and either soybeans, velvet beans, chick-peas or cow-peas as legumes. The use of soybeans was encouraged in view of the high caloric density of this legume. The chemical/nutritional characterization of the cookie product revealed the expected improvement in protein content and quality as well as in caloric density. The cost analysis demonstrated that the cookie would be a relatively low-cost product that could be produced in the rural area; it also proved to be highly acceptable to pre-school and school children as well as highly stable when stoved (up to six months at room temperature).

Implementation of the technology

In the second semester of 1986 and the first six months of 1987, training courses on the preparation of the nutritionally improved cookie were given in various rural villages of Guatemala and met with considerable interest and success. Since the colour of the product proved to be critical in ensuring the high available-lysine content and the high protein quality that were to be expected of the finished product, a colour scale was developed so that the baker could easily and effectively maintain an accurate level of quality control.

The Guatemalan Ministry of Education has since displayed enthusiasm about the product, and has decided to incorporate the cookie into the school snack programme. Two contracts were subsequently drawn up between the Guatemalan Government and the local rural bakers. At present, a 28 g cookie is offered each day to 1,200,000 Guatemalan school children. This is improving local soybean production and income, accelerating the movement of money at a rural level and, hopefully, enhancing the nutrition of the rural school children through a high caloric density food of an improved protein quality. Honduras and Costa Rica are now interested in adopting a similar programme which, in addition, also extends imported wheat flour with locally produced grains which are then given an added value.

Shaping the cookie on the trays provided by rural bakers.

Seismic bricks

Oliver Matheson Bulley

Dragon Ceramex, 5 Nomis Park, Congresbury, Avon BS19 5HB, United Kingdom

British, born 9 August 1936. Director and Manager of Dragon Ceramex. Educated in United Kingdom; Teaching Diploma (Design and Technology) from Loughborough College.

During my work in the field of ceramics, I developed a hand-operated clay extruder which, I soon realized, had considerable potential. Although I designed this machine initially for domestic ceramics, I perceived that it could be used to produce such items as building bricks, drainage and irrigation pipes, etc. Subsequently, I developed die plates for these purposes, together with the relevant handling equipment.

The concept for a Seismic Brick is born

The basic concept of Seismic Bricks came about as a direct result of the tragic events in Armenia in 1988. In 1984, I had decided that my company Dragon Ceramex should go into the full-time production and development of my "Clay Bulley" clay extrusion machines which I had previously had manufactured for me under subcontract. These machines are used for domestic and sculptural ceramics and for the production of building materials, some of them going to developing countries where they can be operated without a power source and by unskilled labour.

At the time of the Armenian earthquake I had just developed a new small clay extrusion machine together with a new method of quickly producing a particular type of die plate. Following the previous work I had done with extruded bricks, I was able to quickly try out, with this equipment, my idea of producing a system for interlocking building bricks. This technique ensures that the bricks remain locked together in the event of a structural disturbance, and even if the mortar bond breaks down. These bricks can be produced on the machines I have designed, and which I presently manufacture and market under the name "Clay Bulley".

Cross-sectional view of seismic bricks. Dimensions 70 cm×100 cm, additional rib height 1.8 cm. For clarity, mortar is omitted.

Ribbed structure offers particular stability

The seismic building bricks that I have designed have a rib form which produces a mechanical lock. If the cement bond breaks down through physical and chemical changes in the bonding mortar, or as the result of severe structural disturbance, the bricks remain locked together. The presence of mortar within the joint structure creates a wedge, preventing the bricks from coming apart. Another advantage of this approach is that less mortar is required between the bricks.

The body of the brick itself has a hollow, lattice structure, which endows it with several advantages over a conventional solid brick, including: economy of manufacture in both material and energy; high thermal efficiency; and lower mass movement when subjected to stress.

These Seismic Bricks can be used in the same way as standard bricks. Where necessary, sections of rib can be removed during construction in order to interlock walls at right angles and to accommodate wall ties in cavity structures. The bricks currently being produced have a cross-sectional dimension of 70 cm by 100 cm, and a rib height of 1.8 cm. However, whilst using the principle of the interlock, it is possible to modify and, where necessary, change the dimensions of the brick and the spacing and the number of rib forms to suit the specific clays and mortar constituents of any particular locality.

Particular strength of curved bricks

During my investigations into the creation of more secure brick structures, I applied a technique which I had developed on my machines for the purpose of producing spherical forms. This is a radius technique which, I discovered, could be used on the bricks; it made it possible to form the bricks with a radius through 90 degrees and thus provide an alternative way of joining outer walls at right angles. Using this technique, it is also feasible to form bricks with a radius through 180 degrees and these can then be stacked to construct very secure columns.

The principle I employ on my machines to achieve the radius utilizes an offset extrusion employing an expansion box. I had previously developed the expansion box in order to produce large hollow extrusions. It is possible to set the radius of curvature of the brick to a pre-determined measurement in order to suit particular requirements. This increases the possibility for the development of architectural forms while producing a brick which will provide a secure structure.

Promoting their use in high-risk areas

These Seismic Bricks have been designed for production on a Dragon Ceramex Clay Bulley extrusion machine although it would be possible to manufacture them on an alternative extrusion machine. I will be making efforts to publicize my work with the appropriate agencies over the next two years with a view to having my Seismic Bricks and their variations put to use in localities which are subject to seismic disturbances.

The Clay Bulley machine makes it possible to form a radius in the blocks to create strong corner structures.

Insect larvae for animal feed and organic waste treatment

Gerardo Lardé

Planes de Renderos/Km. 10, Colonia Los Angeles 13, Avenida Guillén Alvarez, 01196 San Salvador, El Salvador

Salvadorian, born 19 April 1954. Agricultural Researcher at the Salvadorian Institute for Coffee Research. Educated in El Salvador; attended José Simeón Cañas Central American University from 1972 to 1976.

A large number of developing countries face two problems which, although they may initially seem unrelated, are in fact closely interdependent. First, the increasing cost of balanced animal feeds has led to a marked increase in the level of meat and egg prices and has, in addition, hampered the domestic production of animal protein by pushing up production costs beyond the budget of the poorer sectors of the rural population. Second, since there is a lack of suitable disposal and treatment technologies, organic domestic, agricultural and industrial wastes tend to accumulate and develop into a pollution and health hazard. For example, the streets of San Salvador, El Salvador, often contain piles of urban garbage surrounded by clouds of domestic flies and green hover flies which are a significant nuisance for the population.

However, in nature, decaying organic matter is converted by various complex processes into humus, and the insect larvae encountered in this procedure are sometimes eaten by domestic animals – which suggests that larvae can be produced as a high-protein end product that could then be used as an animal feed for chickens, hogs and even fish.

Using coffee pulp for larvae production

Coffee pulp is an important agro-industrial residue in many coffee-producing countries. When fresh, it contains sugars and other components which attract dipterans, and when not suitably disposed of, moist coffee pulp will rapidly develop into a breeding ground for flies; moreover, if the pulp is allowed to ferment, it will start to give off a foul, repulsive odour.

Since 1983, I have researched the use of coffee pulp waste as a breeding material with a view to developing a practical and economic method for the mass production of larvae to be used as animal feed. Early on in the research, it soon became clear that it would be necessary to identify the promising species of dipterans. Consequently, 24 batches of fresh coffee pulp were left in the open air

145

Larvae of dipterans growing on decomposing coffee pulp.

to allow development of an adequate larvae population. This study resulted in the identification of two dipteran species which were then chosen for further studies: a syrphid, the green hover fly *Ornidia obesa*, and a stratiomyid, the soldier fly *Hermetia illucens*. In addition, the study also provided data on larvae yields and on their chemical composition.

Development of a prototype

A prototype breeding unit was built to study factors affecting the distribution and abundance of larvae on decaying coffee pulp and to obtain an evaluation of the type of larvae yields that we might expect to achieve when running the process at a pilot plant level. The brick-built unit is rectangular in shape (355 cm long, 188 cm wide, 84 cm deep), and is surrounded by a water pit in which the larvae are collected; a frame and a plastic-netting enclosure were installed to keep off natural predators and stop the proliferation of domestic flies on and around the decaying matter. At the same time, preliminary trials were under-taken to determine the acceptability of the larvae as feed for hogs and chickens, and these tests provided us with positive results.

146

Future research and development

Much has now been learnt about the parameters that affect larvae growth and the suitability of our pilot plant design. However, since our work on coffee pulp has been successful, it would also be interesting to learn whether other organic wastes could be exploited in a similar way. Consequently, further research is required to: identify promising insect larvae which live on organic residues other than coffee pulp (for example, animal dung, domestic garbage, filter press cake from sugar cane processing, sisal waste, etc.); study larvae growth on various organic wastes under controlled laboratory conditions; install a larvarium on a farm which raises chickens so that we can give a practical demonstration of all phases of the system; evaluate the use of larval protein for fish production; develop a simpler method for the rearing of larvae in which plastic bags would be used as containers for the substrate; and to write and publish a "guide for practical larviculture" which would include all the information that we have collected together during our studies to date.

It is hoped that the technology developed will provide a combined solution for the twin problem of supplying the rural population with a high-quality but low-cost animal feed and instituting adequate waste control measures in both El Salvador and other developing countries.

Gerardo Lardé with his prototype unit for the rearing of protein-rich insect larvae on coffee pulp residue.

A proportional chromatic piano keyboard and musical notation

Henri Carcelle

1 rue de Bruxelles, 62520 Le Touquet, France

French, born 21 March 1954. Pianist, Composer. Educated in France; no further education than high school, piano studies from 1969–1973 with Nadia Tagrine.

The old keyboard and the old system of musical notation have never had any bearing upon the way the piano is played, but were simply the result of the old mathematical systems used in the construction of the music scale and were surpassed 250 years ago by the chromatic "well-tempered" system developed and promoted by Bach and Rameau.

An anachronistic keyboard and musical notation

In order to fully understand the implications of the new keyboard and the new notation, and the aberrations of the old keyboard and notation, it is first necessary to emphasize that music is the manifestation of a series of natural whole numbers. For example, the musical note C is made up of a fundamental sound accompanied by a series of "harmonics" with frequencies that are multiples of the fundamental sound, i. e., vibrating two, three, four or more times as fast as the fundamental sound.

If the fundamental sound coincides with the note C, all these harmonics will correspond to the notes in the scale of C major. This is why this scale has been called the "natural scale" and constitutes the transcendental basis of music. The natural scale was represented on the piano keyboard by the white keys and, until the middle of the 15th century, C major was the only scale and keyboards comprised only white keys. The old system of musical notation was also conceived for C major and each line and space between lines represented a note of the natural scale of C major.

At the beginning of the 15th century, semi-tones (black keys) were introduced to composition, and two mathematical systems were used to accommodate the semi-tones, corresponding to sharps and flats. However, C sharp is not the exact equivalent of D flat or D sharp of E flat, etc. Musical research in the 17th century resulted in the octave being divided into 12 absolutely equal semi-tones – a system which was immediately adopted and promoted by Bach and Rameau.

The prototype of the new "proportional chromatic" piano keyboard and some of the main teaching materials used with it.

Since, although the sound intervals become mathematically false, the differences were so small as to be imperceptible, it also gave us the possibility of playing in all 24 tonalities, major and minor.

With the adoption of the chromatic system, the old keyboard and notation became anachronisms but have been retained in use by entrenched habits and tradition even though they no longer make any sense from the theoretical point of view.

A new, logical keyboard

To remedy this situation I have invented a new proportional chromatic piano keyboard and have developed a new system of musical notation to go with it.

In the old keyboard, when the black keys, corresponding to the old sharps and flats, were inserted between the white keys, the F sharp had to be completely displaced by F, B flat completely by B, and C sharp and E flat had to be spaced slightly farther apart in order to allow the fingers to play the white keys between the black keys as is often necessary. Apart from the octave, for each sound interval, this keyboard offers six different geometrically corresponding intervals. In the new keyboard, with its equal and uniform structure, each sound interval has only one constant geometrical interval, instead of six different ones. As a result, playing the piano is six times easier than before. Every piece of music is played on a well defined tonality and it is necessary to learn all 24 scales. With the old keyboard, each scale or tonality has a different topography, making 24 different topographies in all. The new keyboard has only four different top-ographies or patterns. In contrast to the old keyboard – where there is no logical link between the music perceived by the ear and its geometrical reproduction by the space between the fingers – the new keyboard offers a logical link between the musical sound intervals of the music and the corresponding geometrical intervals of the keyboard. The new keyboard is the exact geometrical reproduc-tion of the sound scale of music.

A musical notation to match the keyboard

The chromatic system of the 24 tonalities has gradually been grafted onto this archaic notation with the addition of sharps, flats, double sharps and double flats. The old notation has become a monster which often frightens people off.

With the new notation, which is valid for all musical instruments, everything is simplified: sharps and flats no longer exist, and each line and each space in between represents one and only one note of the chromatic system, and the 12 semi-tones of the chromatic system are represented in the notation. Moreover, since the structures of the new keyboard and the new notation have the same basis and the same logic, they coincide perfectly. We now draw the lines of the stave vertically; doing so note after note we get: line, space between, line, space beteen; and it is the same for the new keyboard; the lines correspond to the short narrow keys of the keyboard, and the spaces between with the long wide keys: it is absolutely impossible to imagine an easier notation.

It is no longer necessary to learn notes and notation, or to be able to decipher them: reading a musical score becomes elementary. This notation is something like the one used by guitarists, where the six lines of the staff represent the six strings of the instrument. A prototype of the keyboard exists, its great advantage being that it can be made to measure to fit on to a conventional keyboard. Musicians will therefore be able to choose either system on the same piano. The new keyboard simply has to be fastened on to the existing one, and takes only a minute to put on or take off.

I have now contacted several piano manufacturers and have received expressions of interest but no written commitments. However, before I begin serious negotiations, I plan to hold an inaugural concert at which I will demonstrate my invention, which will be given wide television coverage. In addition, I am finishing my teaching method, and am discussing with a computer engineer the possibility of computerizing the transcription of existing scores into the new notation.

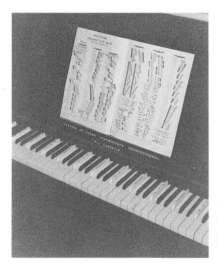

The "proportional chromatic" piano keyboard and pages of score in the related musical notation developed by Henri Carcelle.

Energy from biomass waste by pyrolysis

Prem Chandra Bhardwaj

P. O. Box 11927, Githuri Road, 11927 Nairobi, Kenya

Indian, born 22 August 1931. Technical/Managing Director of Apro Energy Enterprises Co. Educated in India; Diploma (Automotive Engineering) from Institute of Automotive Engineering in 1973.

This project has developed and marketed a range of gas energy savers. It has developed cooking stoves which are practical applications of technology based upon pyrolysis which extracts useful energy from biomass wastes, charcoal being the catalyst agent. Portable bakery ovens have been developed which work in combination with these stoves and have been found useful in rural areas without gas or electricity.

Treatment of amblyopia in children and adults with a game-format mechanical device

Gary R. Diamond

Hahnemann University Hospital, Broad and Vine, Mail Stop 209, Philadelphia, Pennsylvania 19102–1192, United States

American, born 17 January 1949. Department of Ophthalmology, Hahnemann University. Educated in United States; M. D. from Johns Hopkins University in 1974.

The traditional treatment of amblyopia – patching of the better-sighted eye – while often effective, is relatively inefficient and often poorly tolerated. A more efficient and effective treatment would provide threshold targets in a game format with immediate feedback to maintain attention and interest. This project provides such a device, in easily portable format, and has proved successful in adults and children.

Minimizing fertilizer use and water pollution in horticulture

James René Maillefer

25–27 Chemin de Pétray, P. O. Box 38, 1245 Collonge-Bellerive, Geneva, Switzerland

Swiss, born 9 September 1926. General Manager of Diamant Vert S. A. Educated in Switzerland; studied at the Cantonal Horticultural Institute, Geneva, from 1942 to 1945.

This project has developed the "Diamant Vert" system for pot plant production, to replace synthetic substrates. Water reaches the root system by capillary action and the holes in the base of the pot also allow air to reach the roots. Plants produced in these conditions have stronger roots and are more vigorous. This economizes on fertilizer, and minimizes environmental fertilizer pollution.

Robotics to aid the physically handicapped

Jonathan Richard T. Lake

1617 Sumach Road, Caledon, Ontario, Canada L0N 1C0

Canadian, born 21 April 1968. Engineering student at University of Waterloo and Junior test engineer for Magna International. Educated in Canada; currently studying for an Honours Bachelors degree (Applied Science and Mechanical Engineering) at University of Waterloo, Waterloo, Ontario.

This project has designed and constructed a working robot to help physically handicapped people, which can be controlled through a special head brace sensitive to the movements of the head. With the robot, a quadriplegic may perform tasks such as pouring a drink or answering a telephone, all through simple head movements, and restore some of the freedom and independence which many people take for granted.

Computer vision techniques as medical diagnostic aids

Maryellen Lissak Giger

Department of Radiology, University of Chicago, 5841 South Maryland Avenue, Box 429, Chicago, Illinois 60637, United States

American, born 13 November 1956. Assistant Professor at the University of Chicago. Educated in United Kingdom and United States; Ph. D. (Medical Physics) from University of Illinois in 1985.

This project is developing novel computer-vision schemes to aid radiologists detect and diagnose abnormalities in medical images and, in particular, the detection and classification of lung nodules in digital chest images, and masses and parenchymal distortions in digital mammograms. The aim is to increase diagnostic accuracy in cancer detection by reducing the "miss-rates" in radiology interpretations.

Exploring and remote sensing over-the-horizon environments

Li Lewei

China Research Institute of Radio-wave Propagation, P.O. Box 138, Xinxiang, Henan, People's Republic of China

Chinese, born 26 July 1961. Senior Researcher for the China Research Institute of Radio-wave Propagation. Educated in People's Republic of China; Ph. D. from China Research Institute of Radio-wave Propagation in 1987.

This project has designed an advanced, improved system and technique, the Over-the horizon Exploring and Remote Sensing System (OTHERS), which can detect over-the-horizon targets and remote sense the over-the-horizon (OTH) environments to provide information about the sea-surface, wind direction, etc. It can also provide real-time ionospheric data to space stations for launching space satellites.

Improving cork products and their industrial processing (Corksy)

Salvatore Mannoni

Via Silla Lissia 167, 07029 Tempio (SS) Italy

Italian, born 13 November 1948. Laboratory expert, Stazione Sperimentale del Sughero. Educated in Italy; Degree (Chemical Expert) from Istituto Tecnico Industriale Statale, Sassari, in 1967.

This project has carried out applied research demonstrating that new cork processing and manufacturing techniques can result in cost savings of over 40%. It is now planned to: start up industrial production using the methods developed; study the use of cork in new high-technology fields; and carry out studies to evaluate new production processes that will be suitable for new applications in the 21st century.

Variable road pavement structures

Radu Andrei

Bulevardul Independentei No. 21, Bloc B1–5, TR-B4, ET-2, APT-6, 6600 Iaşi, Romania

Romanian, born 13 January 1944. Senior Highway Engineer and United Nations Consultant. Educated in Romania and United Kingdom; studied Traffic Engineering and Motorways at the Polytechnic Institute of Iaşi in 1980.

This project has developed a new concept of road pavement design and construction – the Variable Road Pavement Structure (VRPS) – in which the thickness of the pavement layers is variable and their value is determined by the distribution of vehicle wheel paths on the road lane. The project envisages drafting basic criteria for road pavement design and for appropriate construction technology and equipment.

Isolating cartilage-regenerative cells from bone marrow and dermis

James San Antonio

Department of Pathology, Harvard Medical School, 200 Longwood Avenue, Boston, Massachusetts 02115, United States

American, born 1 July 1957. Post-doctoral Fellow, Department of Pathology, Harvard Medical School. Educated in United States; Ph. D. (Biology) from University of Pennsylvania, Philadelphia, in 1987.

Following demonstration of chondrogenic cells in dermis and bone marrow, this project is developing ways to promote connective tissue regeneration in humans with a view to removing cells from human dermis or bone marrow, promoting their conversion to cartilage *in vitro*, then using the cartilage as an autologous transplant material (i. e. transplantation back to the patient from which it was derived).

Working with Indians – with a little help you can do so much

Antonia Zwollo

Albino Ortega 31, Barrio St. Domingo, Tepoztlan-Morelos, Morelos, 62520 Mexico

Netherlander, born 1 February 1942. Engineer and architect. Educated in the Netherlands; Master of Architecture from the Faculty of Architecture, Delft University of Technology in 1970.

This project aims to study the basic forms and elements that are encountered in Indian architecture in Mexico, and to analyze their meaning and their significance. An illustrated book will then be published in English and Spanish which, it is believed, will be of fundamental value to faculties of architecture and anthropology in Europe and America, and also to government authorities responsible for development aid.

Tracing silver from Potosi and Mexico

Bruno Collin

21 place des Vosges, 75003 Paris, France

French, born 31 October 1956. Head of the Collector's Coin Department, Monnaie de Paris. Educated in France; Doctorate (History) from "Paul Valéry" University of Montpellier in 1981.

This project will trace the routes of 16th century South-American silver in European coinage by neutron-activation non-destructive analysis of silver coins. Analysis of rare elements such as indium in Andean ores and of the presence of indium in Spanish and French coins of the period revealed the presence of Potosian metal in the minted silver. A lead isotope analysis technique for Mexican coins will be researched.

Fortified guano-based organic fertilizer to boost agricultural production

Roman Gammad S. Barba, Sr.

Barba Research Laboratories, Cattaggaman Nuevo, Tuguegarao, Cagayan 1101, Philippines

Filipino, born 23 February 1941. Inventor, researcher and research director. Educated in Philippines; B. Sc. (Physics) from FEATI University, Manila, in 1964.

This project has formulated a processed organic fertilizer from fortified admixtures of guano, farm manure, forestry wastes, industrial wastes, etc. Its purpose is to: restore soil condition in rice paddies that have been depleted of nutrients due to intensive farming and excessive use of of agro-chemicals and pesticides; and boost agricultural production by applying organic fertilizer in combination with chemical fertilizers.

The *White Ship* project

Fukuju Yamada

Tsujikawa Biru, 8–5, 2-chome Akatsuka, Tokyo, 175 Japan

Japanese, born 10 January 1946. Employee Supervisor at Tobu Corp. Educated in Japan; Bachelor of Commercial Science from Chuo University in 1968.

The *White Ship* project, known in Japanese as *Shirofune*, is a concept based on Admiral Perry's opening of Japan with his famous *Kurofune* or *Black Ship*. The *White Ship* will be built from an old American aircraft carrier, and redesigned into a combined recreation/ trade/business centre for the Japanese public to enjoy. It will offer, in Tokyo and other areas, a full range of entertainment, business services and American products, all offered in the American spirit.

High-strength post-expanded bolt for reinforced concrete structures

Pan Li

Institute of Building Structures, China Academy of Building Research, 9 Xiao Huang Zhuang Road, 100013 Beijing, People's Republic of China

Chinese, born 23 May 1953. Research engineer for building structures. Educated in People's Republic of China; Masters Degree (Pre-stressed Concrete Structures) from China Academy of Building Research in 1981.

This project has developed a new type of post-expanded bolt for the repair of reinforced concrete structures. It has a cone-shaped orifice set in an open cross groove at one end and a cone plug set into the cone orifice. When the bolt is inserted into a drill hole in a structural element, the plug is forced into the cone-shaped hole and expands the diameter of the bolt end, thus producing high anchoring strength.

Fold-forming: A new system for sheet metal fabrication

Charles James Lewton-Brain

120, 9th Street NW, Calgary, Alberta, Canada T2N IS9

Canadian, born 16 June 1956. Instructor in jewellery and metalsmithing, Alberta College of Art. Educated in United States, United Kingdom, Canada and Federal Republic of Germany; B. F. A. from Nova Scotia College of Art and Design in 1978.

This project has invented, and will further develop, a system of metal forming which is extremely rapid and permits planar forms and combinations new to metal-working from single, unsoldered or unbrazed sheets of metal. Fabrication benefits result from this. Fold-forming techniques offer advantages for jewellery production. Since tooling requirements are minimal, the method is ideal for small workshops.

Luakela Hydropower Project

David Cole

P. O. Box 21884, Kitwe, Zambia

British, born 16 April 1945. General Manager and Director of Cutler Hammer Zambia Ltd. Educated in United Kingdom; G. C.E. "O" and "A" levels at Sherwood College in 1962.

This project aims to exploit water power in a remote area of Zambia, where the existing, limited power source is operated by a non-renewable energy source, i.e. oil. The project will: provide cheaper, efficient and pollution-free power; supply power to a large hospital and other community services; transfer experience and technology in the development and operation of small isolated hydroelectric schemes.

Ecological studies on combined rubber-tea cultivation

Feng Yao-Zong

Kunming Institute of Ecology, Academia Sinica, 25 East Jiaochang Road, 650223 Kunming, People's Republic of China

Chinese, born 12 January 1932. Director, Professor and Supervisor of research projects at Kunming Institute of Ecology. Educated in People's Republic of China; graduated from the Department of Horticulture, Southwest Agricultural University, Chongqing, in 1955.

To raise the productivity and resistance of the agricultural ecosystem, enhance the environment, and augment economic and social benefits in the tropics, this project is simulating the structure and function of the tropical rainforest and searching for rationally designed multiple-species and multiple-storey artificial combined rubber-tea cultivations as an alternative to traditional monoculture.

A hypothesis for the migraine headache syndrome

Vinod Kumar Gupta

P. O. Box 12005, Jumeriah, Dubai, United Arab Emirates

Indian, born 23 March 1954. Physician-in-Charge at Al-Rasheed Medical Clinic. Educated in India and United Kingdom; M. D. from University of Rajasthan, Jaipur, in 1980.

In its study of migraine, this project has observed a previously unknown combination of eye-signs. It is hypothesized that elevation of intra-ocular pressure is the basic physiological disturbance causing migraine. Drug reduction of intra-ocular pressure has provided consistently gratifying results in reducing the effects of migraine, and offers an attractive approach to the effective management of this syndrome.

Low-cost electronic household gas meter

Albert Kramer

Otto Hahnweg 3, 3731 CC De Bilt, Netherlands

Netherlander, born 17 March 1945. Managing Director of EMS Holland BV. Educated in the Netherlands; attended technical high school and various vocational training courses.

This project has developed a gasmeter with the following features: an accuracy of greater than 1%, including calculation for temperature/pressure influences; a range of more than 1,000 (0.01 m^3/h-10 m^3/h); and a low costing price. The objectives were attained through the application of extremely accurate sensors, few mechanical (moving) parts and advanced computer technology.

Fighting third-world malnutrition with fly-maggot protein

Manuel Marcelo

35 M. Viola Street, Area 3, U. P. Campus, Quezon City 1101, Philippines

Filipino, born 20 January 1937. Director and Production Consultant for LID Agro Industrial Corp. Educated in the Philippines; B. Sc. (Commerce) from the Manuel L. Quezon University in 1960.

This project envisages the development of an integrated bio-system for the mass production and recovery of high-quality protein from the culturing of fly and fruit fly maggots. This new biotechnological system for the production of fly maggot protein capitalizes on the tremendous breeding potentials of fly and fruit fly maggots which take no more than three days to develop to the larva stage.

155

Digital image analysis of tropical rain forest canopies

Paul Martin Rich

Department of Biological Sciences, Stanford University, Stanford, California 94305, United States

American, born 23 February 1956. Post-doctoral Fellow in the Department of Biological Sciences, Stanford University. Educated in United States; Ph. D. (Biology) from Harvard University in 1985.

Digital image analysis techniques promise to revolutionize our ability to characterize the structure of tropical rain forest canopies. The project has developed a digital image analysis programme, CANOPY, to analyze hemispherical "fish-eye" canopy photographs. CANOPY measures the distribution of openings in the forest canopy as seen from below and predicts light penetration through the openings.

The Hydro-Ram – harnessing gravity to pump water

Richard Hamilton Fleming

State Route 723, Box 16, Lowesville, Virginia 22951, United States

American, born 30 December 1924. Farmer, President of Ram Co. and Real Estate Sales Agent. Educated in Norway and United States; B. S. from Old Dominion University, Virginia, in 1972.

The Fleming Hydro-Ram is a lightweight, dependable and inexpensive water pump employing a system of two valves in a closed chamber, it harnesses the force of falling water to generate the power to lift water uphill. It is made of lightweight plastics and gives years of service with little or no maintenance. The pump can provide a flow of water for irrigation and livestock and human consumption.

Dosage device for syringes

James Olson

Torsdagsvägen 40, 86300 Sundsbruk, Sweden

Swedish, born 3 April 1937. Storekeeper and Inventor. Educated in Sweden; self-educated after elementary school.

People with diabetes use syringes to inject insulin several times a day. However, many diabetic patients have diminished sight or are even blind; for them, the task of accurately filling the syringe unaided is a significant problem. This project has invented a device called the "James Tendos" which will allow them to fill the syringes easily and rapidly whilst ensuring the accurate dosing of insulin.

Strong, quiet and affordable energy-efficient foam homes

Carl Louis Hebinck

Alternative Building Concepts, Inc., 53 Highland Place, Land O'Lakes, Florida 34639, United States

American, born 2 March 1933. President and General Manager of Alternative Building Concepts, Inc. Educated in United States; B. A. (Philosophy/Education) from St. Francis College, Loretto.

This project has designed the ABC "Superhome" which is energy efficient and quiet. It is constructed using form-blocks of expanded polystyrene (EPS) filled on site with concrete and steel reinforcement. The walls are faced internally with gypsum board and externally with brick, stucco, etc. The roof is of wooden I-beams in-filled with rigid EPS insulation and topped with radiant foil to deflect solar radiation.

Frankia, a nitrogen-fixing actinomycete, as bio-fertilizer in wetland rice

Ruben B. Aspiras

Microbiology Laboratory, Institute of Biological Sciences, University of the Philippines at Los Baños, College, Laguna, Philippines

Filipino, born 19 May 1939. Professor of Microbiology and Research worker. Educated in United States and Philippines; Ph. D. from University of Wisconsin, Madison, in 1970.

Frankia is an actinomycete endowed with the ability to fix atmospheric nitrogen and serves as a symbiotic partner of certain woody plants. This project has confirmed the presence of Frankia in soils, including flooded rice fields. Laboratory studies showed that Frankia inoculation in rice roots resulted in substantial nitrogen fixation. Field inoculation trials indicate positive contribution of Frankia to rice yields.

Computerized reconstruction of facial features from human skull fragments

Peter Karl Lewin

Hospital for Sick Children, 555 University Avenue, Toronto, Ontario, Canada M5G 1X8

Canadian, born 22 August 1935. Paediatrician and experimental pathologist. Educated in United States, United Kingdom and Canada; M. Sc. (Pathology) from University of Toronto in 1968.

This project has developed a methodology for the computerized reconstruction of human facial features from skull or skull fragments, and has produced stereoscopic see-through images of the skulls of Egyptian mummies. A three-dimensional image of an average adult skull will be stored in a computer programme. Facial features can then be built up, using known data of skin thickness at different facial bone points.

Cancer and the embryo: The role of proto-oncogenes

Marcel Mechali

Institut Jacques Monod, Centre National de la Recherche Scientifique, Université de Paris VII, 2 place Jussieu – Tour 43, 75251 Paris Cédex 05, France

French, born 19 August 1949. Director, Molecular Embryology Unit, Institut Jacques Monod. Educated in France; Doctorat d'Etat ès Sciences from University of Sciences, Paris.

The human genome harbours, in a latent form, genes (proto-oncogenes) which could promote a tumour when escaping normal cell regulation. This project aims to: show that normal gene function is to regulate embryo growth; demonstrate that these genes are decisive in controlling early embryo development; understand why they promote a cancer when their function is altered; and search for prevention and cure.

Cheap and easily erected shelters for areas of natural disasters

Renaud André Mari

"La Lidia", 5178 Cruz Chica, Córdoba, Argentina

French, born 26 February 1955. Self-employed on project work. Educated in Argentina and France; studied at the Institut d'Etudes Politiques, Aix en Provence.

This project has developed a shelter structure with two foundations of reinforced concrete linked above ground by steel H-beams. Its geometric form consists of four detachable segments. The structure is propped at its angles with posts, anchored by buried concrete blocks. The frame units are tensioned by steel wires. Separators maintain the wires at the correct distance, and anchor a covering membrane.

Living with Nature: Low technologies for rural development

Aselo Moncada Jamora

Agral and Technik Inc., 43-H Road 7, Project 6, Quezon City 1100, Philippines

Filipino, born 21 October 1947. President of Agral and Technik Inc. Educated in Philippines; B. S. (Medical Engineering) from Silliman University, Dumaguete City, in 1969.

This on-going project – the preparation of a series of illustrated application pamphlets and a rural development manual, entitled *Living with Nature*, and the actual demonstration of appropriate technologies in selected communities – is intended to teach rural inhabitants and businessmen in the Philippines that nature may be induced to yield more food if her production processes are enhanced and not destroyed.

Sutureless fastener for use in transplant surgery

Leslie Tremaine Russell

11 Laurentide Drive, Halifax, Nova Scotia, Canada B3M 2M9

Canadian, born 18 January 1934. Professor of Mechanical Engineering at the Technical University of Nova Scotia. Educated in Canada; Ph. D. (Mechanical Engineering) from Carleton University, Ottawa, in 1968.

Blood vessels and other fluid-carrying ducts need to be joined in transplant surgery in such a manner that post-operative haemorrhaging is eliminated and that patency is maintained during the healing process. This project has developed a device which eliminates the current technique of suturing (which is prone to leaks), and replaces it with a bio-degradable mechanical fastener composed of only two parts.

A new method of pressure dispersion for body protection

Julius Herman Jacobson

Mount Sinai Medical Center, 1125 Fifth Avenue, New York, New York 10128, United States

American, born 2 July 1927. Director of Vascular Surgery, Mount Sinai Medical Centre. Educated in United States; M. D. from Johns Hopkins Medical School in 1952.

This project has developed a pad which will distribute external pressure to the body as evenly as possible and yet never bottom out. A pad made from an ultra-micro-cellular fibre has been incorporated into a plastic sheath which contains fluid that circulates between the fibres, each of which contains myriads of micro-bubbles. The system is being developed for use in shoes, cushions, mattresses, crash helmets, etc.

A self-trimming vertical axis windmill propelled catamaran

Giuseppe Gigliobianco

Via Novati 12, 26100 Cremona, Italy

Italian, born 31 March 1952. Independent yacht designer. Educated in Italy and United States; studied Mechanical Engineering at University of Bari.

This project explores the possibility of using a windmill for ship propulsion. The windmill is a new design and is directly coupled to a propeller. The windmill will be installed onto a catamaran that, equipped in this manner, should be capable of advancing in the wind's eye. The catamaran will be able to use the windmill sails as conventional yacht sails and to generate electricity when the catamaran is moored.

A synthetic dressing that accelerates healing by 50%

Piero Lovatto

Ignacio Arteaga No. 31, Circuito Navegantes, Cd. Satélite, Naucalpan, Edo. de Mexico, 53100 Mexico

Italian, born 29 June 1923. Owner of Tejidos Reumo-Tex. Educated in Italy

This project has developed a synthetic dressing cloth called "Drenatex" which is non-adhesive to skin wounds, breathes, can be sterilized, is non-allergic, does not promote odours and is re-usable. Fluids from the wound flow into an overlying absorbent pad leaving the wound dry and promoting more rapid healing. Healing time is reduced by 50% The product is ideal for burns, sores, surgical wounds, plastic surgery, etc.

A new and economical route to steelmaking for developing countries

Oscar Gilberto Dam Gonzalez

C. V.G. Siderurgica del Orinoco C. A. (SIDOR), Gerencia Centro de Investigaciones, Est. A10-P01, Puerto Ordaz 8016, Edo. Bolivar, Venezuela

Venezuelan, born 3 January 1946. Head of the Research and Development Department at C. V. G. Siderurgica del Orinoco C. A. Educated in Venezuela, United Kingdom and United States; Ph. D. (Metallurgy Engineering) from University of London in 1983.

This project has developed a new, improved direct reduction process for steelmaking, which combines the carbon dioxide reforming principle and the use of solid metallic iron as a catalyst. This technology makes it possible to combine classical direct reduction units (the reformer and reducing shaft) into a single reactor and offers a simple, economical process that is suitable for developing countries.

Argon-laser photochemotherapy: A new cancer therapy strategy

Daisuke Kato

3–11–10 Namiki, Tsukuba, 305 Japan

Japanese, born 7 August 1942. Senior Research Scientist. Educated in Japan; Ph. D. (Physics) from the University of Tokyo in 1971.

This project is preparing phase-III clinical trials on argon-laser photochemotherapy – a new therapeutic strategy for cancer. Information about this treatment modality and its efficacy will be presented at international conferences, and symposia will be organized to form a global scientific consensus on the establishment of a scientific approach to this aspect of cancer medicine.

Pictures for the blind

Wolf Dieter Seufert

1120 rue Jogues, Appartement 410, Sherbrooke, Quebec, Canada J1H 5N5

Canadian, born 17 April 1935. Teaches Physiology and Biophysics at University of Sherbrooke. Educated in Germany and France; Doctorate in Physics from the Université de Provence, Marseilles, in 1979.

This project has developed a photographic method which will produce tactile illustrations for the blind rapidly and inexpensively. The special illumination used records as grey values in a photograph only that information pertaining to the object's dimensions; these are then translated into levels of elevation by exposing a photosensitive polymer through the resulting transparency to produce a true bas-relief.

A machine to break the human-powered vehicle land-speed record

Thomas M. Caldwell

418 Vista Larga, Los Lunas, New Mexico 87031, United States

American, born 29 June 1946. Educated in B. U. S., University of New Mexico in 1971–1975.

The aim of this project is to break the world land-speed record for human-powered vehicles, multi-person class. An eight-place human-powered vehicle, designed to reach speeds of over 130 km/h, is being built. The machine is constructed from steel and aluminium and it weighs some 150 kg; it will be approximately 6.6 m long, 105 cm in diameter and have a wing-span of some 2.6 m.

Micro-explosion of biliary calculi

Zhang Yangde

Department of Surgery, 1st Affiliated Hospital (Xiang Ya Hospital), Hunan Medical University, 410078 Changsha, Hunan, People's Republic of China

Chinese, born 18 January 1954. Associate Professor of Surgery and Director of the Research Centre of Modern Technique. Educated in People's Republic of China; graduated from Hunan Medical University in 1978.

Intrahepatic biliary calculi, which are common in China and South East Asia, are difficult to cure by surgery alone. This project has developed a micro-explosion technique for crushing gallstones through non-scarring surgery. The toxic and shock-wave effect on the bile duct and adjacent liver parenchyma has been evaluated on isolated human liver and experimental animals. Clinical trials are in progress.

Converting medical debris into safe, useful medical equipment

Francisco L. Hernandez, Jr.

11 Burgundy Lane, Rainbow Hills Subdivision, Avelino Street Extension, Baguio City 2600, Philippines

Filipino, born 9 October 1949. Chief, Department of Neurosurgery, Baguio General Hospital. Educated in the Philippines; M. D. from the University of East Ramon, Manila, in 1975.

In many third world countries, discarded "disposable" medical equipment is used in medical situations entirely different from those originally envisaged. This project has found that these makeshift devices may be comparable to the more costly foreign-made ones. It is therefore proposed to set up a small laboratory for research and development on improving the safety of these devices.

A breakthrough in monitoring breathing in human infants

Hugo Ross Holden

27 Tawariki Street, Ponsonby, Auckland 2, New Zealand

New Zealander, born 19 June 1958. Trainee Intern. Educated in New Zealand; Bachelor of Human Biology from Auckland University Medical School in 1986.

This project has invented a new technique for monitoring breathing in human infants – the aim being to reliably detect breathing pauses in pre-term infants, thought to be at risk from sudden infant death syndrome or infants who have suffered life-threatening events, etc. The new monitor has a specificity for breathing that is not possible with existing monitor systems.

Exploration and Discovery

The projects described in this section were submitted under the category "Exploration and Discovery" which was defined in the Official Application Form for The Rolex Awards for Enterprise 1990 as follows:

Projects in this category will be concerned primarily with venturesome undertakings or expeditions and should seek to inspire our imagination or expand our knowledge of the world in which we live.

Exploration and
Discovery

Marine biogeography of the Baja Pacific

Robert William Schmieder

4295 Walnut Boulevard, Walnut Creek, California 94596, United States

American, born 10 July 1941. Physicist and marine scientist, Cordell Expeditions. Educated in United States; Ph. D. from Columbia University in 1968.

The Pacific ocean offshore from south-central Baja California is a critical boundary between two very different biological provinces, that of cold/temperate water to the north (the Californian province) and warm/tropical water to the south (the Panamic province). Endemic species in this boundary zone should therefore reflect this transitional character, and would help us to understand the biogeography of the east Pacific. However, there have been few studies of the marine biota on the few islands and shallow sea mounts that exist in the region, and practically nothing is known of one critically located island, Rocas Alijos.

We plan to carry out a series of expeditions to this region in order to collect specimens and field data to broaden our knowledge of its biogeography. The principal goal is to reach Rocas Alijos, a group of forbidding and practically undocumented rocks on the top of an oceanic volcano some 300 km offshore, in the middle of the transition zone. We plan to make the first chart of the depths at the site, search for terrestrial plants and animals, dive to collect subtidal organisms, and document the birds and mammals. During the voyage, we will visit several of the larger islands lying off the Baja coast, and document biota along transects between the islands. Subsequent expeditions will explore the series of shallow subtidal reefs lying on the continental shelf of southern Baja, up to 160 km offshore. Together, the results of these expeditions should provide a significant increase in our knowledge of the biogeography of the region and of the processes at work there.

A joint venture

The expeditions will be organized as a joint undertaking by Cordell Expeditions, a nonprofit research organization dedicated to studying the offshore eastern Pacific, and in particular the submarine biogeography of islands and sea mounts, and a consortium of scientists from institutions with special interest in the region.

The Cordell Explorer *at anchor off Pfeiffer Point about 25 nautical miles south of Monterey.*

The expeditions will be carried out in 1990, 1991 and 1992 using the research vessel *Cordell Explorer* which carries a crew of 12; about half will be diver/crew from Cordell Expeditions and half will be scientists from other organizations. Air logistical support will be provided by members of the Cactus Squadron Flight Group, based in Phoenix, Arizona.

The geographic position of Rocas Alijos is not known accurately. We will field a SATNAV receiver to determine the positions of the three major rocks with an accuracy of some metres.

In order to chart the underwater topography around Alijos, we will use an inflatable boat equipped with depth sounder and radio communications to the *Cordell Explorer*. Transponders on the rocks will give us position control. Assuming we are able to land on the rocks, we will search for endemic plants and small animals, taking care to not disturb nesting and roosting birds. We expect our scuba divers to recover some 50 kg of invertebrates from depths of up to 50 metres. Preliminary sorting and fixation of the specimens will be done on board.

The extended cruise to reach Alijos gives us the opportunity to study the other islands and sea mounts along the Baja Pacific coast. Accordingly, we plan to make stops at the following islands: Todos Santos, San Martin, Guadalupe, San Benitos, Cedros, and Natividad. In addition to the island and sea mount stops, we will conduct continuous observations during the cruising. The region is populated by sea turtles, whales, and large gamefish. We have plans to conduct blood sampling, tagging, and censusing of these animals while under way. Assuming permits are obtained from the Mexican Government, we will collect seabirds at Alijos and other islands. We will conduct a continuous surface plankton sample and water temperature record. All specimens will be processed by the participants and colleagues in their respective institutions, and added to their permanent collections.

164

The biogeographic results of the expeditions will be assembled from contributions from the participants. About three months after the cruise, we will hold a symposium, giving the participants an opportunity to present their results and interpretations. Proceedings from the symposium will be published in a journal of record. The results from work during following years will be presented in a forum to be determined after the first year.

Expected results

It is expected that the expedition will result in: the true geographical position of Rocas Alijos and the first chart of its subsurface topography; a collection of terrestrial plants and animals, subtidal invertebrates, algae, seabirds, fish and rocks from Rocas Alijos; photodocumentation and population estimates of the marine mammals and birds; observations of sea turtles, including blood samples and tagging, along the cruise track; and continuous plankton tow samples and water temperature records over the entire cruise track.

The species list and specimens that will result from these expeditions will have immediate significance to our biogeographic understanding of the eastern Pacific. It is expected that there will be many new range extensions for known species, but also it is likely that many undescribed species will be found on Rocas Alijos. As with the Galapagos, the extreme isolation of Alijos almost certainly has produced evolved species. The extent to which they resemble or can be traced to species found to the north or the south should indicate the significance of this interface region.

One of the many very large colonies of hydrocoral photographed during exploratory dives at depths of 40–45 m.

Researching and recording the Maldivian cultural heritage

Hassan Ahmed Maniku

"Guleyseemuge", 55 Orchid Magu, 20–02 Mafannu, Male, Maldives

Maldivian, born 18 July 1946. One-time Director, Maldives Department of Information and Broadcasting and National Centre for Linguistics and Historical Research. Educated in Maldives and Sri Lanka.

The Republic of Maldives occupies a central position in the Indian Ocean, athwart the routes used by ancient traders carrying their goods and ideas from one shore to the other. Most of these traders stopped over on the islands and left their imprint on the culture and language of the Maldives thus placing this small country at the centre of the cross-fertilization of ideas and philosophies and creating a unique society. Records show that the Maldives were in touch with the Roman Empire to the west and the Chinese Empire to the east. In this advantageous position, the Maldives borrowed and adopted from all sides, creating in the process a cultural synthesis rarely found elsewhere. The islands also showed a remarkable resilience to the various forces which passed through them. The language used in the Maldives belongs to the Indo-Aryan group and has developed on its own lines, separate from the mainstream of Indian languages.

Old traditions in danger of disappearance

The old culture is based on a system of ancient folk religion (of which we still know very little), with Hinduism and Buddhism sometimes co-existing with and sometimes dominating it. This situation was drastically modified by the impact of Islam towards the middle of the 12th century and since that date the Maldives has been a wholly Islamic society. It is interesting to note, however, that Islam, after eight centuries as the state religion and as a strong influence on the lives of the population as a whole, has still not proved able to efface the basic ideology in the belief of magic and mysterious beings, which is called Dhevi. The tenets of this magico-religious system have been a guarded secret, generally handed down from father to son. Every aspect of Maldivian life was – and to a great extent still is – controlled by these beliefs. From the propitious time for the coronation of a sultan to the laying of the keel for a new fishing-boat, everything is determined by the "auspicious hours". Deciding on the time of departure to fishing grounds, and the "tuning" of the boat for a good catch are done in accordance to these rights. Though the incantations that are uttered now are taken from the Muslim holy book, the basic practice has undergone little change. In short, this magico-

Coming home with the day's catch. Fishing is the life blood of the Maldivian economy. It provides employment to over 11% of the population and the catch averages 0.3 t per person.

religious system – however alien it may be to the religious beliefs professed by the people – still plays an essential role in their lives.

Recording traditions for posterity

All these aspects of Maldivian life were hidden under the veil of an isolation imposed by the country's political will to remain politically aloof from regional conflicts. This isolation has helped to shield its culture, but today political or physical isolation is no longer possible, especially in such a sensitive area as the Indian Ocean. Gradually, but surely, the Republic of Maldives is shedding its cocoon of solitude. Yet at the same time its cultural and linguistic fabric is also being abraded. The entire weight of modern education and the full force of a linguistic revolution is on the verge of wiping out the old ways. Little, if at all, has been recorded. In my efforts to record such traditions, I have conducted interviews with many old sources, delved into the literature that has been preserved and studied many tombstones and mosque writings in different parts of the country. This has taken me over eight years of labour.

My objective is to compile a quasi-encyclopaedic body of information on Maldivian culture. The areas I have already covered range from names of fish and units of measure to the various names given to the gods in the different religious beliefs. For example, fish names vary from one island to the next. I have compiled these and have documented them along with their English and Latin equivalents. Following the same process, I compiled lists of native medicinal ingredients (especially therapeutic plants), birds and the names of the gods. I have also documented the names that were formerly used to designate both the seasons and the favourable periods for fishing or planting. This kind of multi-purpose calendar, today replaced by the Gregorian calendar, may be lost forever if it is not fully recorded.

To top off all this terminological work, I have produced a lexicon of all the words in the Dhevi language spoken in the Maldives. In another area, I have developed a world bibliography about geological and geographical surveys of the Maldive Islands, with a population census, survey of all the atolls, etc. The documentation that I have developed is not yet as comprehensive as I would wish and my project is to continue to work on these and other subjects such as music, sport, systems of writing, status of women in society, defence and the administration – all of which form additional facets of my Maldivian studies. By recording and preserving the knowledge in these studies, I hope to pass on to posterity something of what the Maldives has accumulated over the ages from its advantageous position on a route so frequented by all the forces that shaped the Indian Ocean littoral. A special case in point is the old *materia medica* and the archaic beliefs. It is for future researchers to dig into this ancient pool of knowledge and bring out something useful to human society.

I am now working on the eleventh part of the project which will record all the archaeological sites found on various islands – both inhabited and uninhabited – together with the shipwrecks that have occurred. These will, when studied, enlighten us not only on the past of the Maldives, but also about all those who frequented our shores or even passed through these islands.

Boat building is a highly developed art in the Maldives. Note the very special axe commonly used by the boat builder. The design is the prerogative of the chief carpenter.

Arctic nesting grounds of the Eskimo curlew

Robert John O'Brien, Jr.

Department of Chemistry, Portland State University, 630 SW Mill, Portland, Oregon 97207, United States

American, born 8 July 1944. Professor of Chemistry and Environmental Sciences, Portland State University. Educated in United States; Ph. D. (Physical Chemistry) from University of Florida, in 1970.

Between 1875 and 1900, the Eskimo curlew (*Numenius borealis*) virtually vanished from the Americas. Shooting undoubtedly played a major role, but it has also been proposed that other human activities, such as conversion of the prairies of the Mississippi Valley and the pampas of South America to agriculture have been instrumental in this development. A change in weather patterns or some weather-related calamity may have played a role too. Whatever the cause, the bird was believed extinct for many years – with scattered sightings subjected to severe scepticism. However, in the past 25 years, definite sight records have been obtained from the Texas coast and from Canada. Nevertheless, in spite of occasional coverage in the specialized press, the plight of this species has still not been deemed worthy of any action.

A recovery plan for the Eskimo curlew

In 1987, American and Canadian biologists made the first step toward devising an Eskimo curlew recovery plan, and it was decided to begin experiments on captive breeding of the closely-related little curlew which nests in the Siberian arctic. Captive breeding is always an attractive prospect for governmental agencies, and has been successful with a number of species worldwide. However, captive breeding of a long-range migrant shorebird such as the Eskimo curlew is problematical.

However, the key factor in assisting the Eskimo curlew to recover some fraction of its former numbers is to locate the bird's nesting territory, study its nesting behaviour and interactions with other shorebird congeners sharing the same breeding habitat, and to identify possible predators. My plan is therefore to find, study and photograph the breeding curlews and to heighten public awareness of the need for conservation of the curlew and all shorebird species.

The search will take place in Canada, and in Alaska, on the historic staging grounds near Kotzebue and northward, where the curlew is thought to have

Closest North American relative to the Eskimo curlew, a whimbrel explores the upper beach, coated the previous night by wet blowing sand.

bred. A presumed pair of Eskimo curlews were located near Lake Rendezvous in Canada in 1987; however, in Alaska only one unconfirmed sighting of this curlew has been made over the past 100 years.

The search will be made on foot, which will require spending several weeks at a time in the field with the necessary provisions. Enlisting the aid of a native as a guide for this search would contribute to its safety and probable success. I have corresponded with an Alaskan guide who is familiar with the territory where the recent Alaskan sighting occurred, in the Arctic National Wildlife Refuge. If permission from the Canadian authorities for study of the Eskimo curlew can be obtained, the area of the Anderson River would probably offer the greatest likelihood of success.

Some of the questions which must be answered for successful management of the Eskimo curlew are the following. Does pair formation occur on the wintering grounds in South America, on migration or in the Arctic? Does staging occur upon arrival on the breeding grounds, or do the birds disperse immediately to their nesting territories? What is the breeding density? Is there evidence of colonial nesting? Is polygamy occurring? Do birds remain paired for more than a single season?

Obviously, my own studies cannot answer all of the above questions. Only long-term research by a number of scientists can provide the necessary information for successful restoration of this species. Thus my own work will be carried out in co-operation with whatever studies may be initiated by the Canadian Wildlife Service or the United States Fish and Wildlife Service.

Specific tasks to be accomplished

In mid-May 1990, my plan is to travel to Kotzebue, Alaska, to search the Sound there for staging Eskimo curlews. Particular areas to search are the estuaries of the Kobuk and the Noatak Rivers, where the curlew occurred in large numbers during the last century. In late June 1990, I would travel to the Anderson River area of the Canadian Northwest Territories to begin searching for and/or study of breeding Eskimo curlews there.

During the late summer of 1990, I will again travel to the Kotzebue sound area of Western Alaska to search for Eskimo curlew post-breeding staging in this historically important area. This region will again be searched by motor boat, with landings being made at appropriate sites. During the spring of 1991, I will travel to the Canadian North West Territories again, this time earlier in the year to study curlews during their pre-breeding and nesting period. Nest observation will be carried out from a blind, and behaviour and predation of any other nests found will be studied by time-lapse video-photography.

Photographic study of Arctic-nesting shorebirds

In addition to the information developed for the Eskimo curlew, other species of Arctic nesting shorebirds will be studied and photographed for the ultimate publication of a comprehensive book on their status and ecology in North America, which could appear in a timely fashion during a period of rising concern for the future of shorebird populations of many species worldwide. It is my goal to produce a book which focuses on their behaviour and ecology, and not to duplicate any currently existing books, many of which deal with identification. Any profits from sales of the book would be donated to the International Council for Bird Preservation which will be invited to sponsor its publication at the time when a draft becomes available.

The book is not to be directed solely at shorebird enthusiasts (although their numbers are growing), but rather it will be intended for all people interested in the natural world, since my goal is to aid in developing a popular demand for shorebird conservation among the general public and their elected legislators.

Related to the curlews but with straight rather than curved bills, the godwits can use their bills adroitly to seize a food morsel 15 cm underground.

The mountain-bike Equa-Tour

Tilmann Robert Rüdiger Waldthaler

Honourable Mention
The Rolex Awards for Enterprise – 1990

Waldmann Expeditions, 39058 Sarnthein, Italy

Italian, born 24 March 1942. Adventurer. Educated in Austria; completed middle school in 1956.

I have had a passion for mountain bikes ever since I was a pastry cook and travelled from country to country for my work. I have now made bicycle trips my occupation. At the age of 36, I cycled 55,000 km from New Zealand to the North Cape on my 18-speed all-terrain bike. Later, I crossed the Sahara from Algiers to Tamanrasset and went on numerous other expeditions that were true exploits. I have already written a book and have produced several reports on my past adventures. My new project, the Equa-Tour, is to cycle round the world from west to east keeping as close as possible to the equator. I will make this journey alone, with no help, and will cover 30,000 km overland.

The Equa-Tour is not a scientific project, rather this solo mountain-bike tour around the equator is a challenge to the mind and the materials used in the equipment employed. The starting point will be Bamako in Mali in July 1989 and, from there, the solo expedition will continue from west to east, first through the sub-saharan regions of West Africa then along the equatorial regions of Central Africa and, finally, the African part of the voyage will end in the East African regions along the equator. Due to difficult terrain and possible political disturbances along the proposed route, I will follow a line between approximately 12 degrees north and 12 degrees south of the equator. This will allow me to avoid various potential problems of either a political or natural origin. The Asian section will start on the Indian subcontinent and follow the same equatorial trajectory as in Africa. One of the journey's many highlights will be the wide range of travelling conditions in South America. The enormous Andean mountains, the vast jungles of the Amazonas, the climatic differences – in other words, a challenge of considerable magnitude.

The psychological challenge

Since I will be travelling single-handed throughout the expedition and will have to depend on purely personal motivation to continue, I believe it will be very difficult to achieve my goal. This is most probably also my main reason for

For Tilmann Waldthaler, cyclist along the equator is a tremendous experience, not only to understand the limits of human capabilities but also to experience the forces of nature..

undertaking this expedition by myself, for I have experienced similar situations on previous bicycle tours, and to compromise with others when the going gets tough is something of an obstacle. Humans are capable of enduring much more than we think. Unfortunately, only too few know their own resources; it is in order to find out how much I can really endure and achieve that I am embarking on such an expedition.

In a world of rapid advances in high technology, I feel that somewhere the average human has lost contact with the reality of nature and life; moreover, we have little understanding for the incredibly sophisticated details of modern advances in chemistry, electronics, medicine, etc. This leaves us with three possibilities: we can take an active part in these advances; we can use the results they offer; or we can reject the achievements they bring. For most people, participation is not possible, and the majority are content to enjoy the results of technology even if in only a mundane way. In most cases, rejection is a question of not wanting or not understanding.

I personally have decided to take an active part in progress. This does not mean working in a laboratory; riding a bicycle can be a step in progress towards a better way of living. Bicycles do not pollute, they are quiet and are generally accepted as a healthy way to travel. At the same time I feel I can make a small contribution to the cycle industry by producing test reports after each "bike expedition" on various product evaluations (bicycles, tyres, clothing, tents, panniers, etc.)

An opportunity to meet my fellow men

In earlier expeditions, I had the impression that people did not understand the reason for my bicycle expeditions or why I should expose myself to situations like the bombardment of Teheran during the Gulf war, climb to an altitude of 5,200 m on an ordinary touring bike, travel through tiger parks in India, cross the Sahara, etc. However, I now feel that my way of life appeals to many people, because it contrasts with the problems of modern civilization they see around them. So many people want to escape, but nobody really knows where to; and finally escape is not the answer. To travel is important but to travel with a purpose is more so. Wherever I have travelled on my bike, most of the people I have met are worse off than we are; they had little food, poor housing and bad health; however, they had the loveliest smiles my eyes could see, the most honest laughs my ears could hear and the sweetest words their mouths could pronounce.

The reason behind my travels

Here we have a reason to travel: to share ideas with others and to comfort the confused. Whenever I am on the road I feel privileged to make my contribution to progress and to better understanding between the peoples of this world. And the reason I can say this is because I have learnt that a cycling adventurer will spend about two hours a day talking to people who are amazed to see a European on a bike.

The South Tyrol is a fantastic training ground for Tilmann Waldthaler's mountain-bike expeditions.

Photographing Lake Baikal in Siberia, USSR

Ashvin Mehta

"Tulsi", Tithal 396006, Gujarat, India

Indian, born 17 July 1931. Freelance photographer. Educated in India; M. Sc. (Medical Biochemistry) from University of Bombay in 1955.

Lake Baikal is one of the natural wonders of the world. Reflecting clear blue skies or veiled in mist, frozen from January to May, alternately placid and stirred up by violent storms, Lake Baikal presents the ever-changing spectacle of a freshwater sea. Cradled between forested mountain slopes in central Siberia, USSR, about 4,000 km east of Moscow, it is on an average 50 km wide, 640 km long, some 31,000 km^2 in area, and a maximum of 1,621 m deep.

A lake of outstanding characteristics

Besides being the deepest lake of the world, it is also the world's largest body of fresh water with a total volume of 22,900 km^3 which is approximately the same as the Baltic and the Kattegat put together. It would take almost a year for the total outflow of all the rivers in the world to fill Lake Baikal.

At different locations around the shores of the lake, for example at the mouth of the Barguzin River, one encounters hot springs. By the end of December or the beginning of January, the lake freezes over and remains frozen usually until late May. As a result of the effect exerted by this mass of water, the summer climate is cooler and the winter climate warmer than that of the surrounding region. Over 300 streams flow into Lake Baikal, most of which are mountain torrents, in addition to the major rivers which are the Upper Angara, which flows in at the northeast extremity, the Barguzin, which joins it in the east, and the Selenga which arrives in the southeast. The sole outflow is the Lower Angara which passes through a rocky cleft on the west shore.

Lake Baikal is completely sorrounded by mountains except at the Selenga delta: to the south is the Khanar-daban border-ridge which rises to a height of 1,800 m above the lake; between the Irkut and Angara Rivers, there is a massive deeply ravined highland; to the northwest, there are the Ontt and Baikal ridges; in the east rises the Barguzin range; finally, the Ulanburgasi mountains encroach on the Selenga delta.

Cradled between forested mountains slopes in central Siberia, Lake Baikal has an average width of 50 km, is 640 km long and descends to a maximum depth of over 1'600 m.

A lake of antiquity

Some 20 million years old, it is one of the oldest lakes in the world. At times it may have stretched westwards into what is now the valley of the Irkut and northwards and eastwards up the lower valleys of the Upper Angara and the Barguzin; however, it has probably never been in contact with the Arctic Ocean. It is a very old relict lake, a deep depression among great mountains, which is still progressing, and earthquakes are frequent along its shores. More than half of the 600 kinds of plants and 1,200 animal species living in its waters are found nowhere else in the world. The fauna may almost be considered a sort of fresh-water museum of ancient species. The waters swarm with fish (sturgeons and *Salmonidae*), and herring is widely available. It also contains many native species of sponges, worms and crustaceans and a native species of seal.

A lake full of fascination

As an Indian, I have also had a fascination for the ancient ties that Lake Baikal has with India; there are more than 30 Buddhist monasteries where "Stotras" of Ganesh and Tara were recited, where Ayurveda was practised, and Ramayan read in "Kalamukh", a language similar to Sanskrit. In natural beauty, it reminds an Indian of only one lake – Lake Manasarovar in Tibet, on the banks of which is located the holy Mount Kailas.

I propose to photograph Lake Baikal, for a book of photographs similar to my other books: *Himalaya: Encounters with Eternity* (1985); and *Coasts of India* (1987). Both of these were published by Thames & Hudson, London.

I am essentially interested in depicting artistically – and not documenting journalistically – various geographical and cultural aspects of the Lake and its unsurpassed natural beauty.

I propose to make three or four expeditions to Lake Baikal and each of these will last 10–15 days. They will be spread over the year so that I can photograph the wonders of each particular season. I have already contacted the USSR Ambassador to India and have been assured that the necessary help will be available for my travel arrangements.

The shores of Lake Baikal serve both as an area of leisure and distraction and as the startupand finishing point for numerous navigation routes.

Computerized mapping of prehistoric tombs in southern Spain

William Clayton Mathers

1 Guilford Avenue, Gillshill Road, Kingston-upon-Hull, North Humberside
HU8 0LA, United Kingdom

American, born 15 January 1957. Post-doctoral visiting scholar at the University of Cambridge. Educated in United Kingdom, Spain and the United States; Ph.D. (Neolithic-Bronze Age Communities in southeast England) from Sheffield University in 1986.

Southern Spain is rich in archaeological evidence of mortuary practices for the period between the Early Copper Age and the Late Bronze Age (circa 3000–1300 BC). Evidence from more than 3,000 Copper and Bronze Age tombs in this region constitutes one of the largest and best documented samples of funerary data for this period in prehistoric Europe.

Earlier surveys lacking in detail

Nearly half these tombs had been discovered and excavated by the beginning of the Second World War, and formed part of a major catalogue of sites published in 1943. Unfortunately, this catalogue of sites contained no detailed distribution maps, or any rigorous analyses of tombs and their contents. Since then, intensive archaeological survey and excavation in southern Spain has more or less doubled the number of known funerary monuments, and has vastly increased our knowledge of the diversity of mortuary practices during the second and third millennia BC.

This evidence reveals that, by the beginning of the Early Bronze Age, there were pronounced changes in funerary monuments and mortuary rituals throughout much of southern Spain, marked – as in other areas of Europe – by the replacement of collective burial practices by more individualized ones. This dramatic transformation was accompanied by a range of other changes, which have yet to be explained in any systematic fashion.

I have already undertaken a qualitative analysis of selected Copper and Bronze Age tombs from the three provinces of Granada, Murcia and Almeria, in southeast Spain. I would now like to carry out a broader, more comprehensive and quantitative analysis by: extending the geographic scope of the analysis to cover the additional provinces of Jaen, Córdoba, Malaga, Cadiz and Sevilla; and incorporating the full range of tomb types found in southern Spain during the second and third millennia BC.

Construction features of a prehistoric tomb in southern Spain.

The reasons behind changes in mortuary practices

As yet, there have been no attempts to exploit the real potential of these data for understanding mortuary practices in southern Spain as a whole, or for comparing patterns of development within this region. To evaluate some of the major characteristics of societal organization and variability in southern Spain over this period, I will examine: how mortuary practices changed through time; why they changed; and why these changes varied from one area to another. My principal objectives will be to: complete a computerized inventory of all published Copper and Bronze Age tombs in southern Spain; create distribution maps of different tomb types, artifacts, etc.; develop and test hypotheses about the mortuary practices using spatial/statistical analyses; and display the conclusions using a range of computer graphics.

This body of data will not only be a valuable source of information for archaeologists working in Iberia, but will also be of considerable interest to colleagues seeking to make general comparisons with other parts of Europe and the Mediterranean. Approximately one-third of these tombs have already been catalogued as a result of work which I have already undertaken in southeast Spain.

The computerized maps that are produced will be particularly useful in trying to assess the differences in mortuary practices (both qualitative and quantitative) in southern Spain. By examining the attributes of tombs and grave goods at a variety of different geographic sites, it will be possible to define important contrasts with respect to: access to prestige goods; the scale of investment in funerary ritual; the concentration of political power; and stylistic diversity.

New insights into prehistoric societal organization

This will be the first time that this type of data has been systematically plotted or compared in southern Spain, and therefore promises some exciting opportunities for new discoveries. Furthermore, since so many tombs are being damaged or destroyed by modern agricultural and industrial development (e.g. the expansion of vegetable farming in Almeria, the construction of reservoirs in Granada, and the extension of irrigation schemes in Murcia), accurate maps of this kind are extremely important for understanding the present distribution of sites. More significantly, perhaps, these maps provide us with clues about the locations of new, and as yet undiscovered, sites. Spatial information of this type is crucial for assessing the significance of sites, and in making decisions about how best to preserve the prehistoric heritage of this important region.

The use of multivariate statistics, together with various methods of spatial analysis, will make it possible to systematically compare many different aspects of funerary monuments and grave contents throughout southern Spain. In addition, these analyses will provide information about the strength of particular sets of relationships; for example, the degree of correlation between tomb size and exotic grave contents, tomb forms and artifact types, or construction features and specific geographic areas.

By transforming the results of detailed quantitative analyses into a simple, visual form it will be possible to interpret them more easily and to see patterns and relationships which might be obscured by tables of numerical data or lists of significance values. An added advantage of using computer graphics is the large number of techniques for presenting the results of complex, spatial and statistical analyses. Collectively, these different techniques offer the opportunity to identify patterns, and dimensions of significance, which would be far less apparent without employing these varied forms of graphical representation.

One of the prehistoric tombs in southern Spain studied by William Mathers.

180

Weddings around the world

Israel Talby

5 Jerusalem Street, 38382 Hadera, Israel

Israeli, born 12 February 1948. Self-employed author and photographic journalist. Educated in Israel, United States and United Kingdom; Diploma from the New York Institute of Photography in 1974.

As a photographic journalist I am regularly assigned to photograph stories and produce photo-essays for magazines and books. My "strongest" side is the human-interest angle of the situations I encounter. "Human interest" is the kind of material for which I will devote myself for hours; frankly, it is because of the human interest that I like photography so much. If I ever had any hidden wish, it was to put aside the daily and routine "non-important" work, and go for the one project which has for a long time been in my mind, "weddings around the world". My idea was to go from one country to another, attend wedding ceremonies, and candidly photograph the events. Starting before the actual day, during preparations, cooking, make-up sessions, etc., and going right through the day itself. From early morning till late at night, when the celebration is over.

At this moment of writing, after completing some 60% of my project, I can say that I have done just what I planned, plus a little more. Luckily for me, I was never on any payroll, always self-employed, free-lancing from job to job, being "my own boss". So I did not have any problems to "quit" anything. Moreover since I had been thinking about it for the past 15 years, the time was ripe this year to turn towards the project and get to work on it. My wife, a full-time high school teacher, was behind me as were our four kids; and that was what made it possible. In order to finance the project we sold our car, took out some of our savings, and planned the next couple of years to be tighter than usual. My hope was, and still is, that at the end of the project I will be able to offer my work as a book and get some of my investment back.

Five months of planning

I set myself a few basics for my project: research wedding material in libraries and museums; talk to professional people; dig through archives; get an anthropological adviser; cover the entire world, all religions, races and continents, young and old, poor and rich, most of mankind; keep exact notes of my

The bride and groom travelling by gondola on their wedding day in Venice, Italy.

recorded subjects; collect wedding paraphernalia, such as invitations and menus, from the weddings I would attend; and do the project non-stop.

Starting at the Library of the Hebrew University of Jerusalem, I sat for five months, researched, read books, took notes, fed them into my computer, and analyzed the things I found. I made comparisons, found out about different religions, honeymoons, raising a family, divorces, learnt about customs, dating, courting, engagements, ceremonies, ageing, and realized from one day to another how little I actually knew. I gathered information about weather conditions, festivals, the best season to marry, the most sought-after day, taboos in the community, in short – tried to familiarize myself with my topic. At the same time, I paid visits to embassies and consulates, trying to establish contacts. I then wrote to registrars of marriages, priests, bridal salons, etc., and was astounded by the quantity and warmth of the replies I received. In addition, before starting off around the world, I got in some practice by touring around doing impromptu photography of weddings in my own country.

My voyage begins

Then on 7 March 1988 I flew out, first to Paris and then to New York and Las Vegas, my first overseas wedding spot. I booked into a motel, rented a car, circled the city, taking notes about wedding chapels and gathered information from a local paper. Next, I stopped at Candle-light Chapel, introduced myself to the chaplain, and was welcomed to attend ceremonies. As simple as that. The only thing which was required was to get permission from the couples. But because of a casual atmosphere of the city, no one objected, though – a few were rather curious.

Next came Honolulu: a big Filipino wedding at St. Andrew's Cathedral and a party at a nearby army base, later in the evening. Then the Fiji Islands: a Sikh wedding which lasted a couple of days, a very colourful ceremony and a most picturesque event. Afterwards, New Zealand: a couple from Samoa marrying at a very small and empty church, a touching ceremony, plus a civil marriage which was followed by a champagne party at Auckland Domain. In Australia, a wedding at the Museum's Garden of Darwin, with a boat-people's ship in the background. Then came Singapore, Buddhist ceremonies, with photographic sessions at the impressive botanical gardens and tea ceremonies.

Thailand is another exotic place for weddings, where they pour sacred water on the couple's hands, set birds free from their cages, serve monks with special gifts, etc. However, there was a problem in Japan – how to get access to a traditional and very private Shinto ceremony, being such a stranger? But luckily, Rotary has priests as members, and Rotarians are known to be helpful. Gypsy weddings in Hungary, belly dancing at a wedding in Egypt, a gondola-style wedding in Venice and on and on and on.

A feeling of satisfaction

Throughout my journeys, I take notes about what I see and photograph and about the interesting information I am told. I collect my personal wedding invitations, as part of the project. I observe anthropological features, jotting down information about habits, what people wear and eat, who stands next to whom, what presents are given, who pays for what, how many children the couple "plan", what do their parents think about it, what are the hopes, fears and expectations, and in short I try not to drive them crazy with my questions. The more weddings I attend the better my questions get, as are the answers.

Today, after some 22,000 exposures and countless kilometres of travel by every possible means of transport, I can testify that recording weddings around the world is a unique experience. I have a feeling that once completed and exhibited, my recordings will help bring people closer together, create better understanding – remind us who we are, and how similar we are. Personally, I will know that I have done something I felt worth doing – and that I did it all by myself.

Unusual decoration on the brides' hands at a wedding attended and photographed by Israel Talby in the Fiji Islands.

The dawn chorus project

Gordon Walker Hempton
Honourable Mention
The Rolex Awards for Enterprise – 1990
The Sound Tracker, P. O. Box 9063, Seattle, Washington 98109, United States

American, born 25 April 1953. Small business operator. Educated in USA; B. Sc. in Botany (High Honours) from University of Wisconsin in 1976.

This project plans to record the dawn chorus of birds at different locations throughout the world. These recordings will then be combined sequentially into a programme in audio-cassette form that will continuously offer the musical sounds of dawn – a never-ending wave of bird song that follows the rhythm of the earth's rotation as if the sun never stopped rising and the birds never stopped singing.

A combination of beauty and precision since time immemorial

Each day when the sun reaches six degrees below the eastern horizon, enough ambient light is created to distinguish objects and the avifauna begin to vocalize. This event is so well regimented that some bird species have served as early morning alarm clocks. Birds evolved to vocalize at dawn, presumably to take advantage of the transmissive, non-turbulent atmospheric conditions which are frequently present at this time of day. Vocalizations may range from simple calls to elaborate songs and serve a variety of functions (e. g., territory identification, mate advertising, family bonding, etc.), depending on the species involved and the season.

Dialects distinguish one dawn chorus from another, and the order of species vocalization further characterizes each locality. Insect-feeding birds are the first to sing; grain-feeding birds are the last to sing. The composition of the dawn chorus is so expressive that it is possible to correctly identify a place, the season and time of day on the basis of the recorded chorus alone. The dawn chorus, like dawn itself, has circled the planet as an endless wave for millions of years. In this respect, the global dawn chorus is one long song with a composition that has paralleled the evolution and population dynamics of birds. It is precisely this perspective, "Planet Earth as a musical instrument," that this project will explore.

The global dawn chorus circles the globe at approximately six degrees in advance of sunrise. Time of year, latitude, temperature, wind and cloud cover all

The Sound Tracker system that will be used by Gordon Hempton to record the dawn chorus at different sites throughout the world. (© 1989 Earth Sounds ™ CD's & Cassettes.)

affect the onset of singing, chorus complexity and duration. Generally, the dawn chorus is best developed during spring in temperate latitudes, and may last for hours. Summer chorus is less pronounced while fall often has a peak chorus similar (but weaker) than spring, caused by photo-periodic hormone production; winter chorus may be much reduced or even appear absent on unfavourable days. However, while the dawn chorus in one hemisphere is seasonally waning, the dawn chorus in the opposite hemisphere will be gaining; thus, the global dawn chorus transcends local conditions. At any given time a wide spectrum of chorus development is present across the face of the earth. In this respect, the surface of the earth, or more specifically, the vegetation (which ultimately supports avian populations) may be viewed as a living and dynamic musical score. As the earth turns, this musical score is released by the sun's rays toward silent space as if by one, colossal piano.

Site selection and recording procedure

I propose to survey the global vegetation and develop an itinerary that will allow me to follow the dawn chorus of songbirds as it circles the globe and that will establish a connection between songbirds and man or, more specifically, the dawn chorus and civilization. If we examine the different vegetation types, we can see that grasslands and the cereals they produce have had an important role in the development of the dawn chorus and the dawn of civilization. It was here also, particularly when diversified by shrubs, trees and surface water, that the oscines or songbirds have sung the long history of vocal evolution. So it will be across the grasslands of the globe that the Dawn Chorus Project will be executed to link both bird and man, time and harmony. It is not the earth, after all, that will be played as a musical instrument, but instead it will be the imagination and attention of the listener across a field of many possibilities.

185

Six representative grasslands will be selected from the different continents around the world on the basis of similarities in climate and seasons, vegetation structure and associated topography. Avifauna differences will not be controlled, but rather, because different social environments will exist in the separate avian communities, similarities in the basic sound qualities will be distinguished by an expressive vocal heritage. Site visitation will be planned to coincide with either the spring or fall peak chorus activity and to emphasize nuptial rather than territorial songs. Special consideration will be given to the Egyptian site of Amenhotep in the ancient city of Thebes. It is here, over 5,000 years ago, that two colossal statues were constructed in such a way that the first breeze (generated by the influence of solar radiation on a non-turbulent air layer) would cause the stone cavities to resonate and, thus, "speak" at the gate represented by dawn.

The dawn chorus for everybody

The field recordings will be deposited at Cornell University's Library of Natural Sounds, the world's largest facility of its kind. The Library's studio facilities will be used to assemble the global dawn chorus audio programme. The final programme will be produced and distributed on audio-cassette under the title, *The dawn chorus: A special time to listen*. Descriptive literature will also be distributed to stimulate radio broadcast network interest, both public and private, for interviews and broadcasts. It is my hope that the binaural recording aspects (which will allow audiences to experience a three-dimensional sound sensation) will attract considerable attention to the project's concept and create a very intimate feeling on the part of the listener for the global environment as a whole.

Each day when the sun reaches six degrees below the eastern horizon, enough ambient light is created to distinguish objects, and the avifauna begin to vocalize (Photo: NASA).

Walking unsupported to the North Pole

Roger Paul Mear

6 The Little Boltons, London SW10 9LP, United Kingdom

British, born 15 February 1950. Freelance photographer and writer. Educated in United Kingdom; B. A. (Hons. Sculpture) from Norwich School of Art in 1972.

The claims made by the American explorers Cook and Peary each to have been the first to reach the North Pole have largely been disputed. The first indisputable attainment of the North Pole over the sea ice was made by the American Ralph Plaisted and three companions in 1968 after 42 days of travel by ski-doo, during which time they were resupplied from the air. Subsequently, all parties travelling the surface of the frozen ocean to the North Pole have relied heavily on support from aircraft to drop food, fuel and replacement equipment. The goal, first attempted by Nansen and forsaken by Amundsen who turned his attention to the South because he thought himself forestalled by Peary, has yet to be attained without the use of aircraft.

On 11 January 1986, after skiing 1,412 km in 70 days, Robert Swan, Gareth Wood and myself became the first unsupported party to reach the South Pole. For the first time the South Pole was reached without recourse to supply depots, motor vehicles, dogs, air support or outside assistance of any kind, indeed we took with us no radio and manhauled all our supplies. I now plan to apply the same concept of unsupported travel in an attempt to reach the North Pole.

Crossing the polar ice-cap on foot

It is 774 km from the northernmost tip of Canada to the North Pole, i. e. some 640 km less than the distance we successfully manhauled in the Antarctic. The terrain however is dramatically different; while the route to the South Pole lies over ice shelf, mountains, glacier and Polar ice-cap, the route to the North lies over a frozen ocean. Pack ice that is continually shifting and drifting under the influence of wind and ocean currents is sometimes split by leads of open water, as the plates of ice pull apart, or alternately raised in great ridges of pressure-ice where the floes meet head on. It is not uncommon for the progress of sledge parties to fall to but 2–3 km a day when faced with such difficulties.

187

Two of the typical inhabitants of the region that Roger Mear will be crossing on his unsupported expedition to the North Pole.

Together with my colleague Paul Rose, I plan to walk from Ward Hunt Island, the northernmost point in Canada, across the 774 km of floating ice to the North Pole completely unsupported. Covering an average of over 30 km per day we expect to reach the North Pole in about 30 days in contrast to most parties, no matter whether travelling by ski, dog sledge or ski-doo, which seem to plan for at least 60 days. I do not think that an unsupported party has any chance of success if a journey of such duration is contemplated since a period of 60 days means that the journey must begin in early March if the Pole is to be reached before the summer break-up of the pack-ice in May.

Beginning the journey in early March means very slow progress because temperatures are generally very low. Every task takes three or four times the amount of time normally required, breakfast might require two or three hours to complete. Melting snow for food and drink consumes massive amounts of fuel, and the calories each man requires per day to combat the cold also increase dramatically. Both these factors add to the weight of the food and fuel that must be carried and thereby make fast progress impossible.

A duration of 60 days means sledges that weigh in excess of 140 kg at the outset. I believe that it is impossible to go unsupported to the North Pole in such a manner. An unsupported team must be able to travel fast and light and maintain a daily average in excess of 30 km, and this will be feasible only if the starting weights per man can be reduced to some 70 kg.

Travelling light

We plan to arrive in Resolute Bay in early March 1991 and stay there ten days to adapt to the cold; on the twentieth day we will set out to conquer the Pole.

"Unsupported" means without aircraft, motorized vehicles, dogs or weapons, but we will each have an Argos beacon and a VHF radio so that we can be found in an emergency. We will pull sleds containing our survival gear: food (calculated on a basis of 30 days), cooking equipment and fuel, tents, sextants and maps, first aid kit, repair kits, sleeping bags and insulating mattresses; we will each pull a sled load of about 55 kg. We will keep in touch with base camp on Ward Hunt Island by means of a 50 W two-way radio. At the base camp there will be a five-man team comprising a camp director, a cardiologist and a radio operator and two cameramen who still have to be chosen.

The cardiologist in the base camp team is a specialist in cold-related problems, and will be in charge of the expedition's medical needs. He will also take blood samples before and after the trip which he will pass to Mike Stroud of the Institute of Aviation Medicine. Stroud took part in the 1986 expedition and did the medical research for it. The data gathered will allow him to calculate the amount of energy expended by the men and to study the effects of exposure to the cold on the immune system. This research will give a better understanding of weight control mechanisms, and the effects of hunger and physical exertion in the cold.

Our studies of energy consumption will make use of a recently developed technique in which the men drink water containing special isotopes. In the study of the immune system, Mike Stround wants to confirm his 1986 observations, in which he found abnormal inflammation indicators in the blood of the three men, indicating infections. His goal this time will be see if strenous exertion really does weaken the immune system.

We will do intensive training beforehand. We will work on our skiing technique for six weeks and then do various types of physical training for four weeks. Then, for 11 weeks, we will become accustomed to the fatigue and exertion of pulling sleds while on a special diet. We will then gradually ease off for the last four weeks so that we do not go into our adventure exhausted.

The project should cost about US$100,000, half of which is just for the flights from London to Montreal, Resolute Bay and then Ward Hunt Island, and on the return from the North Pole.

Roger Mear during his expedition with Robert Swan and Gareth Wood during the first unsupported expedition to the South Pole in 1985–1986.

Researching historic European artillery until ca. 1880

Rudolf Roth

12 Farrow Close, Great Moulton, Norwich, Norfolk NR15 2HR, United Kingdom

Swiss, born 9 June 1950. Full-time researcher. Educated in Switzerland; attended school for eight years in Switzerland, and has taken a short course on the conservation of archaeological artifacts at the National Maritime Museum in Greenwich.

None of mankind's creations has influenced our history more profoundly than the ship and the wheel, enhanced with the introduction of firearms and especially artillery from the 14th century to the present day. Warships from the 17th century onwards were, by design, purpose and classification floating artillery platforms. A similar influence and change occurred in land warfare, fortification and financial burden to individual countries. Artillery itself is man's first practical utilization of a chemical reaction. Although the casting of metal was practised two millennia previously, the manufacture of artillery was the only heavy industry for centuries.

A shortage of reliable information about weaponry

Building ship models for over 20 years, I was continuously hindered by the scarcity and unavailability of practical and reliable information about naval armaments. Towards the end of a course on the conservation of archaeological artifacts that I attended in spring 1985, I decided to inform myself about British naval artillery. After six months of intensive efforts, I achieved a higher degree of confusion and little additional information. The study of publications and manuscripts merely emphasized the strange absence of coherent information about naval artillery and – in fact – all artillery in general.

It was at that point that I resolved to repair this failing by undertaking a research project that would return to the ultimate source of information – the guns themselves. The project consists of three major components: the photographing, measuring, drawing and registration of surviving historic artillery; dissemination and publication of the information that I have compiled, including the publication of a number of books on historic guns; and the restoration and revival of the historic Royal Brass Foundry at Woolwich Arsenal.

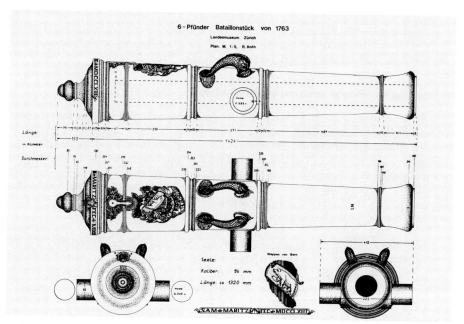

A drawing by Rudolf Roth of a six-pounder cannon from the Landesmuseum, Zurich.

Putting guns down on paper

The systematic physical measuring of surviving guns has, to my knowledge, never been undertaken. The physical discomfort of measuring guns, and possibly also the fact that most researchers are more scientifically and historically minded than technically, might be the reason for that. My initial search on British naval artillery turned very quickly into a fascinating and intellectually rewarding occupation which now includes all types of artillery. During the past four years I have photographed, measured and drawn more than 400 historic cannons in minute detail.

The measuring of a large number of guns constitutes in time the equivalent of an inventory. From the outset, the publication I foresaw was one which would provide quite comprehensive information and answer the majority of questions on artillery for the model-builder, archaeologist and researcher alike, and also include the chronological development and armament of artillery; additionally it would deal with all related information on carriages, design, manufacture, terminology, performance, ammunition, gun-drill, etc. It will in fact become a reference work for many years to come. The conclusion of documentary research might take a year but the number of guns still to be measured is unknown. At the present, I believe that, by around 1997, sufficient information will be available to present at least the first volume for publication. Further publications are intended and the subject titles have been established with reasonable certainty.

18th Century Gunfounding is considered the most comprehensive existing modern publication on gunfounding; however, financial constraints at the time of publication meant that much of the available graphic material was not

191

included. Republication of this important work is now under consideration. The new publication will include the original full-size drawings in colour, a number of sources from unpublished manuscripts, various additional chapters and the revised and unabridged manuscript of the author Prof. De Beer.

Restoring the Royal Arsenal at Woolwich

The Royal Arsenal at Woolwich is strictly speaking not part of my research project although this establishment is of very considerable importance to all artillery-related matters in England. The researcher will therefore invariably come into contact with past activities of the Arsenal which, together with the Royal Artillery Institution at Woolwich, is a continuous point of reference. In 1651, the first proof butts were set up for trials of ordnance manufactured by contractors to the Crown. In 1716, the first and only Royal Brass Foundry was built there and the first Master Founder was the Swiss Andrew Schalch from Schaffhausen.

The entire building of the original Brass Foundry has been restored and is used today as an archive. The Verbruggen House nearby is under restoration at present and at least the ground floor should house a modest exhibition. This is indeed a unique opportunity for a working museum – a place of research, learning and entertainment for the history of industry, artillery and tourism alike. A restored Brass Foundry, Artillery Museum, etc., could play a significant part in the wider context of tourism along the River Thames, with Greenwich, the Cutty Sark and the Thames Barrier in the vicinity.

I intend to present a practical proposal on the realization of this idea at the seminar of the Ordnance Society and meetings with the Historic Society of the Arsenal and the Dutch Study Group towards the end of this year. I intend to commence a co-ordinated effort and organize support on a broad base towards the preservation of the historic Woolwich Arsenal. Success would not only be a personal professional culmination but also a great contribution to the surrounding community in general and to artillery in particular.

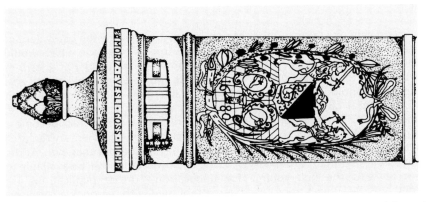

Detailed cross-section showing the ornamentation on a thirteen-pounder (1680) drawn by Rudolf Roth.

Archaeological study of a pre-historic settlement near Turin

Carlo Viberti

Via G. Balla, 9, 10137 Turin, Italy

Italian, born 22 April 1963. Aeronautical Engineer on the Columbus Programme in the Space Systems Group of Aeritalia. Educated in Italy; graduated (Aeronautical Engineering) from Turin Polytechnic in 1987.

The archaeological remains which I discovered 11 years ago are surface structures, built of undressed stones without the use of mortar. Consequently, they are vulnerable to destruction by natural forces and by man, which would render interpretation of the remains much more difficult, if not impossible. The stones have not been dressed into regular shapes, so it will be virtually impossible to decipher the form and method of construction of the buildings once they have fallen down or are dismantled. Also, it will no longer be possible to discern the configuration of the cluster of environments, which could be important in working out the hierarchy of the former inhabitants.

Studying the stones before they are disturbed

My intention therefore is to build on the preliminary study by carrying out a thorough, but careful, investigation of the site. The purpose of this will be to make an accurate record of everything which is visible above the ground, by means of measurements and photography, supported possibly by some excavation and by dating any artifacts that may be found. The results will then be presented in the form of a paper for publication.

I am hopeful that this would then stimulate other more experienced archaeologists to make more extensive investigations, perhaps by means of a full-scale "dig", as unfortunately I have previously been unable to interest local archaeologists in the site.

A fortuitous discovery

I made the discovery whilst I was carrying out field research in the area in July 1978. Just by chance I entered into the depths of a wood growing along a little waterway that I was following, in an interesting area close to Rubiana, a country village some 30 km west of Turin, Italy. At first sight, what I had in view, levelled by the distance, seemed an ordinary heap of stones extending into the

193

Wall structures observed by Carlo Viberti at the pre-historic settlement near Turin.

rich vegetation of the wood. However, on approaching the site and inspecting the remains more carefully, it was easy to see that, on the contrary, the heap of stones was a rationally structured ensemble composed of some 30 small circular environments defined by perimeter walls of stones about the height of a standing person; the stones had been set without mortar and there were no traces of a roof or other kind of covering.

The overall settlement has a rectangular shape about 70 m long and 30 m wide, slightly sloping, with the longer side in line with the slope and with a waterway flowing some 20 m away. Its orientation is approximately north-south and its altitude is about 600 m above sea level.

A large part of the circular walls is still perfectly intact, and each of the structures has a door-like a gap to let a person in. From within the structures, the particular logic of the dried buildings is better understandable: the structure begins from the pavement, where stones of the typical gneiss of the region are set up to form a sort of load-bearing mosaic. Transferring load very effectively, the stones fit in perfectly well with each other up to the basis of the perimeter circular walls which rise up from this pavement structure, with the same load-bearing concept.

The average dimensions of the stones vary from about 30×20×20cm to 70×50×30cm and in some cases more; however, the shapes and dimensions depend on whether the stones form part of the pavement or the wall. The upper

194

limit of the settlement is close to a natural heap of stones located in a large open area, in which the same kind of gneiss is to be found, and this seems to be the most likely source from which the builders obtained the material for the settlement. The buildings closest to this limit, that is at the top of the slight slope on which the cluster has been built, have dimensions which are somewhat greater than the average (5–6 m in diameter versus 3–4 m for the others, and walls 1.8–1.9 m high versus 1.5–1.6 m for the others). The largest of all is located a little more towards the centre, but still forms part of that upper area.

A prehistoric structure of the castellum type?

In view of its distinctive characteristics, the settlement could well be identified as a habitat of the so-called prehistoric "castellum"-type architecture. A working hypothesis is that the circular stone walls were designed and constructed to bear the load of an original covering structure which was composed basically of wooden poles or entire tree trunks, fixed externally around the perimeter and linked and interlaced together at their top to create a frame over the building.

This wooden frame would have been covered with bushes and mud or hides in order to ensure that the roof was watertight. The basic construction elements, the stones, could have been easily transported from the nearby heap (thanks to the natural slight slope); the particular position of the largest buildings (i. e., the ones located in the upper area) could have defined a somewhat hierarchical priority within the social community.

Many of the above-mentioned details lead one to assume that the origin of this settlement could be the same as that of the various wall markings found throughout the region, and which belong to the Neolithic period.

Further analysis, measurements and configuration studies are undoubtedly needed, together with excavation, recovery and dating of any artifacts found; within this framework, it would be a really desirable effort to implement a project such as this.

An overview of some of the wall structures showing the wall construction technique and an impression of the wall dimensions.

195

Archaeological exploration in Patagonian archipelagos

Dominique Legoupil

Honourable Mention
The Rolex Awards for Enterprise – 1990

14 rue Thouin, 75005 Paris, France

French, born 28 February 1948. Research Worker, Centre National de Recherche Scientifique. Educated in France; Ph. D. (Anthropology) from University of Paris V in 1976.

The aim of this expedition is to make a systematic archaeological survey of the Patagonian archipelagos, a complex labyrinth of fjords, channels and more than 5,000 islands, which extend over a range of some 1,600 km from the large island of Chiloe in the north, to the Cape Horn in the south. So far, little is known about this territory as far as geography (maps of the coasts have not been plotted) and, in particular, archaeology are concerned. The only data available about the ancient inhabitants of the area are anecdotes dating from previous centuries and related by such personalities as Bougainville, Byron, Fitz-Roy, etc., and a few reports made by anthropologists at the end of the 19th century or the beginning of the 20th century.

For ten years now, we have been carrying out archaeological research on the populations at the boundary between the archipelagos and the pampa. Now that this has been completed, we plan to undertake a survey of this very large maritime area where we believe we are likely to find the solution to the main problems that confront us in documenting the history of human settlement in the extreme south of South America. We hope to achieve three objectives. The first is to verify our hypothesis on how the southern part of the continent was peopled. Secondly, we want to collect information on the morphology, physiology and funeral rites of the Indians who lived there before European colonization. Finally, we plan to study the eating habits of the natives both before and after the arrival of the Europeans to see whether they changed significantly. It is possible that the European hunters and fishermen depleted the marine fauna, upsetting the natives' system of self-subsistence and thus leading to their disappearance.

Documenting human occupation of the Patagonian archipelagos

Discovery, close to the Strait of Magellan, of marine sites dating from the 4th millenium BC raises the problem of the origin of the human settlement of this territory. The most common hypothesis until now is that the American Indians,

The Patagonian sea lion (Otaria flauescens) has for many thousands of years been the most common catch for the Indians. The massacre of these animals by the Whites during the 19th century led to a precipitous fall in the number of sea lions which parallels the demographic decline of the Indians (Photo: J. M. Yvon).

who settled in both the American continents from the Bering Straits in the north, progressed to the extreme south through the Argentine pampa, since the archipelagos route was impracticable for them owing to navigational difficulties. The archaeological sites of marine hunter-gatherers found in the Strait of Magellan would be in line with a population of terrestrial hunters gradually being forced to adapt to a marine way of life when they reached the end of the continent (maybe under pressure from other more powerful groups).

In contrast, our hypothesis is that these nomadic populations were, from the beginning, halieutic groups, and that they gradually moved south, invading the Pacific coast, slowly adapted to a maritime environment and became more and more specialized in the exploitation of the marine mammals in a manner similar to that of the Eskimos of the North. This supposition is founded on the technical affinities found between the tools of populations from the Straits of Magellan and those of the coastal populations of the Pacific area located close to the north of the archipelagos. It will be necessary to search for the missing link (ancient archaeological sites) over a range of some 1,000 km in the centre of the archipelagos, to support this hypothesis. We will first search for remains of ancient populations on the high marine coastlines (the lowest were below sea level in those ancient periods) in the centre of the archipelagos.

Physical features and burial rites of the populations

Reports in the logs of ancient navigators and verbal descriptions given by contemporary fishermen contain facts about unusual funeral rituals in this area. Mummies, probably cadavers desiccated by the wind, have been found, enveloped in seal skins or pieces of tree bark. Byron, in the 18th century, reports that these mummies were laid out on wattles, whereas other sources indicate they were under huts in a cave.

However, we now have no concrete evidence of this ritual of a population whose last survivors are currently disappearing. In addition to the natural risk of degradation which threatens these mummies, it seems that the superstitious fishermen, who are the only persons working in this area, have been known to destroy these mummies, thus endangering a fragile archaeological heritage. We have drawn a map of the main sites of mummies indicated by written or oral information that has come down to us and will make on-site checks of their existence. The exposed mummies will be studied *in situ* (morphology and morphometry analyses) and we will take samples for studies of rhesus factor, nutritional status, etc. At least one of the best preserved of the mummies will be transported in a vacuum container to the Santiago Museum of Natural History where it will be presented to the public.

Evolution of marine fauna and its historical impact on population

Our third objective will be to look for recent archaeological sites (post-magellanic periods) in order to analyze the nutrition of the people who lived in the archipelagos immediately prior to the arrival of the White population which has destroyed their culture and is responsible for their disappearance. We will study the environment and the available animal resources (especially otariids and marine birds) who formed a fundamental component of this economy. In particular, we will try to evaluate the impact of the hunting of marine mammals by the Whites during the past century and the contribution that hunting has made to the disappearance of some species of pinnipeds and therefore of the Indians who lived on them.

Archaeological findings are often hidden by the dense virgin forest in the area (Photo: D. Legoupil).

A glowing Christmas tree

Clarence I. Kado

Davis Crown Gall Research Group, Department of Plant Pathology, University of California at Davis, Davis, California 95616, United States

American, born 10 June 1936. Professor of Plant Pathology, University of California. Educated in United States; Ph. D. (Plant Pathology) from University of California, Berkeley, in 1964.

Light production in nature has been observed for centuries and has continued to arouse the curiosity of many people who have described luminous organisms in great detail but had little understanding of the precise mechanism of light generation. With the development of modern biological tools, particularly those in molecular biology, it has become possible to isolate precisely a gene of interest and, in our case, the lux genes that lead to the production of light. With the lux genes on hand, we have been able to show that light can be produced by other organisms normally not equipped with such light-generating genes.

Many of us have seen ocean waves glowing greenish or bluish at night while walking along a beach. This light is produced by luminescent bacteria that exist as part of the planktonic population. Bioluminescent bacteria also reside in the gut and on the skin of marine organisms, and in specialized light organs of certain fish and squid. The ecological significance for the host in these symbiotic associations has long been recognized. Luminescence is used by marine animals for a variety of purposes such as attracting prey or mates, for communication and for escaping predators. A number of light-producing bacteria have been identified and recently some of them have become the subject of intensive characterization.

Extracting the glow from nature

We have focused on the bioluminescence system of the marine bacterium *Vibrio fischeri*, in which the light-producing set of genes has been nicely identified. Light production by this bacterium, which resides in the monocentric gland of the Japanese Popcorn fish *Monocentris japonicus*, is catalysed by enzymes encoded by a specific set of lux genes. We have isolated these lux genes and are now able to manipulate lux outside of its natural host, *V. fischeri*.

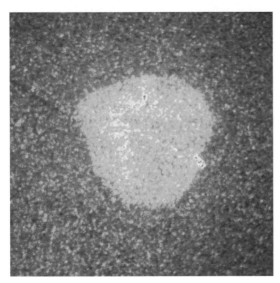

Video image of a glowing leaf taken off of a genetically engineered tobacco plant containing the lux gene-set. The image was measured by Dr. Koji Okumura on a Hamamatsu Photonics camera and computer. Dr. Okumura is a member of the research group which helped develop the glowing tobacco plant.

We have also constructed plasmid shuttle vectors and a transposable DNA element containing lux that can transfer lux to other organisms so that these heterologous hosts can produce light autonomously. Among the test organisms are symbiotic and plant pathogenic bacteria and plants such as tobacco and tomato into which lux has been transferred and inserted stably. The fact that light can be emitted for the first time by plant pathogenic bacteria has enabled us to monitor continuously the infection process well in advance of any symptom.

Transferring the glow from fish to firs

Because of the potential applications of having plants self-glow in the dark, we would like to continue our efforts on tailoring the lux gene-set and in the design of lux delivery vehicles. Thus, the objectives of this project are as follows: tailoring the lux gene-set to optimally produce light in ornamental plants; design and construction of efficient shuttle vectors for transfer to ornamental plants; and transformation and regeneration of the ornamental plants (including Christmas trees and shrubs which could be used to line highways).

It is significantly more difficult, however, to transfer a group of bacteria genes into the cells of higher plants than into other bacteria. To do this, the latest genetic techniques must be used. *Escherichia coli* will act as the first host in the genetic manipulations, and it will be necessary to create a more "compact" lux cluster with a strong promoter, so that once the gene becomes a single entity, it can express itself easily in the cells of higher plants. *Agrobacterium tumefaciens*, the pathogenic bacteria widely used for introducing new genes into plants, will then take over to transmit the lux to tomato and tobacco plants, the two plants best known to geneticists. Finally, to obtain the glowing Christmas tree, we will use cultures from the Douglas fir tree, a species that is fairly well known genetically and that is grown commercially for sale as Christmas trees.

All of these operations must obviously be done on plant cell cultures that will have to be multiplied so that the best strains can be selected according to their capacity to give off light. The cell cultures will then be placed in the proper conditions to produce plant embryos which, in turn, will be planted in a greenhouse. The project provides for fairly extensive planting in one of the University's greenhouses to give a real night-time demonstration of what bioluminescence can do.

The last stage of the project will be to identify any physiological problems that may arise in plants whose genes include the lux cluster, and to try protect the trees against them before they are finally put on the market.

The potential of the use of glowing plants in the ornamental industry is vast and the concept of light-emitting shrubs lining highways and thus improving the safety of night driving is extremely attractive.

Glowing cultures of Erwinia corotovora subsp. carotovora containing the lux gene-set, on agar medium on petri plates and in liquid medium in a flask. The light produced is of sufficient strength for one to read a book with out artificial light (Photo: J. J. Shaw).

Operation Drakkar

Luc Chrétien

81 rue Jean-Jaurès, 92300 Levallois-Perret, France

French, born 19 March 1956. Professor at "Université de Paris Sud-IUT de Sceaux".
Educated in France; Ph. D. (Viking Navigation and Ships) from La Sorbonne, Paris.

Before becoming a god, the Feathered Serpent, a dweller of a distant country, landed in Mexico. He became ruler of an ancient people, the Toltecs. It is said that he was the most handsome of mortals and his hair and beard were the colour of the sun's rays. The legend relates how Quetzalcoatl taught men to fashion useful and beautiful things, and how he instructed them in the art of melting metals and of cutting precious stones. It is also said that rivalries forced this ruler to abandon the country. Before his departure he declared to the people: "One day, other men, white and bearded like myself, will come from the East to re-establish my ancient kingdom." Then, he set off into the Gulf of Mexico with a few faithful companions, and disappeared beyond the Ocean.

By searching into the memories of the Mayans, the Venezuelans and the Muiscas, one could find evidence of his passage. Among these tribes, he was known as Kukulkan, Zume and Bochica. Still later and farther on South, in Peru, a bearded white man appeared once more... Viracocha. Some five centuries later, face to face with Spaniards, the Aztecs and the Incas were sure they were dealing with the bearded god of their legends. But how mistaken they were! These were the conquistadores Cortes and Pizarro, the great vanquishers of the empires of the Americas.

A sea-faring people

In distant times that some would situate in the tenth century, which people living along the Atlantic Coast and known for their beards and light-coloured hair could so have impressed the Indians of Mexico to the point of entering into their legends? Which people indeed, if not those bold seamen the Normans, the only ones capable of defying the ocean with their drakkars in the High Middle Ages? For we find portraits of Europeans in Meso-America and in Peru, in the forms of sculptures and frescoes, blond mummies in the Museum of Anthropology in Lima, a script strangely reminiscent of the runes in Paraguay, a nordic style ship stamped on a gold crown in Lambayec in Peru, Aztec (tamascal) and Mayan

Luc Chrétien and a model of the viking ship he will use for his expedition.

(sampulche) saunas... and even a map bearing the precise outlines of South America, even before the discovery of the Pacific by Balboa or Magellan's voyage.

Traders in the New World

At the end of the 13th century in Rouen, Brazilian wood appears among the items listed in "Droitures, coustumes et appartenances de la Vicomte de l'eau". Moreover, during the same period, customs in Harfleur and in Dieppe levied duties on logs of sapang, a tree of reddish hue found in Central and South America. Following in the wake of the courageous Norman navigators of the Middle Ages, a gentleman from Honfleur, Captain Paulmier of Gonneville, landed in Brazil in 1503, and Jean Denis, a sailor from Honfleur, explored the mouth of the St. Lawrence River three years later.

There was once, long ago... an expedition

In Manaus in the heart of the Amazon, at the time when I had just completed the Orellana Expedition on a balsa-wood raft, I asked myself once again about the legend of white, bearded men figuring in precolumbian history. And indeed, some studies indicate the possibility of contacts between the Normans and the pre-Columbians. I recapitulated mentally the possible itinerary of these navigators: towards the tenth century, a group of Normans touched upon America in the Gulf of Mexico, and then landed in Venezuela. These men subsequently crossed the Orinoco River basin (Los Llanos) before turning to the Pacific Coast to continue their peregrinations. This is supposedly only a legendary route, but in fact, nine times out of ten, archaeological students tend to confirm the details of legends. And so it came to my mind that the only way to validly compare this mythical itinerary with reality was to reproduce the voyage using the same ship and the same route... by drakkar.

Unearthed in 1880 from the blue clay of a funeral mound in southeastern Norway, the *Gokstad* provides the archaeological specifications needed for the construction of a tenth century Norman ship. The *Gokstad*, with its klinker-type hull made entirely out of oak, can carry a crew of 35 men. A low draught factor (0.90 m), and the presence of 16 pairs of oars permits it to manoeuvre rapidly in the shallow waters of rivers and in coastal areas. GUIP Shipyards, French specialist in traditional naval wood construction, has been charged with the task of building the 23.3 m drakkar which commenced in spring 1989 and which will be completed in spring 1990. I plan to try the boat out at sea during the spring and summer of 1990 and will set off across the Atlantic aboard the drakkar around September, hoping to reach my destination in January 1991.

Luc Chrétien at an exhibition where he was presenting the Atlantic route for his future viking ship voyage. In the background a 6-m model of the viking ship.

Expedition in search of the Tasmanian tiger

Gilles Martin

38, place Rabelais, 37000 Tours, France

French, born 14 May 1956. Dental Mechanic. Educated in France; obtained a diploma (Dental Mechanic) from Technical School, Tours, in 1974.

The Tasmanian tiger, *Thylacinus cynocephalus* (or Tasmanian wolf as it is also known) is in fact the largest carnivorous marsupial; it resembles the wolf but is smaller in size. It has a sharp and fox-like face and, although grey-brown in colour, the whole of its back down to its tail is marked with brownish-black stripes. It measures some 1.8 cm in length from its nose to the tip of its tail, and is around 60 cm in height at the shoulder. Its marsupial pouch opens backwards; however, little is known about its reproductive habits since the animal has not been bred in captivity. It feeds on wallabies, small animals and birds. It is a very strange animal in many ways and is reputed for its ferocity. When sheep were introduced into Australia, it preyed on them and as a result was nearly exterminated. As far back as 1840, rewards were offered for Tasmanian tiger hides, and this extermination went on until 1936 when the animal was at last protected by law.

Is the Tasmanian tiger now extinct?

Fossils of the Tasmanian tiger dating from the Pleistocene show that it was once present on the Australian mainland and in New Guinea; however, it has now for long been confined to Tasmania. The history of human interest in the Tasmanian tiger goes back to 1863 when the famous naturalist John Gould expressed concern about the animal's fate. In 1933, a specimen of the animal was caught for the Hobart zoo; however, by 1936, this last survivor had died. In 1937, a substantial expedition was organized and set out to find the animal in the wild but only its spoor was eventually discovered. In 1961, a male was killed accidentally at Sandy Cape but a new expedition to the northwest coast that was organized in 1963 once again came back home empty handed.

In fact, for many years, the Tasmanian tiger was thought to have become extinct – until photographs of it were published in the *New Scientific Magazine* of April 1986. These photographs had been taken by an Aborigine, Kevin Cameron, and were not of the highest quality; the animal's head is not clearly visible

205

A bushman of a hunting, fruit-gathering people photographed by Gilles Martin during one of his earlier expeditions to Tsodilo Hills, Botswana.

and certain scientists have contested the fact that this animal is really a Tasmanian tiger. Consequently the controversy continues to exist – has the Tasmanian tiger completely disappeared from Tasmania?

New search for a tiger

We have decided to organize a six-month expedition that will first track down and photograph the Tasmanian tiger and then go on to study the life and surroundings of the Aborigines of the Australasian continent. The first four months of the expedition will be devoted to the marsupial and will be divided up into two equal halves: two months will be spent in Tasmania in September and October (the end of the Australian winter and the beginning of the Australian spring) and another two months in January and February (at the end of the Australian summer). During the months of November and December that lie in between, it is our intention to travel to the Northern Territory of the Australian mainland to photograph and record the lives of the Australian Aborigines.

Although our four months in Tasmania will be devoted primarily to our search for the Tasmanian tiger we will, of course, study a wide range of the other fauna and the flora and landscapes of Tasmania. For example, we hope to put together a valuable collection of documents about the water mole and other species endemic to Tasmania such as: the Tasmanian echidna *(Tachyglossus sotosus)*, the Tasmanian devil *(Sarcophilus harrissii)* and the various species of birds endemic to Tasmania. The Tasmanian devil is another Australian marsupial – a large heavily built relative of the dasyures, with a broad muzzle, an enormous skull and extremely powerful jaws. In taking photographs of animals that are as elusive and wild as the Tasmanian tiger, we will be using 36-mm reflex cameras fitted with telephoto lenses (focal lengths of 400 mm and 600 mm).

The Aborigines

During the two other months of this expedition, we will travel to the Northern Territory to study, photograph and record the Australian Aborigine – one of the last hunting and fruit-gathering people left in the world. On the basis of these encounters, we shall be able to compare the habits and daily life of the Aborigines with those of another hunting and fruit-gathering people – the Bushmen with whom we lived for two months in the Kalahari in Botswana.

Throughout this journey, we will once again be photographing the flora, landscapes and the unique fauna in Australia – all of which form an intrinsic part of the Aborigines' life (insects, reptiles, mammals, birds, etc.). We will visit the main sacred sites of the Aborigines, for example, Ayers Rock, the biggest monolith in the world and which, for the Aborigines, is a symbol of fertility. There is a likeness between their belief about Ayers Rock and the Bushmen's beliefs about the Tsodilo Hills in Botswana. For these Bushmen, the Tsodilo Hills are a representation of the womb of the earth which gave birth to life in the Kalahari Desert. So we can find among these two peoples living in different continents the same belief with a strange and interesting similarity.

In spite of these similarities, it is not our intention to elaborate a theory about a possible link with these two peoples. Nowadays, it is known that they have derived from very distinct origins. We will only try to study these people, their beliefs and their life styles, and then compare our observations. The notes, photographs and recordings we made in 1987 when we were with the Bushmen in Tsodilo Hills will be compared with those we will make with the Aborigines from the Northern Territory.

These studies and the evidence they are likely to produce are part of an emergency programme because the traditions of these primitive people are fast disappearing.

Rock paintings photographed by Gilles Martin during his expedition to Tsodilo Hills, Botswana, in 1987.

Investigating the last voyage of the *San Pedro de Alcantara* (1784–1786)

Jean-Yves Marc Blot

Honourable Mention
The Rolex Awards for Enterprise – 1990

Apartamentos Santa Rita, Apartamento no. 31, Praia de Santa Rita, 2560 Torres Vedras, Portugal

French, born 20 November 1951. Archaeologist and Writer. Educated in France; M. A. (Cultural Contacts) from Tours University in 1974.

Everything started with a shipwreck, two hundred years ago but everything surfaced again 11 years ago, when historical research led to the discovery, off the coast of Portugal, of the underwater wreck of the *San Pedro de Alcantara*, a Spanish man-of-war lost in 1786 on the final stages of a voyage from Peru. After having been cut off from Spain due to the American War of Independence, the Spanish Viceroy of Peru had put on board that warship one of the richest cargoes of all time, the equivalent of more than a year's foreign trade for the South American colony.

A shipwreck with extensive consequences

The loss, near the Portuguese fishing village of Peniche, had widespread and lasting effects: bankruptcies; over 10,000 pages of manuscripts in the Spanish archives; extensive reporting of the events in most European gazettes; five oil paintings by the French master Jean Pillement then in Lisbon; and three more engravings of the Peniche accident by Spanish artists.

In 1977, following two years of research in the archives and museums of Spain, Portugal, France, the Netherlands and Italy, I rediscovered the wreck; it became the subject of my first university thesis in 1982 and is now further described in the PhD thesis which I am preparing. Since then, I and my wife, Maria-Luisa Pinheiro Blot, an archaeologist, have, in collaboration with the Lisbon National Museum of Archaeology, carried out a series of research expeditions to recover artifacts and elucidate the history of the wreck.

The objects we found on the seafloor in 1977 were deposited with the National Museum of Archaeology and subsequently, in 1986, it was decided to recommence work on the *Alcantara* wreck. Despite the interest and the potential of underwater research at Peniche, field work started in 1986 with the excavation on land, near the cliff of the accident, of the bodies of the victims. Manuscripts showed that these included Indian prisoners from a revolt led by the Inca Tupac

A painting by the French artist Jean Pillement (1728–1808) showing the shipwreck of the San Pedro de Alcantara, *which was acquired by the Instituto Portugues do Patrimonio Cultural for which Jean-Yves Blot has been carrying out archaeological excavations near the scene of the shipwreck since 1986.*

Amaru, considered a pioneer of modern Peruvian independence.

The remains of 22 humans, two with non-European features, have now been excavated, and three months of underwater research were also carried out in summer 1988. However, even after all this work, many aspects of the wreck still require to be clarified by using the wealth of available documentation to establish links between archaeology and such disciplines as history and naval architecture. Consequently, my project is to concentrate on three aspects which go beyond a normal archaeological programme.

Elucidating the design, cargo and loading of the vessel

I now need to make two expeditions that will enable me to complete my research on the *San Pedro* and finalize my PhD thesis on the subject.

The first expedition consists of diving on the wreck of another ship which is lying off Venezuela, and which I discovered was also named *San Pedro de Alcantara*. The carcass of the ship was discovered in 1955 by amateur divers and has been well preserved on the muddy bottom at a depth of 24 m. This ship, sunk in 1815, was built in Cuba in 1788 at the same shipyards as the other *San Pedro*. This expedition is therefore the perfect way to find out what the ship that sank off Portugal looked like. Despite my research, I have not yet found any plan of the *San Pedro*, and contemporary descriptions or narratives are too vague. Furthermore, there is no chance of redrawing the plan by studying the wreck north of Lisbon because most of the hull was taken out of the water at the time and broken apart on the beach to free the silver pieces, which had been distributed

209

about the ship's structural elements as ballast. For this first research component, which would last two months, I have contacted Jean Araud, former chairman of the Lasalle Foundation in Caracas, whose help will be crucial.

The cargo of the *San Pedro* also contained the collection of botanical findings put together by two Spanish botanists, Ruiz and Pavon. On my second expedition, I want to retrace the voyage of the two botanists in order to identify what kind of objects they accumulated during their ten years of travel in South America. Their travel notes give precise details concerning both their itineraries and lengths of stay but say very little about the actual objects collected. I plan to spend three months on this trip between May and November 1990 travelling through Lima, Huanuco, Pucallpa and Chancay to find the exact locations and visit any possible archaeological sites and private collectors. This expedition should make it possible to assess the historical value of the objects which, according to the archives, are still buried off the coast of Portugal.

With the information gathered in Venezuela and after further investigation in the archives in Madrid and Seville, I should finally be in a position to retrace fairly accurately the six-month voyage of the *San Pedro*. We already know that, after setting out from Callao (Peru) en route for Spain, the ship called at Rio de Janeiro to repair damage suffered on Cape Horn. We also know that the ship had serious navigational problems because the cargo was improperly distributed.

The last part of the project will be to reconstruct the ship on computer and to study its manoeuvrability with the cargo it had on board. This study will be carried out by Jean-Marie Finot, a French engineer who is a pioneer in this field.

A skeleton found during Jean-Yves Blot's 1986 campaign. Although the skeleton was originally named "Manolo", this was switched to "Manola" when anthropological examination revealed that "he" was a woman. A number of women were aboard the San Pedro de Alcantara: *Spanish ladies returning to Spain and several female political prisoners.*

Cataloguing wooden statues from ancient Egypt

Julia Carol Van Dijk

31 Sulgrave Road, Hammersmith, London W6 7RD, United Kingdom

British, born 22 June 1962. Doctoral student at University College, London. Educated in Ireland, Federal Republic of Germany and the United Kingdom; studying for a Ph. D. at University College, London.

I am preparing a catalogue of non-royal wooden tomb statues from the Old and the Middle Kingdoms of Ancient Egypt, from circa 2600 BC until circa 1700 BC. These are mainly statues of the owner of the tomb, either male or female, placed into it at burial to assist him or her in the afterlife. Often several different varieties were placed into the same tomb and ascertaining why this was so is just one aspect of my research. I am also examining a particular variety of offering-bearer figures placed into the same tombs. These statues became popular in the 4th Dynasty – the same period as the building of the Great Pyramid at Giza – and remained a standard part of the equipment of burial until the end of the 12th Dynasty. After the 12th Dynasty, Egypt was invaded and settled by outsiders for the first time and her subsequent history is full of the influences left behind by this people, known as the Hyksos.

During the later periods, wooden statues continued to appear, but not so frequently, and their original purpose seems to have been forgotten or superseded. In general, these statues measure 35–40 cm in height, although some as small as 10 cm and others of more than life size have been preserved. There is great variety in their style; this is not surprising if one considers the time period they encompass, but it is surprising when one knows how strictly the craftsmen adhered to the Canon Proportions. This is the set of regulations governing the production of any representation of the human figure, whether two-dimensional or three-dimensional, and is what makes Egyptian art appear to have remained static since its inception. This great variety in style, when properly recorded and analyzed, should reveal criteria vital for greater understanding of this early period.

The scattering of archaeological treasures

The passion of acquiring Egyptian antiquities during the 19th century resulted in collections being established all over the world. These consist of a wide variety of objects, especially those of a more portable size such as scarabs and amulets.

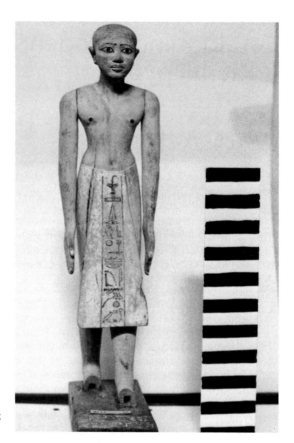

Wooden statue of an Egyptian male tomb owner, circa 2800–1800 BC.

Larger museums and wealthy private individuals stood sponsors to archaeological excavations and received a share of the newly discovered artifacts. As the passion for collecting intensified a black market grew apace, dealing not only in forged antiquities but also in stolen ones. Many early excavators were only interested in the more impressive antiquities, gold and stone statues, for example, and often turned a blind eye to the disappearance of vast quantities of more humble items from their sites. Not unnaturally, dealers were not anxious to publicize from where they had acquired their pieces, and the information we now consider to be the most valuable, for example, information on exact provenance, associated items, position in the tomb and so on, has been lost forever. In the case of wooden statues the situation may not be as hopeless as previously supposed. In many cases the statues bear inscriptions and the translation and correlation of these will reveal many clues to their origins.

The sort of information to be extracted from wooden statues covers an enormous range. The direct information concerns the tomb owners themselves and covers fashions on hairstyles, clothes, ornaments, stance, status – that is, their standing in the community and further afield – the positions they held locally and at court, inscriptions with the names of themselves and maybe their parents – especially helpful in determining genealogies. Female statues often have the "offering formula", a plea to the god Osiris to look after the Ka (soul) of the deceased in the afterlife in return for offerings of bread, beer and other commodities. Very few offering bearers are inscribed but the range of products they carry tell us a lot about the products of the period. The physical identification of the woods used is an area yet to be properly investigated.

A comprehensive database

In order to create an accurate and comprehensive database, access to the material is essential. My material is scattered across the globe, resting mainly in the major museums of the world, but also in many minor collections and even in private collections. It is impossible to locate the statues in the latter category except by word of mouth but those in the former two are readily accessible to scholars who are able to visit them. In general, museum curators have been extremely enthusiastic about my work. At present, it is the exception rather than the rule for collections in museums to be comprehensively published and the only way to determine what material is where is to visit each museum in person. This is both time-consuming and expensive but unavoidable if a reliable contribution to science is to be made. My experiences so far have led me to expect at least three extra statues for every one published – larger museums especially often have no idea of the extent of their collections, much of it lies in basement storage waiting to be catalogued.

The fact that the statues are so widely dispersed has led to the generally prevailing notion that they are few in number and therefore of no statistical value. This is incorrect. I had originally forecast a database of some 300 statutes, that number has increased three-fold and it may well be even higher. Thanks to two scholarships I was able to visit the Cairo Museum in 1986 and some 23 museums in the United States in 1988, and this has provided the information necessary for the completion of my thesis. However, the compilation of a catalogue goes far beyond the range of my thesis and the prospects of completion without external financial support are non-existent.

Wooden statue of an Egyptian female tomb owner, circa 2800–2000 BC.

Round the world by sail steamship – for freedom

Olaf Tormodson Engvig

Villa Torhill, 7100 Rissa, Norway

Norwegian, born 2 June 1937. Freelance photographer and writer. Educated in Norway; attended the University of Oslo, Department of Maritime History, from 1966 to 1975.

The *Hansteen* was built in 1866 by the Norwegian Government as a research ship and for the next 30 years the vessel surveyed and sounded the Norwegian coast; it was also used for magnetic and meteorological observations. Biological and zoological surveys were pursued by the young scientist G. O. Sars who later became the father of ocean research in Norway. As a government vessel, manned by the Navy, the *Hansteen* was, at one point, even used as a royal yacht by King Oscar II. Subsequently, the *Hansteen* served as a passenger steamer for 52 years and a hostel ship for 28 years. However, when, 12 years ago, it was decided that the ship's useful life had come to an end, I organized a campaign to save it and finally became the sole owner of a floating barrack ship for a symbolic price of 1 Norwegian crown. Today, the *Hansteen* is the only passenger sail steamship still afloat on its original hull.

The mid 19th century saw the arrival of a generation of iron ships, like the *Hansteen*, with an extreme clipper hull design and powered by a mixture of steam and sail. However, as the steam-engines became more powerful, reliable and economic, sails disappeared and the sail steamship vanished. This was the fate that befell the ship that I became the owner of.

In 1898, the *Hansteen* became a fjord steamer and several times over the following decades, it narrowly escaped the breaker's yard and finally, when I discovered her in 1976, the hull had been turned into a floating dormitory. Nevertheless, the hull had been constructed to stand up to punishment and even though superficially the ship looked to be in a terrible condition, I was convinced that it was sound and could be restored and repaired.

The *Hansteen* comes back to life

In 1978, I therefore drafted a plan to save the *Hansteen* and laid down the main phases of the operation: inventory every single part; remove all secondary parts, inspect the hull and carry out repairs; install the engine and boiler, fit out the

The Hansteen *in the Trondheim dockyards for refitting during the winter of 1988.*

interior and mount the rigging; train the crew, carry out trials and present this living legend "to the world at large". It was also decided that, in parallel with these activities, we would carry out a programme of research and collect inform-ation about the ship as well as launching a fund raising campaign. Funding did in fact take more time and energy than we had ever expected even though we managed to set up one of the largest support groups of this type in Norway. It also led me to write numerous articles about the ship, its history and the work we were doing to restore her. I hoped at that time also that I would be able to enlist the assistance and support of the museum authorities; however, my hopes proved to be in vain since there was a general belief that the objective I had set myself was not a feasible one.

After the interior of the ship had been dismantled, the contents inventoried and the ship emptied and every part of the Bloomfield hull cleaned and inspected, the damaged parts were repaired to the original specifications using only rivets and, of the original 128 plates, only 26 had to be replaced; conse-quently, some 80% of the ship still dates from 1866. This means that the *Hansteen* is the first Norwegian ship to be restored without a rivet being replaced by a weld and she will also be the first to be 100% finished. All the repairs have been supervised by the Government Ship-Inspection Authority, and the vessel once again demonstrated her seaworthiness when, whilst being towed from the south of Norway to Trondheim, she survived *en route* a 12-knot current and a force nine gale in the Atlantic. When fitting-out has been completed, she will carry cer-tificates for worldwide service for 14 crew and 10 passengers plus 100 passengers for day cruise utilization.

A voyage for prisoners of conscience

With all those who have worked on the restoration over the last ten years, we now wish to take the *Hansteen* on a world tour so that people everywhere can experience the romance of sail and steam in a vessel which is older than the Eiffel Tower or Brooklyn Bridge.

However, we feel strongly that the ship should do useful work and not just be a spectacular sight. The plan is therefore to steam in the name of human rights and freedom. One of the best ways of doing this is to invite Amnesty International to use the ship and the voyage to help prisoners in different parts of the world. I have received strong support for the idea of inviting Amnesty from politicians and other public figures in Norway. Yet, although the project has been in my head for quite a while, it is still in the early planning stage. Therefore this is the very first draft of an old plan. Not until a few days ago did I know that the ship was going to be finished this year and soon be ready for sea.

By spring 1989, the renovation work being carried out on the Hansteen *had advanced spectacularly.*

Angel Falls seen from a different angle!

Silvia Winiger

RD # 2, Box 214, Henderson Street, Oxford, New Jersey 07863, United States

Swiss, born 8 November 1949. Master parachute rigger and Vice-President of National Parachute Industries, Inc. Educated in Switzerland. Degrees in management and computer science and Master Parachute Rigger and Examination Certificates issued by the Federal Aviation Administration of the United States.

Angel Falls, the highest and most dramatic waterfall in the world, became the focus of my attention in October 1988. It all started when I had the opportunity of viewing a videotape showing experienced skydivers hurling themselves over a cliff somewhere in South America against a spectacular background of a thundering waterfall. The video documented an expedition that took place in 1983 – jumpers diving of this 1,000-m high rock situated in the deepest jungle of the Canaima National Park on the Orinoco River in Venezuela. These people were the first officially recognized jumpers to successfully dive from the head of the falls and land in the jungle below. Previously, two unidentified individuals had also made the jump but without the blessing of the Venezuelan Government.

A new challenge to meet

Being a skydiver for over 17 years with a total of over 2,100 jumps to my credit, the jump itself did not look abnormally difficult. But this was a base jump, a different type of jump – and a first for me! Would I have the courage? Normally we skydive out of a plane – no problem – no obstacles to the rear, front, sides – or below for that matter. A base jump, however, is a jump from a stationary object, i.e. a tower, bridge, antenna, high-rise building, rock formation, etc. – anything that is high enough to let a parachute deploy in time to survive the jump. The waterfall's very height does not present a problem, its sheer cliffs drop off in our favour and give the jumper a 10–12 second delay in which to fall stable and pull the main or auxiliary parachute. The only snag is the presence of the fall's cathedral walls that, halfway down the cliff, wrap themselves around the masses of cascading waters, leaving an entrance only about 65 m wide through which the skydiver has to escape. It is a must therefore to pull before that wall and no later.

The preparations completed, we embarked on an Avensa flight for Caracas, and in October 1988, we relaxed on a balmy tropical beach near Caracas waiting for the rest of the group to meet up with us. Next day, we flew inland to Canaima,

217

Into the abyss. Silvia Winiger two seconds after having hurled herself off the top of Angel Falls.

the outpost from which all tourists take river trips or airplane rides away from Caracas. Eventually, we were approaching Angel Falls. It was a cloudy, rainy afternoon, the falls looking forbidding shrouded in mist and clouds. Suddenly we caught a glimpse of them through the tiny windows of our plane and my heart stood still – "I am going to jump off this? I must be out of my mind!"

The approach to Angel Falls

The plane landed in Canaima and, after watching our equipment being loaded onto trucks, we headed up river about 1.5 km to the place where the canoes are kept. From there, a helicopter took our equipment in a huge net to the camp designated for us for the first day. A practice jump out of our helicopter that same afternoon helped us to familiarize ourselves with the altitude and remind us of the task in front of us. A jump from a helicopter simulates a jump from a stationary object; there is no air below the hovercraft, so the body dives into a vacuum in just the same way as on a base jump. The difficulty in a base jump lies in the fact that the body does not dive into an airstream in which one can get immediately stable and fall with a belly-to-earth position. A base jump requires the utmost discipline and concentration with regards to body form especially if exit is less than perfect.

The next day we were off to the falls. The hours in the canoe with only a few stops was rather trying on the entire body but the anticipation and the scenery made the hours fly. Finally the last bend was taken and there facing us were – Angel Falls.

The next day, 4 October, dawned with a breathtaking view of the falls as the first light hit the mountain peaks and cascading waters. It promised to be the perfect day – not a cloud in the sky. The first group was whisked away by the helicopter to the top of the rock formation from where we would jump, and the other groups followed at ten-minute intervals. By 8.30 everybody was assembled at the top and the adventure was to begin.

A leap into space

Finally, it is my turn and the countdown begins, 5–4–3–2–1–go. Remembering what the other jumpers have told me about a base jump, I keep my eyes on the opposite mountain range and waterfalls and my head high. Do not look down! I step off, throwing my body into a hard-arch position. The cathedral walls are coming up at a dizzying speed, but I wait another couple of seconds before I reach for the release handle that activates my parachute. I pull and the parachute opens as it has done 1,000 times before – on heading, within split seconds, clean, driving me away from the cliff, being helped by the powerful air pressure that the waterfall exerts. The walls of the cathedral are left behind and I am free.

Using my experience and know-how from many a tight demonstration jump, I am making my final approach. Spotting the windsock my heart is almost standing still – the winds have changed – I am flying downwind into the target! The winds are pushing from behind me, which means the forward speed of my parachute plus the wind is adding up to an uncomfortably high-speed approach on to the tiny landing-site target. In anticipation, I brake the parachute, pull up my feet and knees to avoid the first set of rocks, missing the boulders but striking a second one with my left foot and crunching into a mess of cut-down brush, nasty tree stumps, bushes, twigs, branches – and I roll… I am limping, but whilst gathering up my parachute, am able to produce a thumbs-up sign and a big smile.

Even now when we get together and talk about this adventure, we reflect on what a jump this was. Anyone seeing Angel Falls and its majestic sheer cliffs and thundering waters will understand what an awesome feeling one can have looking down from it.

Which way up – which way down? Silvia Winiger on her back six seconds from the moment of departure.

Cave exploration in the world's highest limestone mountains, Indonesia

David Robert Checkley

Honourable Mention
The Rolex Awards for Enterprise – 1990

40 Ashford Road, Withington, Manchester M20 9EH, United Kingdom

British, born 9 April 1948. Research Worker, ICI Pharmaceuticals Plc. Educated in UK; M. Sc. (Animal Nutrition) from University of Lancaster in 1972.

At the heart of Irian Jaya, the Indonesian part of the island of New Guinea, is the high Trikora mountain range. Snow-capped, glaciated, remote and uninhabited, these mountains are one of the least visited areas on earth. They flank the wide and fertile Baliem Valley, inhabited by the Dani tribe which had remained completely isolated from western influence until very recently.

These are the highest limestone mountains in the world. They reach a height of 5,030 metres, and are still totally unexplored from a speleological point of view. In 1988, we made a reconnaissance flight by Cessna over the Trikora massif and found many holes that look like cave entrances and rivers that disappear underground at high altitudes. None of this has been explored.

Irian Jaya has had a troubled history, but tourists can now enter the country by obtaining a permit, a "surat jalan" in Jakarta, naming all members of the team. It is then possible to travel within Irian Jaya on a normal tourist visa, provided that one registers with the local police force. The peak of Trikora itself was a closed area in 1988, but farther west there was no access restriction.

Searching for the world's deepest limestone caves

My project is consequently to undertake a speleological expedition in the Trikora. It would last six weeks (from late June to mid-August 1990) and would include ten team members, who have already been selected, plus others now being recruited, as well as inhabitants of Kwiawaggi who would be hired as porters as was done during our 1988 reconnaissance expedition. The ten individuals already chosen are some of the most experienced speleologists in the United Kingdom.

We also may link up with a French group led by Bruno Théry of the Franche-Comté Speleology Federation, Clairvaux, France. They have previously been to the "bird's head" in the west of Irian Jaya. These arrangements are however not

The peak of Trikora at 4,730 m.

formalized at the present time.

The whole team would fly on a regular flight from Bali to Jayapura on the north coast of Irian Jaya, and then on to Wamena in the Baliem Valley which runs along the Trikora massif. From there we would make a four-day walk to the Dani village of Kwiawaggi at an altitude of 3,000 m. Previously, we stayed in an ex-missionary house in this village and plan to use this as our base camp. Finally, an advance camp will be set up at Lake Kulip (altitude 3,400 m) at a day's walk from Kwiawaggi. We will camp close to the lake and will work out from this in teams of two or more.

The region is a mixture of natural grasslands, fern tree pockets and moss forest. The moss forest is difficult to move in but can often be circumnavigated. There are one or two paths to the edge of the area which are used by the Kwiawaggi people when trapping the large marsupial rats that inhabit the area.

Main objectives already identified

We have three major objectives within one to two day's walk of the advance base: a sink cave explored to the head of a very wet vertical section in 1988; a huge shaft seen from the air in 1988 but not located on the ground; and a number of sinks close to Lake Kulip.

During our aerial reconnaissance flights in 1988, we saw rivers disappearing into the ground at altitudes up to 4,000 m and cave features were seen at even higher levels. Where the water reappears is not known. However, we do not know whether there are major resurgences on the northern flank of the Trikora Range. The area to the south was shrouded in mist during our reconnaissance flight, but we believe it to be the site of the resurgences. The land drops away very steeply to the south giving realistic sink to resurgence height differences of 3,000 m. The deepest cave in the world currently stands at 1,535 m in the Jean Bernard system in France. Irian Jaya could be a contender in the race for the underground Everest.

We have the expedition experience in the team. The reconnaissance showed this area to be the most exciting totally unexplored caving area in the world. We are going to explore systems with a realistic possibility of achieving a world depth record.

The reconnaissance plane used by David Checkley to survey the Trikora region – courtesy of the Missionary Air Fellowship.

Ethnic folk arts in China's Guizhou Province

Gail Melinda Rossi

642 Iris Street, Redwood City, California 94061, United States

American, born 10 November 1951. Freelance photographer and writer. Educated in United States; majored in Art at California State University, Humboldt, from 1969–1972.

China's Guizhou Province, aptly named the "Switzerland of China", is a sea of undulating conical hills and mountains where lies hidden a wealth of folk art traditions among its native peoples. A quarter of Guizhou's 30 million population are composed of Miao, Buyi, Dong, Shui, Yi, Yao, Gelao and other smaller nationalities who have retained many of their traditional and ancient customs including an endless variety of exceptional dress. The current drive for modernization in China means, however, that many of these ancient and precious folk arts are on the verge of disappearing. As a visual and living record of a nationality's history and culture, this loss is most unfortunate.

As has happened all too frequently in other countries and already in some parts of China, established folk-art traditions are being sacrificed for mass produced and plagiarized art forms. Commercialized factory work now threatens authentic folk art while at the same time it exploits the indigenous culture and brings scant benefit to the people. The arts of Guizhou are some of the last remaining virtually undisturbed folk art traditions left in the world. Their living preservation is of the utmost importance.

A foundation for the folk arts

Our project is the outcome of nine years spent in China and the teacher training course for rural Guizhou middle-school English teachers that we organized. Combining our twin concerns of rural education among China's minority peoples and traditional folk-art preservation and study, we are setting up the US-China Folk Art Foundation.

The Foundation will have a variety of objectives. First, we intend to help preserve China's ethnic folk arts by promoting an awareness and appreciation of these largely unknown folk arts through exhibitions, publications and lectures, encouraging and establishing collections of prime pieces to be retained and displayed locally on either county or village levels, encouraging the training of

Miao women from Huangping County of Guizhou Province have many opportunities every year to dress in their richly embroidered festive attire, complete with their famed "phoenix" silver headdress.

novices by local master folk artists, revitalizing past skills no longer practised, and gathering information on preserving artifacts and transmitting them to Chinese curators. Next we will research national minority culture, crafts and traditional arts, by surveying the entire province's folk arts, including design, techniques and customs relating to the making and wearing of traditional costume, and by enabling qualified researchers in China to publish articles and books on varying aspects of this area's folk arts.

We also plan to develop sources of income for rural artisans, through the sale of high-quality works. To do this, it will be necessary to: identify saleable folk-art products, ensuring that all items remain true to traditional design; identify and develop overseas markets through exhibits, newsletters, etc.; and provide set-up funds for villages to produce saleable items.

In addition, we intend to provide financial assistance for the education of children in minority areas, and this will come from the money made from selling the folk arts overseas and from anticipated donations. Particular encouragement will be given to education for girls, and we will attempt to demonstrate the compatibility of education with the development or continuation of traditional folk arts. We hope our Foundation can promote further cultural exchanges between China and other countries by helping Chinese folk artists visit foreign countries and vice-versa, and by organizing exhibits of traditional Chinese folk arts overseas, etc.

Getting off to an active start

We have already begun work on many aspects of this project and have chosen as a starting point one particular village in Guizhou's Huangping County in which live one particular Miao group and the Ge-jia nationality. Through visiting Guizhou over 36 times, I'm now familiar not only with the province, but also with local leaders who understand our project. Most importantly, we also have come to know the governor of Guizhou who is of Miao nationality; he has greatly encouraged us and has given us a lot of valuable advice.

Ahwu, who accompanied us when we set up the first exhibition in the United States, lived for three months with us in California where together we studied the market situation. We both manned a booth in a gift show in San Francisco in February where we displayed many high-quality folk arts from Guizhou, resulting in a good amount of orders. Ahwu has now returned to Huangping, sharing her new-found knowledge with the village women. In a few months they will send traditional batik and embroidered articles, ordered at the gift show. Step-by-step we will learn the most effective way to do this work. Since the Guizhou textile exhibit will show in other parts of USA, our foundation will have greater exposure.

Our long years in China have resulted in a deeper understanding of the country, which is of vital importance to the success of the foundation. Our access to central government officials, provincial governors, regional, county and village leaders is something most foreigners cannot attain. We can deal directly with village artisans, avoiding the plague of exploitive middlemen currently running rampant throughout China. We believe we have something that can tap the reservoir of good will that exists between China and other countries.

A common sight in Ge-jia villages are groups of young girls diligently waxing designs onto aspects of their traditional costume.

From the Amazon to the Caribbean by canoe

Antonio Nuñez Jimenez

Ministerio de Cultura, Calle Séptima No. 6614, entre 66 y 70, Miramar Playa, Cuba

Cuban, born 30 April 1923. Chairman of the Cuban National Monuments Commission. Educated in Cuba and Ecuador; Ph. D. from University of Havana in 1952.

This project, which began in 1987, will continue through 1992 as part of the commemoration of the Fifth Centennial of the Discovery of America. The aims of the project are to: re-enact the way in which prehistoric tribes of the Amazon and Orinoco basins may have discovered the Caribbean and its islands; carry out scientific research on the protection of the environment in the Amazon, Orinoco and Caribbean basins and general studies on nature and man in those areas; make a positive contribution to unity and friendship between the peoples of Latin America and the Caribbean.

The first phase of the expedition was carried out in five Indian canoes specially built by the Quichuas of the Napo river basin in Ecuador, who produced these masterpieces using primitive construction techniques inherited from their forefathers and based on ancient traditions.

An expedition covering over 17,000 km

The expedition started out from Quito, capital of Ecuador, where the expedition members, including geographers, geologists, geophysicists, hydrologists, botanists, anthropologists and other specialists from Latin American and Caribbean countries, gathered together to commence their journey. From Quito, the group travelled through the eastern Andes of Ecuador to the town of Misahuallí on the banks of the Napo river where they embarked on a canoe journey that was to last many thousands of kilometres. The expedition followed the course of the Napo river through a large part of Ecuador and Peru up to the point where it empties into the Amazon. It then navigated the Amazon up to Manaus, Brazil, the Negro into Venezuelan territory until it reached the Casiquiare and then, after a short distance, it returned to the Guainia which was followed to the city of Maroa. From there, the expedition travelled 30 km overland to the town of Yavita on the Temi river. The Temi led us to the Atabapo and the Atabapo to the Orinoco which we followed all the way to the Caribbean sea.

226

The expedition leader
Dr. Antonio Nuñez Jimenez
standing among the
Windfield rock carvings on
the Island of Nevis.

Once in the Caribbean the canoes sailed from island to island along the Lesser and Greater Antilles until they reached the island of San Salvador in the Bahamas, the place of the first landfall made by Admiral Christopher Columbus in America. Up to this point the expedition had cover 17,422 km and had visited more than 20 countries in Latin America and the Caribbean. The canoes were rowed by the scientists themselves, both through the rapids of the rivers of South America and the stormy waters of the Caribbean. The scientific equipment and the provisions were carried in support craft which accompanied the canoes for reasons of safety.

A comprehensive symposium programme

The expedition visited some 20 countries and organized symposia or round tables in many of them. In Iquitos, Peru, a symposium was sponsored by the Institute for Peruvian Amazon Research and the Veterinary Institute for Tropical and High-land Research, and brought together delegations from Europe, the United States and Latin America. This was followed, in Leticia, Colombia, by a symposium on management of the Amazon territories, and in Manaus, Brazil, a further sym-posium was organized as a tribute to the expedition by the National Amazon Research Institute. Other meetings took place in Port-of-Spain (Trinidad and Tobago), at the University of Guyana, on the island of Nevis, in the Dominican Republic and in San Salvador (Bahamas). The scientific material obtained by the researchers during the first stage of the expedition is now being processed, and this will take until 1992. The final results of the research work carried out along the Amazon, Orinoco and Caribbean basins will be presented within the framework of activities commemorating the Fifth Centennial of the Discovery of America.

A range of tasks to accomplish

The expedition still has a number of additional tasks that it wishes to accomplish, including: archaeological research on the island of St. Lucia; publication of a collection of children's paintings; and the organization of an international congress. During archaeological research on the island of St. Lucia in the Caribbean, megalithic structures were found under Belfond Forest. They are patterned in the shape of agricultural terraces much like those built by the Incas. More valid conclusions and a final statement as to their precolumbian origin would require more thorough and systematic explorations and studies. Consequently, excavations and verifications by experts are planned on this site to determine whether or not these are Incan ruins.

During the preliminary work in St. Lucia, the expedition had the valuable co-operation of Professor Gregor William, of the Natural Society of the Island of St. Lucia, with whom the expedition promised to collaborate on a more detailed study. The owner of the estate on which the ruins are located has enthusiastically welcomed the project. The determination of the Incan or other South-American origin of the megalithic structures would be of extraordinary importance for science since, so far, no other such cultural findings have been reported in the Caribbean.

Another task to be carried out by the expedition in 1990 is the publication of a book compiling the drawings of children from the native communities visited along the route of the expedition. Children from the major ethnic groups in the Amazon, Orinoco and Caribbean basins drew nature and the world around them and also their view of the expedition.

It is also planned to organize an International Amazon-Orinoco-Caribbean Congress in 1990, with the participation of specialists from Latin America, the Caribbean and other areas to discuss conservation in the regions studied by the expedition. The Congress would study the research findings with a view to reaching an agreement on future actions for the preservation of nature and man in these important regions of our planet.

The canoe Simon Bolivar transporting the expedition team down the Casiquiare River, Venezuela.

The Byzantine monastic movement in the Judean desert

Yizhar Hirschfeld

6 Haarazim Street, 90820 Motza Ilit, Jerusalem, Israel

Israeli, born 6 February 1950. Research Archaeologist at the Hebrew University of Jerusalem. Educated in United States and Israel; Ph. D. from the Hebrew University of Jerusalem in 1987.

For more than 300 years, from the rise of Constantinople and the Council of Nicaea (AD 324), until the conquest of Palestine by the Moslems in AD 638, a unique civilization thrived in the Judean desert. This was a significant social experiment in communal living – the Byzantine monastic movement. What makes this Christian society so extraordinary and important for study is its amazing achievement in a harsh desert environment. This was one of the first and only really successful attempts to establish any form of urban settlement in such a desert. Christian monks turned the barren terrain into a grand "vegetable garden".

The achievement of this society is personified in its very endurance. The monastic movement in the Judean desert did not decay and crumble along with the wider Byzantine Empire; quite the opposite is true. The monasteries in the wilderness were at the peak of their success when Islam took hold. Their termination was the result of severance from the shrinking empire. The moslem forces, although not adverse to the monasteries, cut off all contact with the mother church. The community of monks was forced – through lack of support and proximity – to abandon this amazing way of life.

Fertility in the wilderness

The extent of the success of the Byzantine monastic movement can be easily measured in numbers. In a small barren area of 1,600 km, 60 monasteries with a total population of more than 3,000 souls had prosperous irrigation and agricultural systems which would be the envy of modern farmers. The affluence affected the whole area. The local nomadic and agricultural populations who, up to that period, were the sole inhabitants of the desert, became economic partners to the monasteries. Trade and development prospered. Areas well beyond the Jordan River were influenced. For example, the hill areas of Transjordan flourished from the sale of grains to the monks.

229

Monastery of Euthymius.
Mosaic floor from church
with one of the research
workers explaining his work.

The proximity to the Christian holy sites and the tradition in Christian monasticism brought the Byzantine monks to the Judean desert. But the unique physical conditions which abound permitted them to survive and prosper. During the Byzantine period the desert reached a level of prosperity which has never been equalled. What caused the delicate, abiding balance – between faith and renunciation and economic prosperity – to endure in the Holy Land is a most interesting proposition to consider. What made the monastic endeavour such an amazing success under these difficult conditions is a major question to which I would like to have the opportunity to find a definitive reply.

Researching the durability of the monasteries

I have carried out a systematic archaeological survey which brought to light the remains of 60 monasteries (only 40 of which had been previously recorded) and discovered a chain of military posts along the main byways.

My goal is to select one of these Byzantine monastic settlements and – as a living archaeology project – to recreate the community monastic life as it existed 1,500 years ago. We would reconstruct the complex trough and cistern water catchment network and irrigation system, dam surrounding valleys and rebuild several of the major buildings on the site. Particular attention would be given to the main community edifices and their fine mosaic floors. All this work would meticulously follow the original plans. We would plant the crops grown by the monks – figs, olives, dates, grapes and a variety of other fruits and vegetables – and hopefully enjoy the harvest.

I have two possible sites in mind: Khirbet ed-Deir and the Monastery of Euthymius. These two locations are quite different in nature. Khirbet ed-Deir is one of the most remote monasteries in the Judean desert and, for this reason, has been well preserved. It was quite a small monastery and we have no recorded mention of the site. Excavations revealed an astonishing agricultural system, beautiful mosaic floors, a marble screen, large offering tables, oil lamps, jars, pots, etc.

The Monastery of Euthymius, only 12 km from Jerusalem, was one of the largest and most important Byzantine cloisters. Its founder, Euthymius the Great, was the leader of the monastic movement in the Judean desert during the 5th century. Preservation is excellent. The central basilican church dominated the site; frescoes decorated the walls and the floors were paved with marble and mosaics. It is very well documented and offers considerable flexibility in the scope of the planned project.

The second stage of the endeavour would be to research the significance of the monastic social life in the desert. The monks were far from cut off from their surroundings. Their holy sites and the communal life attracted pilgrims from all over the Byzantine world. These thousands of annual visitors certainly had a very positive effect on the local economy. Much more important was the dynamic economic infrastructure which developed between the monasteries and the local populations. The scope of local trade, the nature of day-to-day relations with local nomads and farmers are topics which are, so far, totally unresearched.

To carry out the economic facets of the research I propose to prepare an exhaustive data base of all prime sources of documents from the period. Such material is stored in libraries throughout Europe, the United States and Israel. Each of these accounts would be studied to glean all references to the daily life and economy of the time.

I believe that this two-faceted project – ethno-archaeological and systematic theoretical research – will culminate in a fascinating functioning site supported by a detailed body of information about life at and around the monastery. I hope we will acquire an in depth understanding of the significance of the monastic movement and its success.

Monastery of Euthymius. The burial crypt of Euthymius.

Rolex Laureate – The Rolex Awards for Enterprise – 1990

Wayne Anthony Moran

Wayne Moran, a physician from Hong Kong with considerable sailing experience, has built a replica of a 13th century junk. He now plans to retrace the maritime Silk Road taken by Marco Polo, compare his own findings with the descriptions given by the Venetian voyager, and carry out research projects to recall the Golden Age of trading and cultural interaction along the Silk Sea Route.

The Marco Polo Voyage

Wayne Anthony Moran

Rolex Laureate
The Rolex Awards for Enterprise – 1990

c/o Shing Ge Fat Shipyard, 25 Po Chong Wan, Shum Wan Road, Aberdeen, Hong Kong

British, born 7 February 1952. Physician, Expedition Leader, Researcher. Educated in Singapore, Federal Republic of Germany and UK; M. B. B. S. from London University in 1976.

Marco Polo is a central figure in the history of the silk routes which, for over 2,000 years, were the means of communication and dialogue between the civilizations of East and West. His overland voyage to Cathay and his 17 years in the service of Khublai Khan are common knowledge. Less well known is his return journey leaving Amoy (Xiamen) by sea in 1292 aboard a junk as part of an imperial fleet escorting the 17-year old Princess Cocachin whom the great Khublai Khan was sending to become bride to the King of Persia. However, whereas the overland silk route was to remain relatively unchanged until quite recent times, the sea route altered within a couple of centuries of Marco Polo's account.

Our project, the Marco Polo Voyage, will, within the framework of the UNESCO integral study of the Silk Roads, be travelling in a replica of a 13th century junk, which we have built, to retrace the maritime silk route taken by Marco Polo, compare our current findings with the descriptions given by the Venetian voyager and carry out a number of research projects to recall the Golden Age of trading and cultural interaction along the Silk Sea Route. We will focus on what has been lost and what still remains of the places, people, creatures, plants and other treasures of the East that he described. Like Marco Polo himself, we will document those links with the past before they are swept away with the tide of advancing civilization.

The construction of the *Cocachin*

Marco Polo provided Europeans with their first description of the sailing junk which he admired because it was so in advance of European vessels in nautical technology. Yet his references contrast sharply with current opinion that junks are not ocean-worthy vessels. It was only when I came to research a vessel suitable for retracing the Silk Sea Route that I discovered that the vessels plying the China coast today are usually coastal vessels and far removed from the ships of Khublai Khan's fleet. I therefore collected engravings and ancient descriptions and used a computer to digest the information I collected and give me the shapes of possible

The stern of the Cocachin, *like that of its illustrious ancestors, is richly decorated with traditional paintings.*

junks that would fit requirements; it also allowed me to choose the one most closely resembling the drawings and descriptions from the past. We finally selected a Yuan Dynasty Fuzhou junk design which originated from the same region of China that saw the embarkation of Khublai Khan's fleet; moreover, its highly decorated appearance suggests that it may have been part of the imperial fleet.

The next step was to build a scale model and have it tested in a water test tank and wind tunnel at the Wolfson Unit of Southampton University. The results proved very promising and this model provided the basis for the construction work. The search for the wood and other materials, and the transport of the keel and the mast, were adventures in themselves – as was also the search for sponsorship to cover the costs. The construction took 18 months and the hull was put into the water in October 1987 after which began the final fitting-out and preparation of the sails prior to commissioning which was planned for 28 April 1988, the festival of Tin Hau, goddess of the sea. The finished vessel is 23 m in length, weighs 75 tonnes and has a poop richly adorned with Chinese carvings; the total cost has been over a million Swiss Francs. During the course of summer 1989, systematic performance analysis will be undertaken using computer-integrated navigational equipment loaned to us for this purpose.

Retracing the route of Khublai Khan's fleet

The itinerary has already been drawn up and will entail sailing down the coasts of Vietnam, Thailand, Malaysia, Singapore, Sumatra, the Nicobar and Andaman Islands, the east coast of India, Sri Lanka, India, the Maldives, the west coast of India, Pakistan, Iran, Oman, South Yemen, Somalia, Ethiopia, Saudi Arabia, Egypt, Crete, Turkey, Greece and, finally, Italy.

During the voyage, we will try to pinpoint the places described by Marco Polo, which remain uncertain or controversial, taking the names, directions, distances and descriptions that he used in order to piece together the jigsaw puzzle of his sea routes; in doing so we will look for what remains of the ancient emporia he described. We will correlate his descriptions of flora and fauna with present-day findings; the abundance of creatures and plants described by medieval travellers contrasts with the current situation, and Marco Polo's description of the "unicorns" in Lesser Java was probably the eyewitness account of the one-horned Sumatran rhino now believed extinct on that island. Our expectation is that the voyage will highlight Chinese maritime activity along the Silk Sea Route which, according to contemporary travellers, was extensive but which was to halt so dramatically during the Ming Dynasty. It is also our intention to test out replicas of old Chinese navigational instruments on board the junk; no less than 11 instruments which indicate North or measure latitude have or will be created. In addition, we will verify the utility of a 15th century Chinese navigational chart that gives the duration of each leg of the journey.

A point of special interest is that we are trying to gain permission for a journey along the east coast of China to visit places related to Marco Polo such as Hangzhou which he described in minute detail and which must have been the finest of all medieval cities, and Quanzhou which was the port of embarkation of the imperial fleet in 1292.

Eight people have already signed on as crew members for the *Cocachin* and two more remain to be chosen to make up the full complement. Also, since the junk can carry up to 17 people, passengers may be taken on from time to time. My wife and three children will accompany me on the voyage but to ensure that the children can continue their schooling, we have arranged for a satellite line with schools in England and Hong Kong. All in all, we believe that the Marco Polo Voyage of the *Cocachin* will make a very positive contribution to stimulating public awareness and interest in the Sea Silk Route and its history through our personal recounting and publications and a television series that are to be produced. Last but not least, it will establish one further link between the East and the West.

The Cocachin, *in which Wayne Moran will be following the sea voyage of Marco Polo, giving ample demonstration of the seaworthiness of its design.*

The Goodwill Constellation: Seattle 1990 Goodwill Games sculpture in space

James Stephen Pridgeon

7108 42nd S. W., Seattle, Washington 98136, United States

American, born 26 December 1948. Research Administrator at the University of Washington. Educated in the United States; B. A. with Honours (English Literature) from Stanford University in 1970.

The Goodwill Games will be an international athletic event similar to the Olympic Games sponsored each four years by the United States, USSR, Turner Broadcasting Corporation and a host city. In 1990 Seattle, Washington, USA, will be the sponsoring host. The Goodwill Constellation is a sculpture in space which will be seen from earth by billions of people. Manufactured in America and launched by the Soviets, the constellation identifies co-operation and excellence as the foremost symbols of the Seattle 1990 Goodwill Games. It is also a unique opportunity for all peoples to share a common vision which combines art, technology and international understanding. Finally, it provides a focus for national involvement and pride because it is a significant international "first".

A technologically feasible project

This is a technologically feasible work which relies on reflected light to be visible from the ground. Consisting of two inflatable Mylarized balloons connected by a long Kevlar tether, the sculpture will look like two brilliant stars moving slowly across the horizon. Each star will be as bright as Venus, with the apparent distance between them being approximately the diameter of the moon. While inflatable satellite technology was perfected by the United States in the early 1960s, tethers are now the subject of intense research efforts at NASA for use in Shuttle and Space Station applications. Thus, tethers offer a significant research component to this project.

The Goodwill Constellation draws upon our oldest legends and most current interests in space. All peoples have a mythology of the stars. Our ancient ancestors wove their heroes and values into patterns in the sky. Today much of our future is involved with the frontier of space. In turn, we depend upon young people to understand the technological challenges and cultural issues of the 21st century.

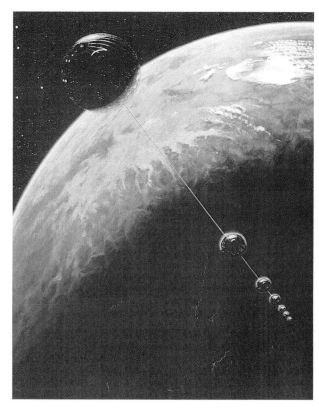

Artist's impression of the Goodwill Constellation. The sculpture as originally proposed with a seven balloon configuration seen from space.

A significant legacy of this project is the potential to engage children in the wonder of space exploration by linking artistic and technological imagination. The constellation provides a substantial educational opportunity. Education directors at a number of science and aerospace centres in the United States have agreed to act as advisers, and the Challenger Center in Alexandria, Virginia, has expressed interest in reviewing the project as potential curriculum material. Two issues of concern to space science must be addressed while developing this sculpture: optics damage and orbital debris. Telescopes with extremely sensitive detectors can be harmed by unanticipated exposure to bright light. Also, orbital debris now comprises thousands of individual pieces which can obscure view and interfere with navigation. Both problems will be solved by a low orbit and short lifespan for the sculpture.

Design and launching

This idea is technically simple. A shiny object in space reflects sunlight. When we pass into night, satellites high above us stay in sunlight long enough for us to see their reflections. Most low earth orbit (LEO) satellites complete one orbit every 90 minutes. Because the world turns below the spacecraft, each pass covers a different part of the earth. It is possible for satellites in LEO to be seen by people all over the world if their orbit is inclined at a 45 degree or greater angle relative to the equator. For example, if the satellite was inclined at 90 degrees (polar orbit) it would circle directly North and South and cover all parts of the ground as the earth turned below it.

The Goodwill Constellation consists of two inflatable Mylar balloons with an adjoining Kevlar tether. The balloons are similar to those used for NASA's Echo programme and are stowed deflated inside the payload canister until deployed. The balloons are inflated by the gradually increasing pressure of a sublimating powder. There is a small on-board computer to control the deployment of the balloons and to communicate with ground controllers for tracking purposes. The 400 pound payload is housed within a thin canister shell which is jettisoned after the launch vehicle deploys the satellite.

Mission scenario

It is anticipated that the sculpture will be manifested as a piggyback payload on a Soviet rocket used to launch satellites or to resupply the Mir space station. Once launched, the satellite will be deployed at a relatively low altitude, thus limiting its useful life. The satellite computer will then deploy the balloons, controlling the tether to minimize the chances of tangling. As the satellite is deployed, the sublimating powder will be warmed by solar radiation, and after some time, the balloons will gradually inflate. Serving as a tracking beacon, the computer could relay useful physical parameters such as tether forces, atmospheric drag, and ozone concentrations. Due to atmospheric drag the constellation's lifetime will be limited. It will burn up as it re-enters the Earth's atmosphere.

A second quarter, 1990, launch window is targeted to ensure the sculpture will be deployed by the July opening of the Goodwill Games. The schedule requires an engineering assessment be completed by May 1989. Assuming positive results, a complete design review would be completed in the third quarter, 1989. Procurement and fabrication could start as early as the third quarter of 1989, with complete fabrication scheduled by the end of that year. Testing would be completed by the end of the first quarter, 1990. Elements of satellite integration would begin in mid-1989 and finish at the end of the first quarter, 1990.

This project draws on both the power and human dynamics of space and the critical role of the artist in exploring these themes. A sculpture in space will not only command attention because of its unique beauty and position in world history, but also because the co-operation which makes it possible is, in itself, a significant international event.

Exploring the sources of the great rivers of Asia

Herman How-Man Wong

China Exploration and Research Society, 4028 Chaney Trail, Altadena, California 91001, United States

Chinese, born 26 August 1949. President of the China Exploration and Research Society. Educated in United States; Degree in Journalism and Art from University of Wisconsin, River Falls, in 1973.

"I stood with one foot on each bank of the Yangtze." At Shanghai, where I made that seemingly overstatement, the river was over 30 km wide and, even on a clear day, one could not see the other bank. But joking I was not; I had just returned from the source of the great river. While man is probing a new frontier in space and distant stars are being discovered every now and then, it is indeed surprising that sources of many great rivers remain undefined or ill-defined on our own planet.

It was with this conviction that I set out in 1985 to locate the source of the Yangtze river. With the full support of the National Geographic Society, I undertook an 18-month expedition which traced the river from mouth to source. Despite tremendously restricting government regulations and logistic difficulties, our team succeeded in studying the river all the way to its known source, Tuotuoheyan, and then proceeded to discover a longer source, Dam Qu.

Now acknowledged by the scientific community as the real source of the Yangtze, Dam Qu's source was established by me in a long summer of hard work. A book, *To the Source of the Yangtze*, will be published later this year in Hong Kong and the United States, describing the adventure.

The Yangtze – the first of a series

However, redefining the source of the Yangtze is only the first step in a series of ambitious plans. The ultimate goal is to explore the sources of the great rivers of Asia that originate on the Tibetan Plateau. However, in undertaking such ambitious projects, I am not driven by a desire for adventure or glory.

The multidisciplinary results of the Yangtze Expedition convinced me that this type of geographic endeavour has much wider implications on other disciplines. For example, much new information was discovered in the field of famine alone. While studying the upper Yangtze, my team discovered fishermen who trained

National Geographic Yangtze Expedition en route to the source of the Yangtze River.

river otters to fish, and scientists who were trying to save the giant Yangtze sturgeon; we learnt about the endangered fate of the Yangtze alligator, the use of mountain goat's gall for the treatment of mountain sickness by Tibetans, and observed the summer nesting grounds of the rarest black-necked crane (*Grus nigricollis*) on the plateau and the little-known Tibetan antelopes, and wild yaks, etc.

The fact that almost all of Asia's great rivers have their sources on the Tibetan Plateau is quite unique. Without doubt, that region remains one of the least known areas in the world. The headwaters of the Yangtze, Yellow, Salween, Mekong, Irriwaddy, Indus and Bramaputra rivers still hold fascination among modern explorers. The Yangtze's drainage area affects over 300 million people, or close to one-third of China's population. Basins of the other great rivers together probably affect a billion people in the world. In the same way that the people living along the foot of a mountain relate to its summit, hundreds of millions of people living along these rivers' drainage areas can relate to the sources.

Modern technology to aid exploration

Modern techniques of remote sensing are crucial in helping us locate the sources of these rivers and we routinely use data from the Landsat, Shuttle Imaging Radar (SIR-A and SIR-B), Large Format Camera (LFC) and Hand-held Photographs from Space programmes. Nevertheless, groundtruthing and final approach to the sites require traditional methods of travelling by jeeps, horses, yaks and camels and on foot. Drawing on experience of the Yangtze Expedition, we would be able to study the geography, climate, hydrology, glaciology, high-altitude lakes, bird and general wildlife and the little-known ethnic cultures of these regions.

240

As principal investigator of the project, I have already accumulated, in China, much of the needed equipment, including a highly modified jeep for off-road use, a motorized inflatable boat, canoes, diving gear and all the essential camping and exploration equipment. I also have in my possession a mass of logistic data and information crucial in putting such an expedition into place. These include space images, large-scale maps, historical text and scientific data compiled by Chinese scientists. However, funds for putting these to use are still lacking. Also, as the result of over 15 years of exploration in China, I have gained the confidence of the Chinese Government and permission for the implementation of such a complicated project. This has been demonstrated by the six National Geographic Expeditions that I have led to China in the past.

A three-part programme

The project can be divided into three parts related to the geographical location of the river sources. Each of these parts will be tackled in one summer of exploration work. The Indus and the Bramaputra both have their sources in western Tibet and they will be taken together on one expedition. The Yellow River and the Mekong have their sources in southern Qinghai and will be explored at the same time. The upper Salween is in northern Tibet and the source of the Irriwaddy in southeastern Tibet: those two can possibly be explored within the same summer. The results of our endeavours will eventually be published in book form which will fill in much knowledge about this unknown region.

Base camp near
Tuotuoheyan, glacial source
of the Yangtze River.

A pharaonic village

Hassan Ragab

Papyrus Institute, 3 Nile Avenue, P. O. Box 45, 16612 Orman, Giza, Egypt

Egyptian, born 14 May 1911. President of Dr. Ragab Papyrus Institute. Educated in Egypt and France; B. Sc. (Electrical Engineering) from Cairo University in 1933.

The idea of the pharaonic village first came to me some 25 years ago when I was acting as technical adviser to the Egyptian Ministry of Tourism and compiled my lectures on tourism into a book. This book proposed to the Ministry of Tourism the building of a "living museum" in the form of a village entirely in the ancient Egyptian style and inhabited by people dressed in ancient Egyptian costume performing all the everyday agricultural, industrial and social activities of the time. The whole village would be a succession of *tableaux vivants* depicting daily life in ancient Egypt which would form a major tourist attraction.

My proposals gained me the reputation of an unrealistic dreamer but I maintained my enthusiasm. In 1962 I began to research the methods employed by the Ancient Egyptians in the production of papyrus paper and started up a small papyrus-making industry to produce copies of ancient Egyptian paintings. It was the need to enlarge my production facilities which brought me to Jacob Island where I started large-scale papyrus cultivation in 1968. It took nearly ten years to develop my installation on Jacob Island by adding plants and trees known to have grown in Ancient Egypt, at the end of which I discovered that I was living in an Ancient Egyptian atmosphere.

In 1976 I put an application to the Egyptian Investment Authority to start an investment scheme of building the Ancient Egyptian Village which I called shortly the Pharaonic Village. The Egyptian Government approved the scheme and I was granted a concession of 50 years on the land where I started my papyrus plantation.

Planning a reconstruction of the past

I had studied ancient Egyptian history and naively believed that my knowledge of Egyptology would be sufficient. I soon found that all the information – and in particular the subtle details – I needed to build a complete ancient Egyptian village were not easily found in history books; and I had to set about searching in

242

The pylon at the Pharaonic Village temple. It consists of two massive symmetrical towers with the main gate between them.

books on Egyptian history, specialized articles in learned journals and in the proceedings of many congresses of Egyptology. Fortunately the Egyptian Museum in Cairo contained much of the information I needed and was easily accessible. However, this did not spare me trips to museums in London, Paris, Berlin, Turin, New York, Boston, Chicago and St. Louis.

The village, which covers 15 hectares, is built entirely in the style of ancient Egypt, although the buildings were constructed using concrete and steel rather than ancient techniques. It is inhabited by about 300 persons, all dressed in period costumes and living according to the usages and customs of pharaonic Egypt. The "villagers" practise all of the agricultural and industrial activities of ancient Egypt using the same tools as those preserved in the Egyptian Museum; social and religious activities are also represented. Located on "Jacob Island" in the Nile up river from Cairo, the "Pharaonic Village" is aimed at tourists who wish to become acquainted with the history of ancient Egypt. At the same time, it is considered a cultural highlight.

It takes about two hours for a guided tour, on floating amphitheatres (a type of gallery-shaped boat). The main parts are: a visit to the Egyptian pantheon by floating down the mythology canal marked out by the statues of the pantheon's 11 representatives (Amon, Thoth, Osiris, Isis, Horus, Khnum, Hapy, Ptah, Sekhmet, Imhotep and Bes); a visit to the pharaonic garden, where the visitor can admire beehives, a reminder of the importance of honey as a food in ancient Egypt; the living display of agricultural traditions, as well as boat-making and fishing; a re-creation of industry (brick-making, pottery-making, perfume-making, etc.); a visit to the temple which is entered through a tree plantation containing every variety recorded in Egypt; and finally, a peasant's house and a nobleman's mansion containing all of the furnishings characteristic of the pharaonic era.

243

One of the features of the peasants' house in Hassan Ragab's Pharaonic Village is a reproduction of a typical ancient Egyptian baking oven.

Taking ancient Egypt into the 21st century

The Pharaonic Village is thus already very well endowed, but I would like – and this is my project – to add new elements that will make my village a greater tourist attraction. In the first stage, I plan to build a pyramid with a classic floor plan, but a variety of functions: a souvenir bazaar on the first floor; on the second floor, an area where ancient pyramid construction would be explained; on the third floor, a department with small-scale models of the seven wonders of the world; and on the fourth floor, a 500-seat theatre where ancient dances would be performed to music played on period instruments. Construction of the pyramid is now in progress.

The second stage calls for the construction of a replica of the famous tomb of Tutankhamen. This is an enormous task, since everything will be reconstructed to scale. The manufacture and construction, under way since 1988, should take about three years. A third stage is planned: the construction of a history museum on writings and paper in Egypt. It is in its final phase. It holds ancient machines and tools needed for paper-making, as well as presses.

The fourth part of the project is aimed at creating a museum devoted to the history of tourism in Egypt. Unlike in Europe, where tourism began in earnest at the end of the 18th century, its history in Egypt is longer than one might think. The first guide to Egypt, written by Herodotus, dates from 450 BC.

Etched in time

Ludwig Jaffe

Via Badetto 18, 25040 Ceto, Brescia, Italy

British, born 12 April 1955. Archaeologist and researcher of ancient rock engravings and paintings. Educated in United Kingdom; B. A. (Social Science) from Polytechnic of Central London in 1981.

Val Camonica, a valley of the river Oglio in the Lombard Alps of Italy in the province of Brescia, extends some 65 km from Lake Iseo to the peaks of the Orties-Cevedale range in the province of Trentino-Alto Adige, near the Swiss border. It is perhaps one of the richest and most significant areas for rock engravings known in Europe and one of the major areas of rock art in the world – a cultural legacy that was registered in the World Heritage List of UNESCO in 1979.

The engravings here form a vast and important first-hand source of information about the past: several hundred thousand figures engraved on glacier-polished rock surfaces recount the story of a people in this remote Alpine valley – images and symbols that reveal the life and outlook of 400 generations that passed their lives here showing their mentality, religion and society and allowing us to see 100 centuries of history, from the hunter-gatherers of the Epipalaeolithic period to the present day.

Research objectives

This project aims to discover, copy and examine rock engravings in selected localities of Val Camonica. The records will elucidate our knowledge of the past in the Alpine region and give us evidence to test the chronological sequence established for the engravings.

We shall lead a team into the field on a programme of exploration, image reproduction and study in the central part of the valley. Zones of interest will be surveyed to locate engraved rock surfaces; we will then unearth, cleanse, high-light, photograph, trace, discern, enumerate and catalogue the depictions. A statistical breakdown of the figures will be compiled, comparisons made, and a report on the results of the research dossier drawn up. Experimental archaeology involving the replication of objects and the reconstruction of structures represented will enable us to check various conjectures concerning the engraved subjects.

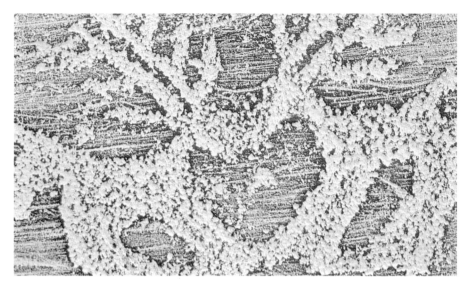

Iron Age rock carving of two deer photographed by Ludwig Jaffe in the Paspardo region of Italy.

Methods

The project consists of 11 processes divided into three stages: discovery; image reproduction; and study. The first two stages involve fieldwork and some time in the laboratory; most of the last stage can be carried out in the laboratory except for procedures that should be verified in the field.

In the discovery process, successively we will: survey to locate engraved rock surfaces; unearth concealed engravings; cleanse the worked surfaces; and highlight depictions – when a rock surface is suitable it may be possible to apply a delicate washable colouring so that the engravings can be deciphered and traced with greater ease.

During the image reproduction phase, we will: trace engraved areas on medium-weight plastic field sheets using felt-tip pens and then transfer them to draughting paper in the laboratory so that they may be helio-copied and photographed; take photographs, picturing the engraved surfaces in the environment, their profiles, the assemblages, details of the scenes, etc.

The study phase involves itemizing and numbering the figures, cataloguing them (typology, size, engraving characteristics and symmetry, delineation, conservation, context, stratigraphy, chronological style) and carrying out statistical analysis and a comparative study.

Finally, the material from the research dossier will be drawn up, results set down, conjectures discussed and impressions expressed. The excellence of each stage affects the successive one; if the figures are not clean and visible, the tracing will not be accurate, the cataloguing may be incorrect, the statistical analysis would be misleading and the results suspect. Each stage needs to be executed with care to ensure that the fruit of the investigation is valid and usable.

A new approach to history

In AD 16, Roman legionnaires entered Val Camonica, one of the many alpine valleys that opened out on to the great plain of the Po river basin. The people they found there already had a complex social organization, similar, in many respects, to that of modern society, and there was a developed commerce involving contact with other populations. Inscribed on the trophy of "La Turbie", a Roman monument in France near the Principality of Monaco, is the name *Cammoni*, one of the Alpine tribes vanquished and subjugated by Emperor Augustus. This modest reference marks the point the Camunnians and Val Camonica entered history, appearing for the first time in written chronicles; it also marks the point at which they disappeared from it again, becoming a small insignificant part of the great Roman Empire.

The traditional approach to history relies heavily on written chronicles, with their inherent biases and distortions. It is usually taken from vanquishers' accounts that tell the story of their leaders, heros and triumphs. Though less easy to understand than the written chronicles, the Camunnian engravings form an original and pure record about the lives of these people. They also had their kings, leaders and heros, though the names of these individuals will probably remain unknown to us.

The Etched in Time project follows a new approach and way of studying and seeing the past. We are trying to puzzle out clues that the depictions give about the Camunnians and attempting to piece together a picture of their lives and social fabric so contributing to an understanding of a heritage that belongs to all humanity. The fruit of the investigation should be an exemplary model analysis that can throw light on past cultural influences in this part of the world and which could be adapted for similar research in other regions of the globe.

A group of volunteers at work cleaning the face of a rock at In Valle, Paspardo, prior to research on the rock engravings that have been revealed.

247

Computerizing the languages of the world

Mary Ritchie Key

Honourable Mention
The Rolex Awards for Enterprise – 1990

University of California, Program in Linguistics, Irvine, California 92717, United States

American, born 19 March 1924. Professor of Linguistics, University of California. Educated in USA; Ph. D. from University of Texas in 1963.

The purpose of this project is to establish a linguistic database where lexical material across the continents is organized by areas, in such a way that comparisons can be based on this documentation. It is aimed towards international understanding and co-operation. It will serve not only as a synonym dictionary, but as an index to meaning and the cultures of various people around the world. This is a pioneering effort that will have global impact.

For the past few years I have been developing the idea of a non-Indo-European dictionary. I wrote a synopsis of the plan and sent it to many linguists who would be likely candidates for co-operating in such a project, asking them to be on the advisory board. The response was enthusiastic, and the acceptance was unanimous. The scholars who were contacted were chosen for their interests in cross-cultural research and for their skills and willingness to give time and thought to the objectives of the International Dictionary Series (IDS). Thus, the project has a charter honarary board comprising my former professors in historical linguistics and an advisory board, with professors from Australia, Chile, Colombia, France, Germany and the United States.

Because of the widespread encouragement, I started compiling the first volume, while also initiating discussions with others who might be editors for the subsequent volumes. Soon I will be retiring and be able to work full-time on the IDS, and plan to continue to guide and direct the project beyond compiling the first volume. To assure continuity, I have engaged younger scholars throughout the network of personnel involved, with the understanding that they will continue after my retirement from the project.

Dictionary plan

The first two volumes (South American Indian Languages and Austronesian Languages) are in the final stages of preparation. Further volumes are being planned, in consultation with experts in the various areas of the world. Our

When a young woman, Mary Ritchie Key (in green sweater) visited the Quecha Indians of Bolivia. She is wearing a native headdress to pose with a highland dancer of the area.

preliminary sketch indicates that about a dozen volumes would cover the major cultures of the world. Each volume will be produced in the same format, which will ensure the elegance of having comparable material. The model we have adopted is *A Dictionary of Selected Synonyms in the Principal Indo-European Languages*, compiled by Carl Darling Buck, which is organized in a topical outline of 22 chapters, with the various subjects treated as separate units. The IDS adaptation contains about 1,300 entries, and these, with identical numbers, will remain the same throughout all the volumes. The entries will be given bilingually or trilingually, with English as the first heading, and the language(s) of the area alongside. In the South American volume, English, Spanish and Portuguese will head each entry.

Each volume will have a chief editor, a group of associate editors, and a group of language specialists who will act as consultants for each language entered in the dictionary. Since the personnel for each volume will be different, several volumes can be in process of compilation at the same time. No salaries will be paid to any of the compilers; the scholarly work will be provided voluntarily by the academic community and other scholars. The languages for each volume will be areally defined and should be representative of the linguistic features of the area. About 35–50 languages will be chosen for each volume. (The Austronesian volume is the exception; it has about 80 languages involved.)

The production of each volume will involve sufficient interaction between the editor and the language specialists to ensure accuracy. During the initial stages of preparation, the editor will acquaint the collaborators with the outline and organization of the dictionary as a series. The word list is distributed to each language consultant and to the associate editors. As the consultants fill in the word list, correspondence with the editor deals with such matters as morpheme division, dialect usage, orthography, and difficulties in finding the correct translations. At this stage the entries are arranged in the topical format with numbers, as in Buck. Thus the consultants will see the material arranged in final format before publication. We are in discussion now with a university press which is interested in publishing the dictionary series, providing we can submit camera-ready copy for each volume. In addition, we are in discussion with Human Relations Area Files to include disks in their CD-ROM series. Thus, we will provide the data in both book and computer form, and the text only in the book form.

Progress to date

I will act as the general editor for the project which will have its headquarters near the University of California, Irvine. While the main work of the IDS will be done on a voluntary basis, there are certain financial needs that must be met: photocopying the final draft to be checked by consultants; postage to the various countries; travel by a few compilers for checking data; travel by the general editor for enlisting participants; travel by volume editors for their particular needs; buying computer disks. Volumes I and II are in the final stages of preparation. Prof. Darrell Tryon of the Research School of Pacific Studies has devised the software for compiling the word lists. The languages are entered individually, and the system permits editing the lists as notes are added and corrections submitted. Then the programme merges the lists into a single listing of each word, with all the languages and their respective footnotes in order.

We believe that the dictionary can be completed in seven years and we have decided to complete at least one of the first two volumes before asking specialists to work on others in order to provide them with a coherent format.

Mary Ritchie Key learns the software programme used in the compilation of the Dictionary, which was devised at the Australian National University, Canberra, under the direction of Prof. Darrel Tryon, who is seated next to her.

Punciid ostracods – a search for a living fossil

Kerry Michael Swanson

112 Westminster Street, Christchurch 1, New Zealand

New Zealander, born 30 September 1946. Geological Technician, University of Canterbury, Christchurch. Educated in New Zealand; B. Sc. (Geography) from University of Canterbury, Christchurch, in 1982.

Examples of "living fossils" occur in almost every phylum, yet within this diversity of forms there apparently exists a number of traits or characteristics which warrant consideration as something unique and worth scientific investigation. To qualify for membership in that exclusive "living fossil" club, an organism must present a number of credentials: it must have persisted over a very long interval of geological time; it must be morphologically and physiologically similar to its fossil equivalents; the geological record of its fossil relatives must extend back to the very origins of complex animals; and it must present a relict (restricted) distribution and have few close living relatives.

However, the concept of a living fossil cuts right to the heart of evolutionary theory. In formulating his concept of gradual biological change through time, Darwin acknowledged a contradiction between that which he perceived (a gradual, progressive modification of form) and that which could be deduced from the fossil record. Examination of the development history, illustrated by fossil remains, indicates the record as very patchy and that gaps between major evolutionary progressions are the norm, i.e. forms morphologically "intermediate" between ancestral and descendant species are not found.

"Punctuated equilibrium" coined in the 1970s as an alternative to Darwin's gradualism required that the fossil record (with all its "imperfections") be interpreted as a true and accurate record of biological evolution. The so called "gaps" were real, illustrating that speciation events occur in "short" sharp bursts in small geographically and genetically isolated populations; these events "punctuate" the often geologically long periods of "stasis" or non-evolution.

A living fossil found in New Zealand?

In 1949 a New Zealand palaeontologist, N. de B. Hornibrook, described the carapace of two new ostracod (Crustacea) genera found in sediments dredged from the northern shelf of New Zealand in about 300 m of water. In his text he

251

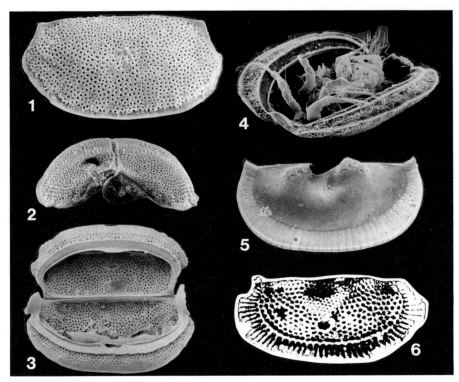

Plate illustrating the New Zealand punciid ostracods and assumed "ancestral" kirkbyacean.
1. Manawa staceyi n. sp. left valves×150. 2. Manawa staceyi valves in "life" position.
3. Manawa staceyi interior of carapace. 4. Manawa staceyi entire animal, ventral
uppermost. 5. Puncia sp. right valve×125. 6. Coronakirkbya fimbriata ×75. Permian,
Texas, USA.

stated "...the author is reluctant to assert that a representative of a group of Ostracoda, which apparently died out elsewhere in the Devonian (400–350 million years ago), is still living in the South Pacific". Unfortunately Hornibrook's material contained no soft parts.

For over 20 years, I have pursued an interest in New Zealand's marine ostracod fauna, with the lure of being the first to find a living punciid ostracod ever present. I began an investigation on the benthic ostracod fauna of the Cavalli Islands in northern New Zealand. To my disbelief, two of those samples produced two poorly preserved specimens of *Manawa* genus of punciid ostracod with soft parts intact. Attempts at dissection were not successful, consequently a resampling programme was undertaken.

From that effort, I recovered an additional two specimens and the next year, a further six specimens. I also found about three juveniles, all of which were carrying a single shield-shaped shell, a feature never previously recorded in the ostracods. I have now convincingly shown that the punciid ostracod is quite unique and that, for *Manawa*, at least a number of characters are of enormous significance when aspects of crustacean evolution are discussed.

In many respects, the work completed thus far represents the tip of the iceberg. I have not made any seasonal, behavioural or histological examinations of *Manawa* although I have established those projects as a priority. More importantly I have still been unable to achieve my original objective, i.e., to capture live specimens of *Puncia*; that animal after all is the one which led Hornibrook to make his original pronouncement about a possible "living fossil" find. In 1987, a colleague from Australia informed me he had found a few valves of the third punciid genus (*Promanawa*) in recent sediments on the west coast of Tasmania. I am quite convinced that using the techniques developed for capturing *Manawa* and given sufficient time, live specimens of that genus can also be recovered.

A search for a live specimen of *Manawa*

My project is to establish a base camp and laboratory on the uninhabited Haraweka Island in the Cavalli of New Zealand; there I will collect, concentrate and examine residues on site until living specimens of *Manawa* and *Puncia* in particular are retrieved. Behavioural (especially reproductive strategies) and ecological studies will then proceed. Subsequently, I will establish a base camp and laboratory at Macquarie Harbour, Western Tasmania where I will collect, concentrate and examine residues on site until living specimens of *Promanawa* are retrieved.

I will also carry out similar research in north Germany and in western Texas, USA, where other researchers have found examples of the three species in a fossil state. In the analysis of the recovered materials, I will work with the Earth Science Research Centre at the Australian National University in Canberra, Australia, which is highly reputed in the analysis of ostracod carapaces. All of the data obtained will be interpreted in relation to ecological interpretations based on faunal associations, sedimentary and geological field data; in addition, the amino acids present in the valves will be determined.

Several species that had originally been described as "living fossils" such as coelacanths or horseshoe crabs have been found, after all, to have undergone some evolution. The punciid ostracods offer great promise of being given this exciting designation. The challenge of this project is now to determine finally whether puncidae are "living fossils" worthy of the name.

The first Cavalli Island expedition gets under way in December 1984.

Iconographic evolution of rock art of the southern Sahara

Christian Dupuy

112 boulevard des Belges, 69006 Lyon, France

French, born 28 July 1959. Researcher writing Doctoral Thesis. Educated in France; M. A. (History) from the University of Provence in 1984.

Documentary data on the subject of the rock art of the southern Sahara are still very few and far between, which is somewhat surprising in view of the fact that the earliest publications in this field date from over a century back. The fact is, however, that the majority of writers in this area have been travellers or amateur historians more sensitive to the aesthetic appeal than the documentary or archaeological value of their discoveries. Hence, most writings and reproductions have concentrated on rock art works of a pronounced, evocative nature.

Expanding on earlier findings

Using these highly selective documents as their basis, certain writers have attempted to establish chronologies and even historical reconstitutions. A number of hypotheses – even though they may seem inspired more by intuition than by scientific observation – nevertheless deserve verification or completion. This is the context that motivated my desire to carry out several study trips during which I listed and traced engravings in regions containing a wealth of rock art but which were hitherto scarcely known. My objectives were threefold: to establish a relative chronology of the rock art of a given region; to mark the limits of the geographic zone of the cultural sequences emerging from this chronology; and to attempt a definition of the natural and cultural contexts and ritual events which inspired the members of pastoral societies to engrave rocks exposed to the elements on the southern edge of the Sahara.

A necessary condition for any rigorous analysis is that of a faithful recording of data on site, and detailed retranscription on to paper. With this methodological precept in mind, I travelled to Algeria in April 1983, where I was able to perfect the recording method that I have since used in Niger, Mali and Egypt. This method consists of taking photographic views and tracings of engraved rock faces onto transparent film; it is relatively simple to carry out, and necessitates no bulky material.

Christian Dupuy tracing a rock carving in the southern Sahara.

Prospection takes place on foot or by camel, enabling complete recording of engravings on a regional level; my Bedouin (Egypt) and Tuareg guides (Niger and Mali) have, on each occasion, been able to supply me with extremely valuable toponymic information as well as recounting to me myths and legends linked to specific engravings. On-site work is then completed by a topographical recording of stations discovered, with a precise localization using the aerial maps produced during the 1960s by the French National Geographical Institute at a scale of 1:50,000. I establish the position of each engraving on the topographical plans so that, at the end of each trip, I have the spatial organization and density firmly and clearly recorded on paper.

A search for a missing cultural link

The material collected in Niger and Mali has enabled me to establish several distinct figurative phases which do not tally with ideas hitherto accepted. Each phase presents an affinity with either rock Art of northern regions, or that of regions to the east. But, with our current knowledge, it is impossible to specify exactly the nature of the relationship linking the rock art with the little known art of western regions situated in southern Mauritania. This is the missing link I wish to find by leading an expedition to this region. It will then be possible to define the geographical limits of each school of engraving and to make serious hypotheses as to the history of populations in the southern Sahara from the Neolithic Age to present-day. It seems certain that, amongst the engravers of distant times, some were ancestors of contemporary Peul und Tuareg peoples. Certain of their pastoral customs are the basis for a strong pre-supposition of that connection.

255

But, once again, these are but hypotheses: at the present moment material proof remains to be found. For this reason – and here lies the second important axis of my research – it is indispensable to carry out multidisciplinary research, in order to situate the birth, identity and the evolution of the ancient pastoral societies with this engraving tradition. Pottery and stone-ware collected in different regions from habitats around rock art locations will be used to determine if influences so far noted on art are also present. If this proves to be the case, habitat structures and rock art could be said to spring from the same cultural phenomenon, and curiosity would be enriched by new knowledge; that of the actual material culture of the artists, which has until now remained completely unknown.

Finally, excavations of tombs near rock art sites could lead to the discovery of the burial of certain animals represented on the rocks, and of funeral artifacts connected to those collected on habitat sites, in association with human skeletons. This would certainly shed light on the identity of rock artists, by measurements of anthropological characteristics. Radiometric bone, charcoal and pottery datings and thermoluminscence would fix the age of different cultural sequences highlighted by the study of a rock art impossible to date by any physical measure.

An effort meriting exceptional resources

The resources needed to carry out this project will prove to be more costly than those for the missions I have carried out so far. But the results recorded during these missions reach farther too. The results of the research planned are of the utmost importance to trace the ethnogenesis of pastoral peoples still present in the Sahara today. Their presence takes its source in a distant past which is probably situated around the time when cattle were first domesticated – that is to say over 7,000 years ago.

One of the hundreds of rock engravings catalogued by Christian Dupuy.

Navigating the upper Yangtze for a children's vaccination programme

Michael Edwin Cole

High Rising, Linton, Ross-on-Wye, Herefordshire HR9 7RS, United Kingdom

British, born 10 April 1935. Director of Short Term Experience Projects (STEP). Educated in United Kingdom; Diploma in Physical Education from Carnegie College, Leeds, in 1960.

Research has been undertaken to produce a load-carrying "hover lorry" which can operate at altitude to deliver essential supplies to remote communities living near previously unnavigable rivers. In April 1990, we will be taking the hover lorry onto the upper reaches of the Yangtze River to provide the last link in the cold chain to deliver vaccines to isolated children.

Adventure with a purpose

In 1990, the British Hovercraft to China Expedition starts its unique attempt to navigate the upper reaches of the Yangtze River using a hover lorry design, to trace the river's source in the mountains of Tibet. Of more importance, will be the medical and scientific projects undertaken. Aboard the two hovercraft will be doctors, engineers and scientists who will be studying and working with the Chinese on rural health, water quality, aeronautical and materials engineering and a United Nations (UNICEF) vaccination programme for children.

The invitation to work in China has been made under the twinning arrangement with exists between Leicestershire County Council and Sichuan Province, and between Chongqing City and Leicester City Council. Appropriately, Loughborough University will lead the expedition's technical and scientific programme in conjunction with Chengdu University. The expedition itself will last three months and will cover the upper third of the Yangtze River's 6,200 km.

The Yangtze journey, which has been described as "the hovercraft equivalent of climbing Everest", will be against the natural current and flow of the river and, in the later stages, the hovercraft will be operating at an altitude of over 5,000 m. At that height, exacting stresses are put on machinery and men. The air will be thin and the weather unpredictable. This is the specific stretch of the Yangtze where we will seek to demonstrate the practicality of using "lorry" hovercraft for medical services. High ultraviolet exposure and weather extremes even in the spring and summer will make it very challenging for the team and machines. The

The hover lorry to be used by Michael Cole for his upper Yangtze expedition, travelling overland.

primary aim of the expedition is to set up a vaccination project for UNICEF in remote areas where boats cannot operate. An additional objective of the expedition will be to study and undertake field trials on materials and structures for hovercraft; tests and field trials will be carried out aimed at making hover lorry technology more efficient by experimenting with various materials under stress at altitude.

A health programme for the Yangtze River

UNICEF is at present involved in a very ambitious project in China to bring "health for all by the year 2000" and "immunization for all by 1990". The children of the people living alongside the upper reaches of the Yangtze River have yet to receive their vaccination against the six main childhood diseases (polio, whooping cough, diphtheria, measles, tetanus and tuberculosis). The team look forward to assisting in this vast undertaking. Vaccines need to be transported rapidly and at low temperature as part of a process called "the cold chain". Hovercraft are expected to play a decisive role in opening up new cold chains, converting difficult rivers into medical highways.

Recognizing that the very best legacy we can leave behind in China is good teaching, we have planned a series of seminars in three main centres where there will be opportunities to share with the Chinese medical workers something of our experience in delivering primary medical care in developing countries. Of course there will be much we can learn too, and we anticipate the stimulation of experience-exchange encounters with particular reference to the Chinese village doctor system. We plan to analyze the drinking water in the villages we visit. In the developing world, some 85% of all diseases are water borne and anything we can do to improve a village's water supply both in quality and quantity will be beneficial to the local people. In conjunction with the Epidemic Prevention Services of China, we plan to analyze river water at different stages of our expedition in order to quantify pollutant levels. There may well be a correlation between the pollutants over different stretches of the river and the disease patterns occurring in the corresponding areas. The prime emphasis in bringing medical care to developing countries needs to be focused on the mothers and the

258

children under five years of age. We shall stress this concept in the programme and we will observe with interest how the Chinese are coping with this key group.

During an expedition of this magnitude it is important that there is adequate preparation before we set out, competent care during the expedition and careful evaluation and screening following completion of the expedition for each person in the team. The medical team will have full responsibility advising team members on vaccination requirements, pre-expedition fitness as well as on general medical fitness during the expedition. There will be contingency plans in case of serious accidents or emergencies.

Exploration to the source of the Yangtze

High up on the northeast side of the Tibetan Plateau lies the Province of Qinghai. Although in land area one of China's largest provinces, it has only four million people. The Yangtze flows through the southern part of this province. Roads cross the river at Yushu and Tuotuoheyan at heights of around 4,000 m and 5,000 m respectively. Road distance between these towns, through Xining (the provincial capital) and Golmud, is over 1,600 km, but the river distance is 865 km. A Sino-US Raft Expedition descended this stretch in 1986 and it is thought to be navigable in both directions by hovercraft. We have learnt a great deal about this part of the river and its peoples from the Raft Expedition leader.

A hover lorry prototype navigating in narrow confines.

Satellite imaging to search for lost Chinese cities of the Silk Road

Derrold Wayne Holcomb

Honourable Mention
The Rolex Awards for Enterprise – 1990

P. O. Box 6257, Venice, Florida 34292, United States

American, born 19 March 1949. Research Scientist. Educated in USA; B. Sc. (Chemistry) from Georgia Institute of Technology in 1973.

Chinese literature documents a series of cities and outposts which formed the Silk Road of antiquity. By following a chain of oases, ancient peoples extended their trade routes to traverse the entire Taklamakan Desert of northwest China, establishing contact with the rest of Asia and the Helenistic culture of the West beyond. While this route is documented in earlier Chinese literature, it first appears in Western writings as the Silk Road of Marco Polo, by which time the area was already in decline. Over the past three millenia, remains of many cities now extinct have been slowly buried in the sands of the expanding desert. An example of this was Loulan near the oasis of Lop Lake which thrived for many generations until, during the Eastern Han Dynasty, the climate turned cold, meltwater from glaciers decreased and Lop Lake shrank. The entire area is now a part of the Lop Nur Desert.

Written record of human habitation in the Lop Nur depression extends back at least to 3,000 BC, a singular record of great potential significance. However, the drought has also effectively preserved traces of the past. Remnants of cities, forts, signal towers and religious structures project out of the sand in numerous places throughout the Lop Nur depression. However, a huge and ever-advancing over-burden of sand greatly limits reconnaissance or detailed excavation.

Viewing the past from satellites

Radar images taken from orbiting space platforms can penetrate the hyper-arid sand sheets of the moving desert, and I have found that computer enhancement of digital images can delineate indicators such as buried stream beds or linear features which may imply human activity. My project is to computer-enhance radar data and use them as a basis for field work to locate significant archaeological sites and define the areal extent of this former kingdom.

In 1986, the NASA Jet Propulsion Laboratory provided the author with about 20 linear metres of film rolls containing radar images taken over China using an

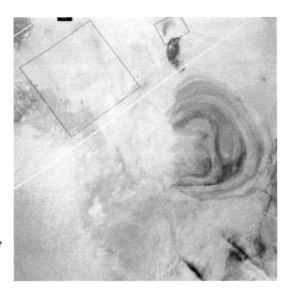

Large format camera photograph taken over the Taklamakan Desert, the world's second largest hyper-arid core.

experimental radar sensor, the Shuttle Imaging Radar, first generation (SIR-A), carried aboard the US Space Shuttle. Lap Nor and desert areas around the Taklamakan oases were included in the areas imaged and computer-based processing of the digitalized images located traces of ancient waterways beneath the sand cover. For sake of verification, I used available radar data to locate images of known archaeological sites in arid areas in the northern Sahara, Egypt, the Arabian Peninsula, Middle East, and the Indus Basin. Digital data from these scenes will be used to develop enhancement regimens applicable to arid regions where suspected archaeological sites have little or no surface expression. Through application of these results to subsequent generation SIR-C image data from the proposed study area, we hope to detect and map archaeological ruins in the study area.

Thus far, all computer image processing has been done at the facilities of Earth Resources Data Analysis Systems (ERDAS) where computer access has been freely available during evening and weekend hours. In pursuit of this project, I have developed an expertise in computer enhancement and interpretation of radar generated images. The NASA Jet Propulsion Laboratory has offered to schedule imaging by SIR-C – the third generation radar sensor – of areas selected by me in support of the archaeological goals of this proposal. Image processor techniques will be refined, and computer regimens that best elucidate the traces of man's activity on the environment will be developed. Through continuation of work in progress, I intend to develop a catalogue of enhancement regimens and techniques that best elucidate sand-buried man-made features. These techniques would then be applied to SIR-C radar data from the Taklamakan Desert, identifying potential sites for field survey or excavation.

Combining satellite images with field research

From the works of Western explorer/collectors of the late 19th and early 20th centuries, I have developed a regional archaeological survey map. Using these archaeological descriptions as a guide, potential imaging areas will be suggested. At least one preliminary trip to Sinjiang Province will be required for on-site evaluation of sites under consideration, in order to document as fully as possible the ground for selection of areas to be imaged. However, the Taklamakan is the world's second largest hyper-arid desert, and it is located in the far northwest corner of China, remote from centres of population. Logistics of supplying an expedition team with food, fuel, water, etc., in such a remote area are complex and expensive. Over the past four years I have worked with How-Man Wong to create the China Exploration and Research Society (CERS), a non-profit organization which has been able to partially fund one expedition per year, but the extended expeditions for this project will require a major funding increase beyond the scope of the CERS.

The region selected for now is known to contain sites and to have been the locale of some archaeological digs. I believe that towns are most likely to be found at the points where rivers meet. Finally, once the SIR-C photos have been received and studied, they will be processed along with the CERS's Landsat images to find possible archaeological sites. Thus one or more post-SIR-C expeditions will also be undertaken. As ruins are known to exist in this area and some excavations have already been recorded, and as applicability of radar studies to this topic have been demonstrated, some level of success is assured. The ultimate goals of this project are to clearly demonstrate the application of radar imaging to desert archaeology, to help identify sites in the Taklamakan Desert worthy of excavation and to initiate and facilitate Sino-Western co-operation in excavation and preservation of these treasures.

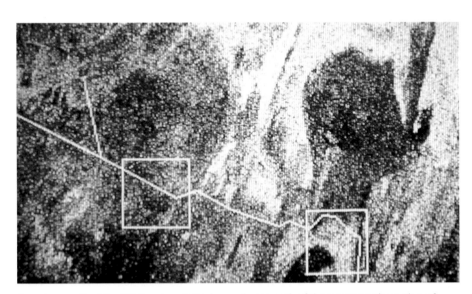

Imaging swath of the SIR-A radar plotted on a photograph of the Lop Nor Lake region of the Taklamakan Desert.

Patterns for living – decorated houses in rural southern Africa

Barbara Anne Ashworth

14 Southern Avenue, Frenchwood, Preston, Lancashire PR1 4NL, United Kingdom

British, born 7 August 1944. Senior Lecturer/Head of Graphic Design at Bolton Institute of Higher Education. Educated in United Kingdom; M.Des. from the School of Architecture, University of Liverpool in 1986.

Southern Africa's rural architecture is of an intensely personal nature, affected by many variables. Traditional design has been modified by close contact with European influences. However, such influences have not yet destroyed the individuality evident in the building of a home. The homesteads and houses of southern Africa vary greatly in their construction and in their decoration. Whilst their construction has been documented to a certain extent, little has been written about their decoration, and no detailed visual record has been made.

Undocumented treasures

This lack of visual documentation seems most reprehensible and I believe that the patterns and forms of decoration of mainly mud-built houses should be recorded. Such a record would display the houses, homesteads and villages in existence today and detail the situation and comments of their inhabitants – those responsible for their decoration. Tribal traditions and family and social backgrounds would be investigated as would the political, economic and geographical situation.

The project is on-going. It began with a "pilot" study in 1985 with the production of 300 35-mm transparencies and over 100 line drawings of the decoration on rural houses in Lesotho, Swaziland and parts of South Africa. The richness of images found led to a determination to further record their existence and document their production and position. Together with my husband, I learnt to speak some Zulu but, at that time, could not find the necessary texts to learn Sesotho, and in September 1988 we set off on a route planned to take us through areas that we hoped would be of interest. Our hopes and our investment were hugely rewarded. In rural areas, we found the images we wanted and were greeted with attitudes of friendliness, co-operation and an appreciation of my interest.

Drawing of a large farming homestead in the Orange Free State of the Republic of South Africa. Doors and windows of these rectangular houses are of particular importance, and all of the pattern is produced from ochres, whitewash and charcoal.

Our journey took us through Swaziland, KaNgwane, Lebowa, Gazankulu, Venda, Botswana, Bophuthatswana, the Transvaal, Orange Free State and Natal, Lesotho, Transkei and KwaZulu. The resulting collection of over 800 transparencies is impressive but by no means comprehensive. It is the largest of its kind in the world and, in fact, the only one of its kind in the world. However, other areas of Lesotho, Lebowa, Venda, Namibia, the Transkei and the Ciskei must be explored in detail and recorded.

Considerable areas still to be studied

Although finance imposes severe restrictions we intend to take out a bank loan to continue with the work this year as far as we are able. We shall travel in areas that we have previously visited and try to build up a more complete picture of the houses of the north and south Sotho during August 1989. We shall visit certain villages and families with whom we have maintained contact. These will be mainly in Lebowa, Gazankulu, Venda, KwaNdebele and the Orange Free State of South Africa and in Lesotho. We are hoping that by then we will be able to communicate, although in a fairly limited manner, in Sesotho.

At the end of 1989 our documentation of some areas should be quite comprehensive but it will still leave huge areas that are inaccessible to us only because we do not have enough cash to hire and fuel the right kind of vehicle. Still much of the creative talent and pride of tribal Africa will be unknown to the world. Further areas of the Maluti Mountains should be recorded as should parts of Namibia and the most northerly parts of South Africa. The world is almost totally ignorant of a 20th century phenomena of beauty and importance.

264

I have contacted various African archives and museums and the Museum of Mankind in London and, although they are aware of Ndebele painted houses in South Africa, they have little or no record of note and virtually nothing relating to the Sotho, Swazi and Tswana. I have visited the Africana Museum and Archive in Johannesburg, the Killie Campbell Archive of the University of Natal, the University of the Witwatersrand and the Phuthodikobo Museum at Mochudi, Botswana, and have been in contact with other researchers. No one is duplicating the work that I am doing or the study that is outlined here.

Art and culture to be displayed worldwide

Rural houses and their documentation are an essential part of the art and culture of southern Africa in the 20th century. They are vital: they are alive: they should not be allowed to die. It is a great pity that the world is not able to see and appreciate the creative and artistic skills of these people. They want their work to be appreciated; they are proud of it; they value it greatly and are pleased when others do the same.

If we are not careful, a whole lifetime and more of visual imagery will disappear: never known, never understood. That cannot be right! Why should the Tswana of Botswana and the Bophutswan suffer the ignorance of the world? Why should the South Sotho, the Basotho of Lesotho as well as those in the Orange Free State be condemned to obscurity? Why should the skills of the Swazi in Swaziland and KaNgwane not be demonstrated to the world?

As a graphic designer I have the necessary autographic and photographic skills to be able to complete this work professionally. My research work at the University of Liverpool has given me the organizational, observational and research skills necessary for it to be academically thorough.

The project is important: it is realistic: it is viable. I sincerely hope that I can obtain the necessary support to bring it to completion.

Elaborate courtyards, gate posts and walls are predominant in the area of Mavambe. These were recently painted because an "initiation" of young men into manhood was taking place.

Graveyards of the British period in the Indian subcontinent

Susan Maria Farrington

Tipnoller Cottage, Wiveliscombe, Taunton, Somerset TA4 2RL, United Kingdom

British, born 10 May 1949. Part-time secretary for the Royal Geographical Society. Educated in United Kingdom; Domestic Science Diploma from Evendine Court, Malvern, in 1966.

The purpose of the project is to record and thereby encourage the interest in and preservation of British graves in South Asia. The graveyards, Christian churches and their monumental inscriptions are of historical, genealogical and architectural interest.

A painstaking survey procedure

The techniques involved include both dictating inscriptions into a cassette recorder, writing notes on the location and general appearance of each cemetery (including a brief sketch map), taking photographs, compiling plotted cemetery plans, and feeding the information into a privately owned computer.

About 3% of the material collected to date has been edited in a final form and published under the title *Peshawar Cemetery* by the British Association for Cemeteries in South Asia in 1988. The inscriptions are transcribed from the cassettes on to hard copy, then card-indexed to hasten retrieval, and eventually will be added to the computer database, which currently contains about half the total material of some 30,000 inscriptions.

Funds are required to help feed material into the computer, to develop photographs, and to continue the work, both editing existing data and travelling to collect more information. Aspects of the work which could be developed are further research into the individuals recorded and their families, and the redesign and replanting of ailing cemeteries, if old plans can be located.

A special aspect of Anglo-Indian history

The work began in 1981 after a chance visit to Peshawar Cemetery (the subject of the first book) while I was on holiday. Since 1981, over 500 churches and cemeteries in Pakistan, India, Sri Lanka, Burma, Bangladesh and Mauritius have been recorded. It is perhaps similar in aspiration to the Irish Memorial of the Dead

Set against a backdrop of the barren Baluchistan mountains rising to an altitude of over 8,000 m, the main cemetery at Quetta has more than 1,200 headstones and memorials.

series, which produced many volumes of Irish gravestone inscriptions at the beginning of this century.

Advances in computer science and photography enable the work to be much broader. There is still the prime interest of recording the memorials, but the computer enables one to distinguish between types of grave or headstone, the wording of inscriptions, causes of death, occupations, time of year of the majority of burials, etc. Even the names of the stone masons are recorded. If support is available, the work can continue and a great corpus of material should become available in time recording one aspect of European occupation of the Indian subcontinent.

Recording graveyards before it is too late

1989 is a critical year for the preservation of British cemeteries in South Asia. It is now over 40 years since British rule ended. In a hot climate with seasonal monsoons, and even snow, the headstones are decaying rapidly, plant growth swallows up cemeteries, and the small expatriate communities are diminishing.

Local people in the subcontinent are interested in and well disposed towards the preservation of the British monuments, cemeteries and churches, but they do not have the funds to support such projects and have other personal higher priorities for their own budgets. The British Association for Cemeteries in South Asia, which published my book, is a small charitable organization which aims to help where it can, but funds are limited and it is unable to support individual work such as this beyond paying for the publication of record books.

267

If funds can be found to finance the pursuit of this work, research can continue leading to further publication of handbooks and guides, thereby increasing the awareness and knowledge of this unique historical resource before the passage of time and the ravages of climate diminish it further.

Inscriptions reflect all aspects of life in the subcontinent – this medical officer lost his life in a river "when leading the Peshawar Vale Hunt of which he was Master".

Saving an old merchant sailing ship to discover the world

Charles Hervé-Gruyer

94 rue de la Meule, 85350 Ile d'Yeu, France

French, born 15 July 1958. Project creator and educational director for *Le Taillevent* charity. Educated in France and the Federal Republic of Germany; Masters Degree in English and Spanish from Université Paris III in 1979.

Since the age of 20 I have worked on the education of delinquent teenagers and, in doing so, have tried to impart to these young people some of the pleasure and personal fulfilment that I have obtained from my contacts with the sea and boats. When I was 21, I bought the *Gwenvidik*, an old wooden boat and, together with the teenagers from the centre for delinquent teenagers in which I worked, we set sail. I knew very little about sailing and the youngsters even less. The boat was old. We had some accidents: the mast broke, the sails were torn, the engine failed... But the impact on these teenagers' personality was so positive that we decided to take the youngsters on board for a whole school year. In 1981, with help of many friends, we built the *Gwenvidik II*, a modern steel sailing boat, and from 1982 to 1985 – with teenagers entrusted to us by the State – we sailed to England, Ireland, Spain, Portugal, Morocco, Tunisia, Italy, Malta, Corsica, Madeira, the Canary Islands, Cape Verde, Amazonia, the West Indies and the Azores. For these youngsters, whose lives had been disturbed by the lack of a family or stays in prison or psychiatric hospital, this type of activity was a revelation. Nevertheless, in 1985, I realized that the job was too much for one person. We needed a bigger boat, able to take on board a real crew. I no longer wanted to have just teenagers with difficulties. At last, I wanted the voyages to become real expeditions, based on a precise and motivating subject.

A new organization and a new boat

With two friends, I founded a not-for-profit organization *Le Taillevent*, sold *Gwenvidik II* and bought *Fleur de Lampaul*, an old Brittany merchant ship built in 1948. She was nearly a wreck but she had a fascinating history and had been one of the world's last merchant sailing ships, working under sail until 1978. It was a completely mad project. There were just three of us, with very little money. *Fleur de Lampaul* was enormous, the work on her was colossal. We knew nothing about this kind of boat. Our only salvation: we are realistic dreamers, very optimistic, and not frightened by hard work!

The Fleur de Lampaul *takes to the high seas again with a crew of young people who, whilst continuing their schooling, will study whales and help in humanitarian activities.*

We rebuilt *Fleur de Lampaul* on the Isle of Noirmoutier. The project created a lot of enthusiasm and we were able to enlist the help of numerous voluntary helpers, together with the advice of the previous owners, two old sailors whose experience was of immense help to us; in fact, at times we had a dozen people, aged 12 to 75 years, working together day and night. We had to work fast because, with no financial help, we had decided that the boat would have to work to earn money. We had signed up contracts and we had to honour them; in addition, we organized an exhibition on board during our first summer, and had 13,500 paying visitors. Just 18 months, and 20,000 hours of work, after arriving in Noirmoutier, *Fleur de Lampaul* was ready to return to the sea, as beautiful as the day she was built – so beautiful that she has been classified as a historical monument and awarded two prizes.

A new life for a venerable ship

We now have this magnificent 30-m ship back at sea and, guided by her former owners, we are learning to sail her and are ready to pursue two objectives: to protect our national maritime patrimony; and to offer educational opportunities to young people.

We believe that the French public is not sufficiently aware of its national maritime heritage, so we undertook to carry out our own public education programme through the media; in addition, during the summers of 1987 and 1988, we organized two cruises in which 35 publishers displayed 15,000 books on board the *Fleur de Lampaul* and we sailed from the harbour to display our precious cargo to over 270,000 visitors. It was this voyage of nearly 130,000 km to 80 harbours that provided us with the funds to carry out our young people's expedition.

In search of "Moby Dick"

In September 1987, five teenagers, aged from 12 to 17, embarked for ten months. Two of them, entrusted to us by the State, joined us with major problems; the others were well-balanced and had been entrusted to us by their families. The purpose of this first expedition was to bring to reality a childhood dream: to sail the South Seas in search of whales and dolphins – a search for Moby Dick!

Less than two years after the day I bought her, *Fleur de Lampaul* sailed towards the high seas, called at Portugal, put in to Madeira where we studied sperm whales with the last whale fishermen and played at Robinson Crusoe on a desert isle. In the Canary Islands, we did a lot of skin diving and friendship slowly began to replace aggression amongst the teenage crew members. Over a two-month period we met with innumerable cetaceans and were, after a while, able to swim with killer whales, pilot whales and bottlenose dolphins. My dream had become a reality.

When *Fleur de Lampaul* returned to France in May 1988, the teenagers had changed fundamentally. They were happy to live and full of projects for the future and they were actively involved in radio and television reporting of their experiences. We presented our results to a meeting of the European Cetaceans Society and even received another prize.

Long-term plans for teenagers

However, we still have much to learn and improve if we want to achieve our objective of making a voyage with seven children each year. In summer 1990, we will operate a travelling exhibition on saving human lives at sea and then in September 1990 set out on our second children's voyage to study killer and sperm whales off the coast of Africa, making two films for international distribution on the way. Then every winter *Fleur de Lampaul* will offer a number of children the opportunity to discover the world, men and nature.

Our purpose is two-fold: to allow these youngsters to live their lives fully by a true encounter with the world, by community life, by team work together with scientists and media professionals; to have them carry out useful work, recognized by the society, in spite of their young age.

The youngsters on board ship learn the multiple aspects of sailing a large boat and have day-to-day contact with a variety of sea dwellers.

Investigating the loss of the British James Knight expedition

Owen Beattie

Honourable Mention
The Rolex Awards for Enterprise – 1990

University of Alberta, Department of Anthropology, Edmonton, Alberta, Canada
T6G 2H4

Canadian, born 3 June 1949. Associate Professor, Department of Anthropology,
University of Alberta. Educated in USA; Ph. D. (Anthropology) from University of
British Columbia in 1981.

In spring of 1719, Captain James Knight, with the frigate *Albany*, the sloop
Discovery and some 50 men, sailed from England to North America in search of
gold, copper and a Northwest Passage. Knight, in the employ of the Hudson's Bay
Company, was nearing 70 years of age and had a long and distinguished history
of service with the company. Though he was expected to return before the
winter of 1719, little alarm was felt when this did not occur. However, by 1721 the
Hudson's Bay Company issued orders for a search for the missing ships and men. It
was discovered that Knight's expedition had wintered in 1719–1720 at Marble
Island, located 25 km off the northwest coast of Hudson Bay, but substantive
information on the loss of the expedition did not surface until the islands were
visited in 1776 by Joseph Stevens, Magnus Johnston, Samuel Hearne and others.
Reports indicate that, by summer 1720, half the men had died and the rest were
affected by "sickness and famine". By spring 1721, all the remainder had
perished. The circumstances surrounding the loss of so many men are not known,
nor is there any information on the location of the graves.

Interpretation of an 18th century disaster

The proposed research project has three phases: the search for and documentation of archaeological sites from the Knight expedition; the excavation of discovered sites for the purpose of interpreting the disaster; and the development of
facial reconstruction methods which will allow accurate representations of the
appearance of these sailors to be constructed. The first phase will be completed in
summer 1989, and is funded by the Boreal Institute for Northern Studies. The
second and third phases remain to be undertaken.

Very little has been written or researched about Knight's expedition (most
information comes from sources based on Hearne's account and some Hudson's
Bay Company records from Fort Churchill). A colleague of mine has just completed archival searches in England in an effort to compile information on Knight
and his last expedition. Apparently, little primary information is available. Hud-

An Inuit campsite on Quartzite Island dating from the time of the Knight expedition. Hundreds of these campsites can be found in association with the location of Knight's house.

son's Bay Company records in Winnipeg (already an important source of information) will be thoroughly searched in the autumn of 1989. Rediscovery of the expedition's burial sites would be a key first step towards excavation of the graves, on-site analysis and facial reconstruction of Knight's men, and grave site restoration. Further excavation of Knight's house and other sites from his expedition will also take place. Forensic, anthropological and archaeological investigation of the disaster would provide information on possible health and victualling problems that could have contributed to the men's deaths, as well as the role of any violent confrontations with Inuit groups.

The field research in 1989 will involve a systematic archaeological foot survey of the four islands that make up the Marble Island group. The focus of the survey will be the location of sites directly related to Knight's expedition. Sites interpreted from surface artifacts, associations and logical locations to be from Knight's expedition will be mapped, described, and tested through limited excavation. Artifacts discovered through these tests will be recorded and collected for laboratory analysis. Any human bones discovered (as well as associated artifacts) will be recorded but left undisturbed. Sites relating to Knight's expedition discovered in the 1989 survey will be excavated thoroughly in summer 1990 by a team that includes a forensic anthropologist/archaeologist. Skeletal remains will be studied for evidence of health status, cause of death and identity. The skulls will be photographed in detail and plaster casts will be made of the facial features for later facial reconstruction. After analysis, the remains will be reburied and the graves reconstructed.

All discovered bones will be measured and analyzed to provide information on stature, muscularity, life style characteristics and indications of pathological conditions and/or trauma. The age profile of the men, which can be assessed from bone, would provide interesting insight into crew selection.

Putting a face to history

I am refining methods for facial reconstruction utilizing advanced video techniques and, employing magnetic resonance imaging (MRI), I hope to be able to reconstruct from skulls the appearances of historical figures with a high degree of accuracy. For example, we have not been able to find any portrait of James Knight, and it appears that none was ever drawn or painted of this important explorer. If we find his remains, we will be able to build a portrait through our facial reconstruction techniques; in other words, we will be putting a face to history.

The discoveries made during the project will be of considerable anthropological and historical importance and will form the foundation for the major research planned for 1990. Information on the skeletal biology of this expedition, along with the facial reconstructions, will be compiled in the fall of 1990 with the results of the research being presented at various conferences. Publications on the results will be quite varied, and include papers on bone pathology and radiology, forensic anthropology, facial reconstruction, dietary determinations and clothing and other preserved perishables.

Knight and his men spent nearly two years on these islands before the last man perished. Although the house discovered there has been identified as Knight's and archaeologically tested in 1971, and although a few additional sites were found during the summers of 1970 and 1971, most parts of the islands remain unexplored. I expect that the field survey will reveal many additional sites associated with Knight and his men, including one or more burial areas. In fact, it seems probable that the burials constitute the largest feature(s) still awaiting discovery.

The foundation of the James Knight house built in 1719 on Quartzite Island. The foundation is located in the middle of the photograph with the protected harbour seen on the left.

Cataloguing and studying South-American colonial organs

Cristina Dinorah Rauss-Garcia Banegas

University Music School of Montevideo, Juan Paullier 1126, 11200 Montevideo, Uruguay

Uruguayan, born 1 March 1954. Professor of Organ at the University School of Music of Montevideo. Educated in Uruguay, Switzerland and France; studied at the Public Lyceum from 1959 to 1970 and the Conservatoire de Genève from 1979 to 1984.

I have for many years heard stories from several Latin-American countries about organs that had been brought to this continent during the 17th and 18th centuries and which are still to be found in, often very remote, localities; for the most part, however, these organs are in a very poor state of conservation. Some of them have suffered the shameful fate of having been dismantled by tourists who carried them away pipe by pipe and took them home as souvenirs of the places they had visited. This has been the fate of organs in places such as Ouro Preto, Minas Gerais, Brazil. Other organs have been sold for scrap, the pipes melted down and the wood used to make benches and tables or just to light a fire. In all cases the organs' voices have been stilled for ever.

Desecration of historic musical instruments

On the other hand, there are some organs that have been restored by unskilled workmen who have taken advantage of the ignorance and enthusiasm of the population to maltreat a defenceless historical instrument. Moreover, there is no law that forbids a parish or an institution from modifying the interior of its organ; in some cases, even though the external structure has been preserved, the original mechanism has been replaced by modern electronics. In addition, it is common knowledge that certain very valuable organs have been sold at very low prices and exported from the country in question.

The organ is the king of musical instruments, and the one for which, over the centuries, the most beautiful sacred music has been, and still is being, composed. However, in Latin America, this instrument is being treated with such disrespect that I have vowed to put a stop to this desecration. The music of the golden age of Spain will be lost in its original conception if we do nothing to halt this vandalism.

To provide a basis for this preservation task, I have already catalogued the 34 organs of Uruguay. The most valuable of the existing organs was built in 1900 and is sited in the Cathedral of Canelones. With the collaboration of Umberto

275

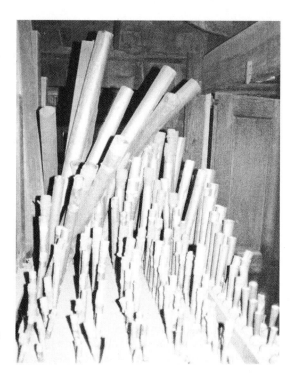

Present condition of the pipes in the organ at Diamantina, Brazil.

Pineschi, Head of the Accademia Italiana per Organo de Pistoia, Italy, this organ is to be repaired.

Of the many organs that existed in Paraguay, only one remains and this not even in Paraguay but in Bolivia. It was this situation that gave rise to my project. There are many organs in Peru, Ecuador and Colombia, which will, I am sure, eventually suffer the same fate as those in Paraguay. I feel that my mission is to save them. For example, during my recent concert tour in Colombia, I saw in a convent an organ built 150 years ago, which still works without electricity, with the original bellows. This jewel, as so many others, should be preserved in its original state.

A mission of conservation

To rebuild these organs I think that the best idea would be to apply for funds from the respective communities, dioceses and other official and private institutions. Once a given organ has been rebuilt, the next step would be to encourage the local population to develop an interest in the instrument, select and give scholarships to one or more gifted persons so that they can study in Uruguay with me and then, when they return home, they can pass on what they have learnt and thus form new schools of music.

I therefore propose: to search for, investigate, catalogue, save, and document South American colonial organs before it is too late; to make recordings of the reconditioned organs to prove their value; to make an inventory, documented with photographs, of the characteristics of the instruments and of the places in which they are located, date of construction and their present state of conservation. The research would be carried out in Peru, Colombia and Ecuador. In view of the situation in Latin American where there is virtually no knowledge about this specialized field and where the necessary resources are practically inexistent, I plan to: travel to various historical sites in the countries in question; catalogue the technical aspects of the instruments such as the date and place of construction, mechanical state of the keyboards and the pipes, etc.

It would also be necessary to evaluate the stops and the repairs to be made to the structure, mechanism and pipes. All this needs to be photographically documented step by step. If only the box of the instrument remains, it may be possible to carry out an approximate restoration of the organ to its former state. Every phase of this study should be published in a catalogue. When the instrument is ready to be performed on, I would make recordings so as to make its particular characteristics known all over the world. These recordings could be distributed by the cultural departments of the embassies of the three countries in question.

As a musician born in Latin America I feel an obligation to do something for the instrumental heritage of this continent. I have to stop the vandalism that has been going on for too long now. Having devoted so many years of my life with love and dedication to music – and especially to organ music – and having acquired the knowledge to fulfil my mission, my objective is now to acquire the funding necessary to carry out my mission. In Mexico, Guy Bovet, under whom I studied on two occasions, has undertaken a similar task. He is an outstanding musician and I will certainly seek his advice. Nevertheless, I think that it is for a Latin-American musician to preserve the instruments that exist in his or her part of the world.

The dilapidated keyboard of an organ in a church near Bogotá, Colombia.

Scientific cave exploration – new perspectives for mankind

Gerhard E. Schmitt

Im Neurod 16, 8750 Aschaffenburg, Federal Republic of Germany

German, born 25 January 1954. Manager of the Pollution Department of NUKEM/ Hanau. Educated in Federal Republic of Germany; Ph. D. from University of Frankfurt in 1988.

Since 1976, I have been exploring the cave systems of the Taurus mountains in Turkey and have made a series of interesting discoveries. In particular, we have explored the Altin-Besik cave which at intervals floods explosively and is flushed out by an immense amount of water, and have determined the cause of this phenomenon. We discovered and explored the "Toter Hund" cave and descended to a depth of 340 m under the earth's surface – the deepest cave known in Turkey. During a 1987 expedition to the Sarph-Daglari in Turkey, I discovered what is probably one of the world's best examples of a round cave pearl with a diameter of 52 mm, and a difference between the smallest and largest diameter of only 0.1 mm.

Moreover, in exploring caves all over the world, we have also had the unique opportunity of observing rare species of cave animals such as spiders, salamanders, scorpions and bats. Since, in caves, there is no alteration of hot and cold, day and night, wet and dry, cave animals need a minimum of life energy and are, therefore, able to live long periods without food. Most of them are blind. For their orientation, they usually have long antennae, chemoreceptors and an excellent memory of their surroundings.

Ongoing exploration on the Sarph-Daglari plateau

My project is in two parts, and the first relates to an interesting phenomenon that occurs in the "Sugla", a wide flat valley some 24 km in length and totally encircled by mountains, which, although normally dry, is periodically (every 5–10 years) inundated with water and turns into a lake some 10 m deep. This lake remains for about five years and then the water level gradually falls and the lake vanishes. After an interval of 5–10 years this cycle starts over again.

We explored the Tinaz mountain which is located to the west of the Sugla valley and were surprised to find two large sinkholes there. Although it was August, huge amounts of water were still arriving from the higher mountains to

The Sugla Valley in a dry period (1983).

the west and vanishing into the caves under the Tinaz. At that time, we were able to explore only one cave – apparently part of an older cave system – which was inactive, dry and located in the higher west flank of the Tinaz. We found huge rooms with white formations and pure calcite crystals. Our compass told us that this cave went direct to the Sugla Valley. However, after 900 m, the cave ended in a room 100 m long and 60 m high, the walls of which were covered with millions of calcite crystals. Four years later the Sugla Valley was a 10-m deep lake.

Why a dry valley periodically becomes a lake

When the Sugla is dry, the population is employed in agriculture and cattle breeding; however, when it turns into a lake, nothing can be done and the population is destitute. Our exploration of the Sugla valley and the surrounding region showed that water reaches the Sugla Valley through underground galleries from sink holes located in the Tinaz mountain area to the west of the valley where it is joined by local ground water. The water drains out of the valley through sink holes at the southern end of the valley. However, in periods of heavy precipitation the karst water from the Tinaz mountains and the local ground water build up, and the sink holes, which normally drain off the water, become plugged and the water rises and becomes a lake. Once this finding had been made, it was possible to take the necessary remedial action and ensure that the valley is no longer subject to flooding.

Nevertheless, we have not so far been able to traverse the whole distance of the underground galleries between Sugla and Tinaz and I am planning to return to the region in 1990 to dive in the Guversin siphon in the Sugla valley and explore the final link in the chain to the Tinaz cave.

Regular water supply for the plateau population

The second part of my project is to explore the Sarph-Daglari, a plateau measuring some 50 km in length and 7–10 km in width and located at an altitude of 2,500 m, once again in the Taurus mountains. This region has no large rivers, only cave springs which flow periodically (karst water). As a result of this, the inhabitants are chronically short of water. Consequently, I have developed a plan to explore the caves in this region since we are convinced that they will give us access to new water sources that will provide the population with the essential water supply it requires. At the same time, the isolated nature of the plateau indicates that we have a strong likelihood of finding new species of cave animals in the region. Finally, from our analyses of the local geology we have the hope that this massif contains the deepest cave system in Europe and that we will be able to explore and document it.

The Sugla Valley during a period in which it has been transformed into a lake (1981).

Exploring ancient precolumbian Peruvian canal networks

Charles R. Ortloff

FMC Corporation, Central Engineering Laboratories, 1205 Coleman Avenue, Box 580, Santa Clara, California 95052, United States

American, born 30 July 1937. Principal engineer. Educated in United States; undertook Ph. D. work at University of California, Los Angeles, from 1961 to 1965.

Precolumbian societies of the ancient Peruvian north coast used complex canal-based irrigation systems for millenia to provide water for extensive agricultural field systems. These systems provided the agricultural base for sustained population growth and the development of civilizations of increasingly complex nature during the Late Intermediate Period of Peruvian history (AD 800–1450). In a typical major north coast valley, literally hundreds of kilometres of ancient canals chronicle centuries of intra-valley canal design, construction, modification, abandonment and reconstruction cycles by successive societies and civilizations. Many large canals, some 80 km in length, interconnect different river valleys to shunt water from rivers to large land areas without a close-by water source. Three such mega-systems are known from the Late Intermediate Period (Chicama-Moche Valley Canal, Lambeyeque Valley System, Rimac Valley Canal System) but are as yet little explored. The success of these complex inter- and intra-valley water distribution networks is demonstrated by the fact that at AD 1400, the amount of land under cultivation was 50% higher than at present. Almost all of the ancient mega-canal systems are in excellent state of preservation and are as yet unstudied in detail.

For the past 13 years I have applied my engineering experience on numerous archaeological projects throughout South America to extract the long-hidden hydraulics knowledge of ancient civilizations and present it to the scientific and lay communities through publications, lectures and TV documentaries. The analysis process involves extracting canal geometry and properties data from field excavations and then recreating the fluid mechanics of these canals by computer simulation.

Ancient knowledge of irrigation hydraulics engineering

Previous work on the 80 km long Chicama-Moche Intervalley Canal has produced highly revealing results. We measured the slope of the canal from one kilometre survey points along its length, and local slope variations, wall roughness details

Intervalley Canal perspective. View north of the destroyed aqueduct section near Quebrada del Oso, Peru. The scale of the installation is indicated by the workers located at the excavation trench towards the centre of the photograph.

and canal cross-section geometry every 5 m in certain "interesting" canal areas characterized by rapid variations in cross-section geometry. Results were assessed by analysis of the computer-generated water-flow patterns. Large hydraulic models were also made and tested for other interesting canal sections and results observed. Final results were very informative. Observed for the first time were hydraulic control mechanisms relying on the interplay of canal cross-section shape, wall roughness and local slope in the presence of sub- and supercritical flows. Since each flow category has different effects when operated upon by channel geometry changes, the net result was one of unanticipated sophistication in canal design.

Such sophistication in channel design was commonplace in ancient Peruvian hydraulic societies relying on irrigation agriculture far before the invention of formal hydraulic science in Europe in the 18th and 19th centuries. Given the 2,000 years of hydraulics experience and empirical know-how possessed by ancient engineers of different north coast societies under a wide variety of situations requiring adaptive engineering responses, the depth of demonstrated knowledge is not surprising.

Extending our insight into precolumbian engineering techniques

The proposed project is a continuance of work begun earlier on the Chimu Intervalley Canal and represents a personal goal to complete. Previous work through 1980–84 involved ground survey of only certain segments of the canal. Some 70% of the total canal length remains as yet unexplored. These segments undoubtedly contain a repository of cumulative hydraulic design information of the Chimu state and its predecessor civilizations.

View of a destroyed low aqueduct section of the Intervalley Canal facing north. Low aqueducts are spanned by multiple eroded gullies along the canal length.

The project will entail mounting an overland expedition to traverse the entirety of the Intervalley Canal and adjoining territory while recording and photographing canal geometry and slope data in unexplored areas. Full aerial photographic coverage of these areas is on file. Since no excavation is envisioned (as the last canal phase is in an excellent state of preservation) only ground survey is required. Once necessary data are gathered from several weeks in the field, work will commence back in the United States on interesting channel sections.

To date, a number of publications detail results obtained from past work. By project continuance, the complete catalogue of hydraulic control techniques available to Chimu canal builders can be explored and analyzed. Results to date indicate a strong contribution of indigenous American civilizations to hydraulic knowledge with undoubted further contributions from future research. Although the north coast civilizations apparently did not develop conventional writing (or its presence has not yet been discovered), nevertheless examination of hydraulic designs and engineering accomplishments of these ancient Andean civilizations provides insight into alternate means to solve complex problems of water supply and distribution as well as system preservation mechanisms in the presence of destructive natural forces. By completion of this survey and analysis task, our understanding of ancient American contributions to engineering history will be enhanced and the recovery of lost hydraulics techniques for desert agricultural promoted. Work to date in this new field has provided new insights into the technological cornerstone that supported growth of hydraulic coastal civilizations.

Windsurfing across the Pacific without a support boat

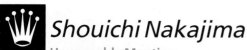 *Shouichi Nakajima*

Honourable Mention
The Rolex Awards for Enterprise – 1990

1–27–25 Takaido-Higashi, Suginami-Ku, Tokyo, 168 Japan

Japanese, born 13 February 1946. Businessman, owner of Channel Co. Ltd.
Educated in Japan; B. A. (Physical Education) from Kokushikan University in 1968.

The history of man's conquest of the sea is a long and enthralling one. Initially, he probably used driftwood to keep himself afloat; then, as time passed by, the wood was shaped into a board and an oar so that he could control the direction he desired to travel. It did not take so many years for man to discover the advantage of sail as he observed the steady blowing of the wind. As he sailed, he wanted to go farther and farther and faster away from the shore in an attempt to reach the horizon.

His physical endurance and courage were very important factors in achieving his desires. From his repeated experiences he learnt the nature of the ocean tides and currents, and the seasonal changes of the wind also affected the duration and distance of his voyage. He perceived the basic laws of nature and he analyzed and exploited them in sciences which later brought about our current highly advanced technologies.

Nowadays, technology makes ocean travel accessible to virtually anybody. Physical endurance and courage are no longer priority factors for an ocean crossing.

In continuing pursuit of ocean endeavours

At a young age, I asked myself whether our modern high-technology world still had any need for human physical strength, wisdom and courage in the endeavours undertaken to cross the waters. The positive response that I perceived drove me to enter into numerous long-distance swims: I was 20 years old when I first swam the Strait of Tsugaru. Since then, I have swum the Straits of Dover, Palk, Malacca, Gibraltar, Magellan and many others. In a way, I think, I have tried to prove the importance of physical endurance and courage as the essence of human success in a technological world which tends to overlook such characteristics.

*Shouichi Nakajima during
a previous exploit
windsurfing between Guam
and Japan.*

However, when I look back at my past achievements, I find they would be incomplete without such modern technology as weather forecasting, water-speed measurement, the measurement of medical parameters and so forth.

Thanks to modern technology, we are better equipped to exploit our knowledge in achieving what our ancestors might only have dreamed about. How can man and his wisdom provide mutual support for each other? Is man a powerless creature in this high-technology world? These are the questions that were behind my motivation to take up the challenge of windsurfing across the Pacific Ocean.

Power boats or yachts do not create a unity between man and his vessel. In the challenge that I have taken up, man has to take the initiative in controlling his vessel. This is why I chose a sailboard as my vehicle for my crossing of the Pacific Ocean.

On a sailboard, the mast and the sail must be constantly supported by the sailor to catch the wind; moreover, the sailboard does not have a rudder and the sailboarder has to shift his weight to change direction. Primitive though the concept may seem, my equipment will be designed to withstand 11,000 km of long-distance sailing and, in particular, my physical fitness will be tuned to its peak. Our only piece of equipment will be a radio so that we can remain in contact with the land. To find our position at sea we will use navigation by satellite. From the medical point of view, we will regularly check body temperature, blood pressure, urine and weight and will eat a specially designed diet.

An uncompromising schedule

The journey will last from January to June 1990 (180 days, of which 160 will actually be sailing time). The distance covered will be 11,000 km and the passage will be from San Francisco, USA, to Honolulu, Hawaii, and finally to Yokohama, Japan. The sailboard will be of a tandem design and will be crewed by Hiroaki Nakajima and myself.

Over the 3,600 km from San Francisco, USA, to Honolulu, Hawaii, we expect to sail 1,800 km at a rate of 70 km per 8-hour day, i.e., for a period of 25 days; the remaining 1,800 km will be sailed at a rate of 100 km per 8-hour day, i.e., a period of 18 days. With the trade winds blowing northeast, our daily advance will be improved.

From Honolulu to Yokohama, Japan, we expect to sail 5,400 km at a rate of 100 km per day, i.e., for a period of 54 days, by catching the trade winds. Therefore, the total 11,000 km will be completed within our self-imposed timetable of 180 days. This schedule is based not only on wind and currents, but also on my previous achievements.

The board has been specially designed for transpacific windsurfing, with an overall length of 7.2 m, a waterline length of 6.6 m, beam of 1.2 m, draft of 0.14 (with centre board up) and 0.8 m (with centre board down), a fully loaded weight of 450 kg and a wishbone sail rig.

No supporting vessel will accompany us. The sailboard will, however, have a small amount of living space because of the long sailing distance, and durable materials will be used that will withstand the punishment of adverse weather. The board will have two masts and sails but the sail area will be kept relatively small in order to minimize energy consumption.

Primitive though the concept of the sailboard may seem, Shouichi Nakajima's equipment will be designed 11,000 km of long-distance sailing.

On the trail of the legions

Raymond Selkirk

25 St. Cuthbert Avenue, Chester-le-Street, Co. Durham DH3 3PS, United Kingdom

British, born 30 March 1931. Archaeologist. Educated in United Kingdom; obtained Air Traffic Control Officer's Licence from College of Air Traffic Control, Hurn Airport, in 1962, and various aircrew licences.

Since the great ice sheets melted from Britain 10,000 years ago, we have, locked in our top-soil, 8,000 years of unwritten prehistoric archaeology, 400 years of very sparsely documented Roman occupation, even less information on the Saxon invasion and the two Viking invasions. It is, in fact, only from the Norman invasion onwards that we have a reasonable record of this nation's history. This project is designed to improve our knowledge of that ill-documented Roman occupation.

The shortcomings of archaeological search techniques

Unfortunately, most of our archaeological information comes from chance finds by land developers; and, when a find does occur, the historical investigators are given little or no time to examine the evidence. Also, on many occasions, funds are not available for "rescue digs". Aircraft have been used by several universities for archaeological searches but the usual method employed is a "square search". This is extremely expensive and even Cambridge University has been forced to dispose of its aircraft on the grounds of economy. Much time is spent by archaeologists in the scanning of the complete set of aerial photographs of the whole of the United Kingdom taken by the Royal Air Force for mapping purposes. Yet, relatively little information is to be obtained from these photographs since they were taken at a time of day when maximum lighting of the landscape was to be expected, i.e. at midday; however, photographs taken in the low-angle early-morning or late-evening sun are required if we are to see the shadow marks which betray the presence of archaeological sites. In addition, the crop marks which reveal hidden sites show for only short periods of time, consequently an archaeologist has to be extremely lucky if he or she is to observe any such traces on military survey photographs. Strangely enough, more archaeological information has been obtained from captured Second World War German Luftwaffe reconnaissance pictures that were taken of Britain than from Royal Air Force sources; this is because the German photographs were taken by aircraft sneaking across the defences at dawn or dusk – times which are ideal for archaeological show marks to manifest themselves.

Roman coins found by divers along the line of the Roman bridge at Piercebridge, discovered by Raymond Selkirk. These coins were probably votive offerings, thrown into the river to placate river gods. Coins date from AD 70 to AD 380.

In view of all this, the situation is far from satisfactory. We must wait for land developers to strike evidence, and the chances are that, even if given enough time for an excavation, the funds will not be available. Moreover, funds for expensive "area searches" are difficult to come by, and the available military photographs (with the exception of a few captured German prints) are not suitable.

A tactical approach to archaeological searches

How much better it would be if we found a method of actually calculating where the Roman sites should be. An aircraft could then be despatched direct to the site, get its photograph, and return to base at very little cost. The ground searchers could then confirm the pilot's evidence. This project proposes that the search for Roman sites should be undertaken using new techniques which I have described as "Tactical archaeology", i.e. the calculation from all manner of sources as to where the Roman sites are most likely to be found. By this, I mean a method of aerial prospecting for ruins that is guided by a line of reasoning worked out in advance. For some ten years now I have been surveying in small planes the region around where I live and have already identified roads, six bridges, several forts, and a treasure in a river (votive offerings thrown in the water by the Romans).

The way I approach the search is to look for signs that help me locate places where the Romans may have constructed buildings or highways, so that I have to make only short flights over specific areas; this is important in maintaining costs at an acceptable level. Using this approach, I have already discovered a network of over 320 km of Roman roads in northeast England.

My manner of proceeding is based on the fact that Roman geometricians must have had some sort of compass to lay out their roads – which they liked to keep as straight as possible. In my opinion, there was only one reason for a curve in a road: to go around an obstacle. Consequently, I use a British army astro-compass that has the same characteristics as the Romans' solar compass: instead of indicating the magnetic north, it points to geographical north as deduced from the position of the stars.

A procedure that has demonstrated its effectiveness

Using this method, I studied a known ancient road that follows a fairly winding course. After calculating the headings of the road's straight sections and some of its major detours, I surveyed the region by plane starting at each of these road segments, and in each case holding the same heading. I quickly identified the continuations of the road sections, which were almost rectilinear. Calculating their heading thus enabled me to deduce where they led, and that was where a Roman settlement was located. Everyone of them led to an existing fort, city or village.

I would now like to extend the coverage of my "Tactical aerial archaeology" surveys, using information from all available sources. Some of these sources have not been used before; for example, it was not realized that certain Roman masonry techniques could be recognized in 6th century Saxon churches where the Saxons had re-used Roman material, thus indicating that there was a Roman site close at hand.

The only answer to our search dilemma is "Tactical aerial archaeology". It has not been practised before but it is hoped that this project will bring it to the attention of the general public. The idea of tactical archaeology has already proved itself by the successes it has achieved in the past and its cost is only a fraction of an "area search". The technique should be repeated over the whole of Britain and other parts of the former Roman Empire.

A hitherto unknown Roman road discovered by Raymond Selkirk.

Manned exploration of the abyss

Andreas Buchwald Rechnitzer

1345 Lomita Road, El Cajón, California 92020, United States

American, born 30 November 1924. Professor at San Diego University, California. Educated in United States; Ph. D. (Zoology) from University of California, San Diego, in 1956.

Exploration of the abyssal depths of the world's oceans has until this century been accomplished by blindly lowering sampling equipment by wire from a surface ship. As a result, interpretation of the resources – and their potential value to mankind – involved varied hypotheses; and extrapolation and conjecture were used in attempts to describe the abyss, its inhabitants, and its value to mankind. The creation of a craft that would allow human intervention to all depths of the sea was accomplished by Swiss scientist Auguste Piccard. Jacques Piccard was the person with whom I worked in establishing a world record for deep diving on 15 November 1959. I have since continued my involvement in bringing deep submergence science and technology to its present state-of-the-art, and have been a scientific participant in recent highly successful scientific deep-sea research and explorations.

On 23 January 1960, I was privileged to be the scientist-in-charge of the first, and to this time the only, dive to the ultimate depth of the world ocean – 11,600 m. The family of deep submersible vehicles has grown significantly from that day, yet the number of manned vehicles capable of reaching depths of 1,000 m is only five. Since Piccard's bathyscaph *Trieste* was retired, none can go deeper than 6,000 m.

A joint US-USSR deep-sea exploit

The USSR has recently acquired two such deep-diving vehicles for scientific exploration of the abyss. A USSR Academy of Sciences invitation has been extended to selected US scientists to participate in a series of dives in Lake Baikal in 1990 and in the Indian Ocean and Red Sea in 1991, and I am fortunate enough to form part of that team of American and Russian scientists.

Lake Baikal's fauna, ecology and lake-floor features are singularly unique among the deep fresh-water bodies of the world. Long isolated from the sea, this fresh-water body of unusual depth has undergone unique faunal developments. Little is known about the environment, habitats, ecology and behaviour of the

The manned submersible MIR I of the Soviet Academy of Sciences, P. P. Shirshov Institute of Oceanography being placed in the ocean off Bermuda in July 1989. The vehicle can carry two pilots and an observer. Numerous giant six-gill sharks were attracted to tuna bait placed on the sea bed by the MIR I manipulator.

organisms living in the deep portions of the lake (maximum depth 1,620 m). Deep submergence technology and field experience are now available to conduct meaningful scientific investigations of Lake Baikal throughout all of its depths. Direct, close-up observations of animal species, their behaviour and their environment can be augmented by advanced data collection and recording techniques, and the use of unique sampling equipment that will bring living organisms to the surface for further study and display. In addition, the geological history of the Lake Baikal basin strongly suggests that hot water vents will be found associated with lake bottom fracture zones.

Highly productive baiting techniques will be used to attract a broad spectrum of deep-water organisms into the viewing and collecting area of a manned submersible where they will be observed to establish their inter-relationships with their environment. Quantitative measurements and sampling surveys will be conducted to augment the visual observations. Precise navigation will be used to support surveys of the lake at various depths and in a variety of locations. Advanced photography and video-technology will be used to acquire images of the fauna and the lake floor. This field exploration effort is expected to develop significant new knowledge and to serve as a catalyst for establishment of a new ecology centre to foster additional studies involving expanded and international participation. The expedition findings will likely provide new scientific findings and fresh material appropriate for publication in scientific journals, the *National Geographic* magazine, worldwide television and public lectures. I propose to include this expedition in a book.

We also propose to explore each of the major abyssal basins of the Indian Ocean and the Red Sea using manned deep submersible facilities to determine the influence – present and past – of sea-floor physical barriers on the distribution of faunal species. The scientific approach will be similar to that described above for Lake Baikal. The Indian Ocean is the smallest and geologically the most youthful of the three oceans. It differs from the Pacific and Atlantic Oceans in two important aspects. First, it is land-locked in the north and does not extend into

The MIR I *manned submersible of the Soviet Academy of Sciences, P. P. Shirshov Institute of Oceanography on the sea floor deep in the Atlantic Ocean. The* MIR I *was photographed by personnel in the* MIR II. *The Soviet submersible pair can accomplish tasks that are difficult or impossible to carry out using a single submersible. Our experiments will take advantage of this capability by manning deep sea stations in multiples of 20 hours.*

the cold climatic regions of the northern hemisphere; consequently, it is asymmetrical with regard to its circulation. Second, the wind systems over its equatorial and northern portions change twice each year causing an almost complete reversal of its circulation.

Important to the proposed exploratory research by manned deep submersibles are the number of basins separated by major ridge systems. The largest is the Mid-Ocean Ridge, the greater part of which has a rather deep rift valley along its centre. Most of the ocean basins separated by ridges reach depths in excess of 5,000 m; but all within the depth capability of the USSR submersibles. Determining the impact of these physiographic features on the geographic distribution of abyssal forms is the objective of this exploration and discovery project.

A unique Soviet-American venture

The significance of the proposed effort is reflected in the unique and timely opportunity for American and Soviet scientists to conduct a joint scientific investigation of a unique body of water – Lake Baikal. The USSR has offered to provide a deep submersible and the associated logistic support for the vehicle. Top scientists and technical experts will join in a new approach to studying a remote, but scientifically intriguing body of water by direct human intervention. New knowledge regarding the biology and ecology of the deep depths of Indian Ocean basins will be derived from *in situ* manned observation and data collection using manned submersible and remotely operated vehicles and data collection technologies. The basins to be visited represent virtually pristine areas for direct observation research and precise data collection. Applying the baiting techniques to unprecedented depths within the known range of the coelacanth is expected to shed new light on this living fossil.

292

The petroglyphs of Easter Island

Antoni Pujador

Balmes St. 334–336, 08006 Barcelona, Spain

Spanish, born 12 April 1948. Export manager in a Catalan stainless steel manufacturing company. Educated in Spain; graduated from high school in El Aaiun in 1971.

Its monolithic statues or "moais" have made Easter Island famous throughout the world, and have earned for it the reputation of being the world's largest open-air museum. However, this island still harbours numerous mysteries that still remain to be be given an adequate explanation. For example, the open-air rupestrian (rock) art is, by far, one of the most specific and spectacular manifestations of the Rapa Nuian civilization. Throughout the whole of the 165 km^2 of the surface area of Easter Island one can encounter an astonishing number of rupestrian engravings or petroglyphs.

An uncharted wealth of petroglyphs

The island itself has been the site of a considerable number of ethnological and archaeological investigations over the years – starting with the expedition organized to the Island in 1913 by Mrs. Scoresby Routledge – which we consider to be the first of its type. However, the petroglyphs themselves seem to have systematically been left unstudied by the various investigators, despite the studies carried out by Mr. Henry Lavachery during the course of the Franco-Belgian expedition organized in 1934; this expedition even published a book on its findings although this is unfortunately very incomplete. In more recent times, praise should be expressed on the subject of the work done by Dr. Georgia Lee, of the Institute of Archaeology of the University of California in Los Angeles. Nevertheless it still remains that there is no complete catalogue of the Island's petroglyphs.

The project that we intended to carry out is designed to rectify this gap in our knowledge since we plan to make a study of the petroglyphs, compile our findings into a single publication and, having interviewed and questioned the elders of the island in order to obtain a thorough knowledge of ancient myths and traditions, to link each of these petroglyphs with the corresponding legends. There still remains time to undertake this effort.

A petroglyph of the god "Make-Make" in the Orongo area of Rapa-Nui.

Nonetheless, there are two very important facts that should be born in mind in this context. First, there is the natural erosion produced by the weather combined by the abrasion caused by animals who pasture freely all over the Island – all of which have had and are continuing to have an impact on the condition of the petroglyphs. Second, there is the onset of the tourist phenomenon which is now beginning to affect Rapa-Nui; in particular, in spite of the surveillance procedures that has been put in place, a certain amount of vandalism is still taking place, with a degree of systematic destruction by souvenir hunters, coupled with the activities of pseudo-scientists and the like.

Store of folk-lore still accessible

One feature that distinguishes Easter Island from the other islands of Polynesia and, in fact, from most other parts of the world where petroglyphs are to be found is the fact that on Easter Island – probably owing to the fact that it is one of the most isolated places – the elders of the population still have an extremely extensive knowledge of their ancestor's legends. We know that these people would be willing to collaborate with our team in order to relate to us and establish for posterity this important segment of their local culture.

In the petroglyphs, the Rapa Nuian people have developed and transmitted a form of behaviour standards – a kind of social organization. Consequently, thorough investigation of these petroglyphs will allow us to make a significant advance in our knowledge of the cultural dimension of Rapa-Nui. Even more important than this, however, is the fact that we shall have recovered for science and posterity an irreplaceable heritage. We have, in fact, been working on the subject for several years now, but lack of resources and time availability have meant that the task has not yet been brought to completion.

In particular, we have localized 41 emplacements where petroglyphs are placed, and by completing this catalogue with sector Ana Kena, we will have studied and catalogued some 51 combined units in this sector. There are many places – such as caves in the cliff faces, etc., to which it is difficult to obtain access and which we have not yet had the possibility to research and for which suitable climbing equipment, boats, etc., will be necessary.

A valuable resource for future researchers

The task that lies before us is to finalize the work that has been done to date (both by ourselves and by other scientists who researched this field) and to compile the data for analysis using the appropriate methodology. Once we have finished compiling all the research that has taken place to date, the data will be analyzed using a standardized procedure that will allow comparisons to be made of data from different parts of the Island. Finally, we will record oral legends and traditions , relate them to the individual petroglyphs and publish our results.

We believe that if we are able to publish and compile all this material, the benefits which would accrue to archaeologists of the future would be enormous and we will have made a tremendous advance in extending our comprehension of the rupestrian art of Rapa-Nui. This would also mean a knowledge of the communities that were able to accomplish these achievements in almost complete isolation on Easter Island – thousands of kilometres from anywhere.

Statues on Rapa-Nui. Treasures such as these are highly exposed to vandalism, the elements and even to damage due to well-intentioned "technicians" making plaster casts for exhibitions in Europe and elsewhere.

The Nullarbor project

Robert John Palmer
Honourable Mention
The Rolex Awards for Enterprise – 1990

12 Seabank, Alnmouth, Alnwick, Northumberland NE65, United Kingdom

British, born 18 October 1951. Freelance Writer and Photographer, Director of own Photographic Company. Educated in United Kingdom; Teaching Certificate (Geography) from St. Martin's College, Lancaster, in 1973.

The Nullarbor Desert of Australia is a desolate expanse of limestone in the south-east corner of Western Australia. Bordered to the south by vertical cliffs that plunge into the Great Australian Bight, its arid landscape belies the great blue tunnels that run far beneath the surface of the desert. The Nullarbor contains some of the world's most spectacular underwater caves. The current world record is held by one of these, Cocklebiddy Cave, where a mammoth underwater journey of 6 km is necessary to reach the present end of the system. Other caves offer the potential for greater discoveries and record-breaking explorations.

The caves of the Nullarbor are legendary in the annals of underground exploration. In 1990, an international team containing some of the best cave divers in the world will be exploring over 100 m beneath the sands to establish new standards in underwater exploration techniques and equipment, and hopefully, in the process, creating a new world record in underwater cave exploration. This will involve swimming distances of 12 km and more, committing the divers to underground camps beyond the flooded passages, and creating problems of logistics and decompression previously inexperienced in cave diving.

New caves and world records

The continuing exploration of these caverns offers unique and exciting adventures inside Earth that will take underwater exploration into the 21st century. The team will be using the most advanced underwater equipment available – including specially constructed underwater vehicles, rebreathing equipment designed primarily for use in outer space, and on-site computers to project decompression profiles and analyze logistical problems *in situ*. Previous explorers have concentrated on known caves, and have achieved little at sites which offer potential for important new cave systems. Our efforts will be concentrated on caves which end close to the underground water table with the intention of finding major undiscovered and unexplored underwater galleries. This will form the first stage of the Nullarbor Project.

Pannikin Plain Cave – where a great limestone cavern suddenly plunges underwater in a two-kilometre tunnel far below the arid Nullarbor Desert. Further exploration is for skilled cave divers only.

The main stage of the Project will continue the exploration of known underwater caves, such as the Cocklebiddy and Pannikin Plain Caves, and make new exploration in aquatic caves that are discovered during the first phase of the project. In the Cocklebiddy and Pannikin Plain Caves, rebreathing systems will be used to enable extreme distance penetrations to be made with minimum logistical effort. At other sites, initial explorations will be undertaken using conventional scuba equipment, configured for cave diving, until distance indicates the use of the rebreathers. A third aspect will be the exploration by helicopter and boat of the cliffs of the Nullarbor coastline, where the desert meets the Great Australian Bight. The sheer, vertical edge of the Nullarbor forms the longest unbroken cliff-line in the world. Entrances in the cliffs have been reported and, once their position is established, they can be reached by mountaineering techniques from the clifftop. Reports exist of submarine freshwater springs, possibly the resurgences of the Nullarbor caves. We will also investigate these.

Finally, the Project will examine the hydrology and geomorphology of the caves in an effort to ascertain how such massive conduit development has taken place beneath one of the southern hemisphere's most arid zones. This should have ramifications for similar desert environments elsewhere in the world. Australian aboriginal involvement with caves and freshwater springs in the Nullarbor goes back at least 20,000 years, and close contacts are presently being formed between the project and the Mirning people whose ancestral home is the central Nullarbor. The dreamings of the Mirning hold much about the creation of the desert and its social and ecological environment.

The main field area of the project centres on the tiny community of Cocklebiddy. The nearest jumping-off points, Perth and Adelaide, lie some 1,200 km away and 1,600 km away respectively. This means the logistics of support are considerable, the more so when the desert environment is taken into account. All material will have to be transported, possibly from both Perth and Adelaide, and this includes base camp facilities, diving and filming equipment, generators, food and all ancillary equipment.

Specially designed diver propulsion vehicles will be used to transport both personnel and equipment through the longest underwater sections of the caves. A number of days will have to be spent living underground beyond the underwater passages, and full underground camp facilities will be required, including medical provisions such as pure breathing oxygen for decompression and therapeutic purposes. Due to the extreme amount of time spent underwater, recompression facilities must be available on site, with additional emergency procedures established to evacuate casualties to Perth or Adelaide for full therapeutic treatment in the event of an emergency.

Rebreathers – outer space to inner space

Some of the earliest cave diving was done on simple oxygen rebreathing sets available in the late 1940s, but these were abandoned in favour of the more reliable and versatile aqualung. Recently, developments in underwater breathing technology, have led to the emergence of units which can be used for underwater cave exploration with a high degree of safety. On the 1987 Andros Project, a cave diving exploration of the deep "Blue Holes" of Andros Island in the Bahamas, Rexnord Mk 16 rebreathers were used to place trained cave divers at depths of up to 92 m while breathing a mixture of oxygen and helium. From these dives, Dr Bill Stone of Cis-Lunar Developments, one of the leading team members of the Nullarbor Project, has developed a new rebreathing system specifically for use in hazardous environments, i.e., underwater caves and outer space. The prototype has been successfully tested at depths of over 90 m and for durations of up to 24 hours. The successful use of the Cis-Lunar rebreathers on the Nullarbor Project will herald a new era in underwater exploration.

Cliffs along the edge of the Nullarbor Desert drop vertically for 100 m into the South Australian Bight. In these desert limestones lie some of the world's longest underwater caves.

In search of dinosaurs in the southern Chubut region of Patagonia

Rubén Dario Martinez

Facultad de Ciencias Naturales, Pasaje Alvear 1568, Casilla de Correos 392, 9000 Comodoro Rivadavia, Chubut, Argentina

Argentine, born 3 September 1956. Professor of Natural Sciences at the "San Juan Bosco" National University of Patagonia, Argentina. Educated in Argentina; Professor of Natural Sciences, graduated from the Universidad Nacional de la Patagonia "San Juan Bosco" in 1980.

In November 1984, I assembled a research team to explore the Bajo Barreal formation which dates from the Upper Cretaceous period with the purpose of discovering fossil remains of the fauna (especially dinosaurs) which lived in the south-central area of the province of Chubut, Patagonia about 90 million years ago.

Vast riches of prehistoric fossil remains

Argentina is very rich in mesozoic vertebrates, with fossil remains recorded in at least ten of its provinces. There have been findings of dinosaurs, pterosaurs, crocodiles, rincosaurs, therapsids and primitive mammals from the Mesozoic era. In Patagonia, in the south of Argentina which comprises the provinces of Neu-quén, Rio Negro, Chubut y Santa Cruz, some sporadic explorations have been carried out in limited areas. These explorations were undertaken by Argentine, European and American scientists, guided by reports from members of the local population who had uncovered large bones (generally leg bones or vertebrae from large sauropods).

In Rio Negro and in the northern part of Chubut, there have been findings of dinosaurs, sauropods, theropods and hadrosaurs, and also crocodiles, mammals, birds, etc., from the Triassic, Jurassic or Cretaceous periods. Recently an extensive dinosaur breeding area in Rio Negro, with dozens of nests and eggs also came to light.

These expeditions were always undertaken by institutions located very far from Patagonia – 2,000 km away (in the case of Buenos Aires) or 3,500 km away (as in the case of Tucumán). On account of the great distances involved, such explorations tend to be relatively brief, very costly and quite limited as far as the area they cover. And, of course, the dinosaurs and other reptiles found are never returned to Patagonia. Nevertheless, the southern part of Chubut, in spite of an abundance of mesozoic outcroppings, has not been meaningfully explored,

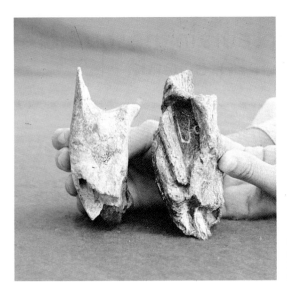

Left premaxillary of a sauropod of unknown family (marked with a red point).

something I took into account when I decided to assemble our investigating team.

We have explored a number of areas over the last four years. During this period we have found a very diversified collection of cretaceous fauna with remains of crocodiles (plates, teeth), turtles (plates), holostean fishes (scales) and, above all, dinosaurs. In fact, one of our outstanding achievements has been the discovery of a new genus of carnivorous dinosaur, Xenotarsosaurus, with a type of ankle unique among all carnivorous dinosaurs. In 1986, we found, about 200 m away from the carnivorous dinosaur, a herbivorous articulated dinosaur almost complete (only the head and neck are missing). This is the most complete specimen of the Titanosauridae family found up to now. The dinosaurs of this family can be found in Argentina, Brazil, the United States, India, Niger, Egypt, Spain, France and Romania. It took us 15 months to extract this dinosaur and we are in the process of examining it now.

A potential for even more exciting discoveries

The project we are presenting for the Rolex Awards for Enterprise is the systematic exploration of the outcroppings of the Bajo Barreal Formation, with the primary aim of finding dinosaurs which will allow us to get to know the evolutionary development undergone by these reptiles with particular reference to the spine, pelvis, extremities, cranial morphology, etc., about 90 million years ago in this area of Patagonia. Sauropods and theropods of the Jurassic (Callovian) and Lower Cretaceous (Albian) periods are already known. These dinosaurs, discovered in sporadic expeditions from Buenos Aires, have an anatomical structure that exhibits primitive traits which belong to a stock we could label as "Middle Jurassic-Lower Cretaceous". The dinosaurs of the late Upper Cretaceous (Campanian-Maastrichtian), particularly the sauropods, have a different, more modern morphology. Therefore, the dinosaurs of the Bajo Barreal Formation, which correspond probably to the Turonian-Coniacian ages, should provide us – given their intermediate position in the time scale – the clue to the anatomical changes that took place during the period – unexplored until now – which extends over some 16 million years.

This is the first time that anyone has found in South America this little known family of sauropods associated with titanosaurids. Our project will, I hope, expose remains that are even more eloquent in describing this new family

We tentatively estimate that it will take six years to explore 1,200 km^2 of outcroppings; for example, it took us 15 months to extract the last dinosaur we discovered. Moreover, exploration can be carried out only between September and March due to climatic factors; the rest of the year, we will concentrate on laboratory work.

Our intention is to divide our team into two which would speed up the work and make it more effective. In addition, supplementary funds would allow us to buy some mechanical excavating equipment since all the work is done with a hammer and cold chisel at the moment.

This project would provide fundamental revelations on the history of the dinosaurs of Patagonia and offer a key to a study of the evolution of the mesozoic reptiles of Gondwana.

A view of the Bajo Barreal Formation with a petrified tree in the foreground of the photograph.

Photographic study of Mediterranean landscape and architecture

Neil Folberg

P. O. Box 151327, Talpiot Industrial Area, 91003 Jerusalem, Israel

American, born 7 April 1950. Free-lance photographer. Educated in the United States; B.A. (Hons.) from University of California, Berkeley, in 1973.

The Mediterranean lands are generally defined as the areas bordering on the Mediterranean Sea that have a Mediterranean climate, and are loosely classed as the areas where the olive is cultivated. The geography of the region ranges from essentially uninhabitable desert wilderness to cultivated coastal areas, from high mountain ranges with a permanent layer of snow to arid semi-desert. The lands that border the Mediterranean include the Iberian Peninsula and Southern France, Italy, Greece, Yugoslavia, Turkey, Syria, Lebanon, Israel, Egypt, Libya, Algeria, Tunisia, Morocco and the Mediterranean Islands. Egypt, though essentially an arid zone with few Mediterranean characteristics, is inextricably intertwined with the history of the Mediterranean lands and the development of civilization.

The unity of the Mediterranean area

The Mediterranean is an inland sea bordered in the north and south by extensive mountain ranges. In many areas, these mountains run nearly parallel to the Mediterranean coast line and can be used to roughly define a zone that has a Mediterranean climatic pattern and that has historically been the centre of development of Mediterranean civilizations and peoples. The different nations that border the Mediterranean have, throughout recorded history, interacted with each other in a way that allowed a constant interchange of ideas and trade between East and West, cross-fertilizing one another so that when one civilization began to wane, its knowledge and culture were usually passed to another civilization on the rise, either by free exchange of ideas or through the military conquest. The existence of a nearly tideless inland sea located in a moderate climatic zone with predictable weather patterns that are favourable even to primitive navigation, allowed the Mediterranean Sea to become a channel for inter-cultural communication.

The reflecting pool in the Alhambra in Granada, Spain.

The civilization of the Mediterranean

The primary symbol and structure of civilization has been the city. It has been said that, since the word "civilization" derives from the Latin *civita* – which means city – to be civilized is to be urban; consequently, civilization, in this strict sense, is the "art of living in towns". Evidence of ancient and modern civilizations remains on the land, in their architecture, both sacred and profane. And most of the great civilizations have left us their cities, dominated by their preferred architectural style set in that part of the land that they found to be most conducive to development and physical security.

As empires spread throughout the Mediterranean basin, they took their architectural styles with them. Successful forms were also eagerly copied by other cultures, so that one finds, for example, elements of Roman and Islamic architecture in North Africa, Southern Europe, Asia Minor and the Levant. Architectural styles provide visual evidence of cultural diversity and interchange that is characteristic of the Mediterranean region. While the styles are diverse, their wide diffusion creates a visual theme that can be easily photographed and followed throughout the Mediterranean lands.

The visual evidence of these civilizations persists today in the changes that they effected on the surface of the landscape. This may also be seen in the pattern of developed agriculture, through the introduction of such plants as the olive tree or grape vine; or through land conservation methods, such as the terracing of hilly areas that is almost universal throughout the Mediterranean region. Irrigation techniques have also left their mark on the land, in the form of irrigation channels and aqueducts. These elements combine to form a landscape that has been altered through human activity until it achieved its present form, one which is easily identifiable as being distinctly Mediterranean.

An outstanding theme for a book

There is a surprising scarcity of books dealing with the Mediterranean region as a unit, whether one looks in the areas of art and photography, architecture, history or geography, though there are books beyond number that deal with a specific period or a single subject that has bearing on the Mediterranean region. A comprehensive series of books encompassing the entire region, an area that has been the locus of development of Western civilization and the theatre of Western history until the discovery of the New World, could fill a major gap.

This series of books could be divided into three volumes, as described below. The subjects described in each volume are merely examples of one of many rich themes to be explored and developed in each of the geographic areas.

The first in the series could be the Western Mediterranean, including Spain, Morocco, Algeria (if possible) and Tunisia. These countries have had historical and trade links over a period of centuries. If Spain on occasion dominated parts of the North African coast, the Moslem Moors controlled Spanish Andalusia for hundreds of years, enriching the agriculture, architecture and arts of Spain immeasurably, leaving behind cultural monuments of incredible sophistication and beauty.

The Central Mediterranean might be the second in the series, including Southern France, Italy, and the eastern Dalmatian Coast of Yugoslavia. Here is the fertile area of development of both Roman and Renaissance culture, and the area dominated by the great maritime powers and city-states, such as Venice. Venice was a Western power with Eastern ambitions, an intermediary between the Renaissance and the exotic east with whom it traded not only goods, but architecture, developing a brilliant and distinctive style.

The final volume could comprise the Eastern Mediterranean, including the Mediterranean areas once controlled by the Ottoman Empire: inland Yugoslavia, parts of Greece, Turkey, Israel and Egypt. This is the meeting point between the olive and the date palm; and the breeding ground of Judaism, Christianity and Islam.

A photograph taken by Neil Folberg for his photographic study of Mediterranean architecture.

The conservation of historic huts in the Ross Sea region of Antarctica

David Lawrence Harrowfield

16 Halton Street, Strowan, Christchurch 5, New Zealand

New Zealander, born 21 August 1940. Historic sites conservator. Educated in New Zealand; B. Sc. (Geography) from University of Canterbury, Christchurch.

Antarctica contains a number of wooden huts which were established as early as 1899. They served as homes, laboratories, and workshops for the pioneers of Antarctic exploration and represent the foundations of present-day science programmes. Today, these historic sites, which also include rock shelters, field depots, cairns, memorial crosses, a grave and the site of an ice cave, are preserved under the Antarctic Treaty (1959) as memorials to the expeditions and famous personalities associated with them.

Of the sites officially recognized by the Treaty, nearly 30 are located in the Ross Sea region south of New Zealand. Two of the most historically important huts are at Cape Adare in North Victoria Land and at Cape Evans 800 km south, on western Ross Island. At Cape Adare are two Norwegian huts constructed of interlocking boards which served as the winter quarters for the Southern Cross Expedition (1899–1900) led by Carsten Egeberg Borchgrevink. A third hut nearby occupied by the Northern Party of the British Antarctic Expedition (1910–1913) has been totally demolished by violent winds. This was confirmed by field observations made in 1982.

Precarious condition of historic Antarctic buildings

Typical problems attributed to wind include the weathering of foundations and wallboards, indentations and embedding of beach pebbles, deformation and splitting of walls, lifting of the roof cladding and the scouring of ground about the buildings. While much valuable information was obtained in the field and from laboratory tests, the field work carried out to date lacked detailed climatological observations.

Photographic evidence obtained from visitors to this remote locality since 1982 has confirmed that wind damage has accelerated. It is now proposed to return to Cape Adare and, using anemometers, including a gust recorder, obtain the wind measurements required. A vertical profile of sediment traps will also be used to

The snow drift against the southeast wall of Captain R. F. Scott's 1910–1913 expedition hut, Cape Evans, Antarctica.

sample wind-transported beach pebbles, and measurements will be obtained of attrition and impaction on hut wall boards. From wind tunnel and other experiments, including impaction tests using samples of present beach materials, it should be possible to obtain an indication of wind velocities which, in winter, exceed 40–50 m.sec^{-1}. The use of a scanning electron microscope will help determine the extent of cell deformation in the wood. It is during autumn and winter that most damage is thought to occur to the huts and the only winter wind records presently available for this locality were collected in 1899 and 1911.

With this information, it should be possible to accurately predict the long-term survival of the Southern Cross Expedition living hut, and to accommodate future conservation work within an overall management plan for the site.

Damage to Scott's hut

The second site to be examined is the largest historic hut on the Antarctic Continent and was erected at Cape Evans in 1911 as the main base for Captain Scott's British Antarctic Expedition (1910–1913). Of different construction to the Borchgrevink huts, it is associated with the ill-fated trip to the South Pole in the Austral summer of 1911–1912, and subsequently became the base for two years of ten marooned members of the Ross Sea Party of Ernest Henry Shackleton's Imperial Trans Antarctic Expedition (1914–1917).

Scott's hut is orientated approximately northeast/southwest. During the winter months of April-June and in the spring month of November, extensive snow drifts form along the southeast wall and around each end of the hut. Observations by visitors confirm precipitation has increased in recent years, and this has tended to remain until late summer (February). The snow drift which accumulates against the southeast wall, in particular, has already contributed to the collapse of a stores annexe erected in 1911 and intact until the late 1950s.

During summer months, when temperatures can rise above freezing point, snow along the hut wall melts and as a result of capillary action, rises in the wall and then freezes on the interior cladding. The resulting increase in relative humidity and accompanying dampness within the hut has severely affected this important building and its contents, particularly, fittings and artifacts of iron.

Planning for future preservation

From a unique set of records obtained in 1986 and recent field observations, it is proposed to again utilize the Canterbury University, Department of Mechanical Engineering, wind tunnel and – with models of the hut and snow drifts – study the airflow about the hut. A smaller wind tunnel may be constructed specially for this work. As with the Cape Adare historic hut, this information will be of considerable value in planning future conservation programmes, especially if a decision is made to replicate the stores annexe as a means of providing protection to the hut and its contents.

Weathered timber on a corner of the stores hut used by C. E. Borchgrevink's Southern Cross Expedition (1898–1900), Cape Adare, Antarctica.

Prospecting for iguanodons

Pierre Gérard G. Capront

Honourable Mention
The Rolex Awards for Enterprise – 1990

Albert Premier, 35, 7980 Stambruges, Beloeil, Belgium

Belgian, born 13 October 1959. Radiologist and Researcher in Palaeontology and Geology, Université Libre de Bruxelles. Educated in Belgium; M. D. from University of Liège in 1985.

In 1878, a coalminer working in one of the coalpits in Bernissart, a small Belgian village close to the frontier with France, uncovered some rather unusual lumps embedded in the soil, which were later identified as the bones of iguanodons. Excavation of the site began immediately but three years later had to be halted because of financial and technical problems. Since 1880, the reconstructed skeletons of a number of iguanodons in particular have been housed in a museum in Brussels. Several attempts were made, without success, to resume exploration. However, in 1987, I as a radiologist and keen amateur geologist, and Pierre Simonet a palaeontologist, decided to make this long-standing scientific dream into reality.

The skeletal bones of the iguanodons were found at depths of over 300 m in sedimentary strata some 200m long and 34 m deep, i.e., a total area worth exploring of some 200,000 m^3; the original excavation explored only 300 m^3 and yet yielded 29 iguanodons, five turtles, four crocodiles, batrachians and several thousand fish.

Bringing the fossils back to the surface

Our first step was to set up "Prospecting for Iguanodons", a non-profit-making association, to raise the funds to re-open the site at Bernissart. Under the authority of the parent association, we are putting together: a group of mining engineers for the excavation work; a body of jurists to advise on finance and administration; and a college of scientists to ensure the site is thoroughly explored. The association has also obtained the co-operation of a large number of politicians and of prominent members of Belgian society.

The full potential of the Bernissart site has not been realized but modern excavation methods enable research to be carried out in the fields of geology and plant and animal palaeontology including studies on iguanodons and other members of the dinosaur family of that era (notably megalosaurus and

308

This vast enterprise envisages creating, at an authentic prehistoric site, a palaeontological research centre of worldwide significance, financed by a unique tourist attraction of high-level educational, scientific and cultural value.

hysilophodon). A number of scholars, all intensely interested in the prospect of re-opening and exploring this mine of prehistoric wealth, have joined forces. The fact that the project promises to develop as an interuniversity one will guarantee the obtaining of optimum scientific results.

Not only is the whole project of unquestionable scientific value but also the retrieval of iguanodons offers a very viable financial proposition. Interest shown worldwide for these dinosaurs in such perfect condition is indeed considerable and this means that it would be feasible to scientifically explore the total area (i.e., 200,000 m^3) and also transform the site into a major tourist and cultural attraction. It has been estimated that the whole project will cost in the region of BFr 3,500,000,000, a huge budget that will obviously need to be spread over a period of 15 years if all plans, particularly the scientific ones, are to be completed.

With innovation as its driving force, the project will inevitably create and promote new ventures of economic opportunity. For example: the development of a unique prehistoric site will encourage the growth of a thriving and prosperous tourist industry in this Franco-Belgian area; proceeds from the sale (or long-term loan) of a maximum of six iguanodons would cover the costs of excavation and a palaeontological infrastructure; and many new jobs would be created in an area where there is at present a high level of unemployment.

A five-point plan for the future

The "Prospecting for Iguanodons" association is drawing up a five-point plan to: record the facts uncovered by the exploration work and draft a document in

309

collaboration with the Belgian Institute of Geology; collect and interpret the excavation plans of the geologists and paleontologists working on the project; supervise the construction of a palaeontological research and world conference centre; ensure the project remains viable both scientifically and financially; supervise arrangements; and create a tourist and cultural park to assure the future profit-earning capacity of the venture and exploit the "dinosaurs" theme to the utmost.

The surface attraction park will be supplemented by an underground attraction since visitors will be able to go down the pit and see for themselves how and where the fossils were discovered.

The region is well served by road and rail transport facilities and "the land of the dinosaurs" will in fact sit astride the Franco-Belgian frontier and would thus become the first non-national tourist and cultural centre in the "United States of Europe".

A joint scientific and private enterprise venture

The facets of "Prospecting for Iguanodons" are closely intertwined and mutually supportive. The whole project provides a highly original and happy alliance between the scientific world and private enterprise without thereby having to call on grants from the State coffers. The completion of scientific exploration and discovery at Bernissart will enable the past to become of service to the well-being of the present, and of the future, of mankind.

Retrieving the numerous perfectly preserved fossilized specimens from this unique prehistoric site will permit the reconstruction, in its authentic palaeontological environment, of a complete biotope of the Mesozoic Age.

Project Condor – a balloon flight from Colombia to Spain

Juan Antonio Bravo-Perea

Apartado Aereo 17858, Bogotá, Colombia

Colombian, born 7 September 1953. Researcher, translator, journalist, English teacher and lecturer. Educated in Colombia, United Kingdom and United States; studied (American History and Literature) at the New York City University.

This project intends to undertake a balloon flight from Colombia to Spain to commemorate the fifth centenary of the discovery of America by Christopher Columbus. It is intended to encourage appreciation of the contribution of Columbus to history and the Jewish and Arabic contribution to the discovery of America. The voyage will also promote support to save the condor.

Portrait from the sea – a rediscovery of Canada

Peter Brock

Minke Foundation, 517 Purcell's Cove Road, Halifax, Nova Scotia, Canada B3P 2G2

Canadian, born 8 May 1933. Executive Director, Minke Foundation. Educated in Canada and United Kingdom; attended Upper Canada College, Toronto, McGill University, Montreal, and University of Edinburgh.

The Minke Foundation is making a television film expedition called "Portrait from the sea – a rediscovery of Canada" to unveil the character of Canada's heritage, beauty and diversity. The rediscovery voyage will be by sailing vessel – the *Minke* – and canoe. The *Minke* will take television viewers on an adventure around Canadian shores, in the cold North Atlantic whilst the canoe follows rivers and lakes to the Pacific.

Exploration of the Mamberamu basin in New Guinea

Antonio Iodice D'Enza

Via Posillipo 316, 80123 Naples, Italy

Italian, born 22 March 1945. Lawyer. Educated in Italy.

The project will explore the Mamberamu basin of New Guinea where six previous expeditions have failed and where, as far as is known, no expedition survivors have ever returned. It is intended to determine the difficulties and obstacles previous expeditions encountered and, if possible, reconstruct their story. Each phase of the journey will be video-taped.

The Sri Lankan maritime heritage project

Prasanna Upali Weerawardane

14 St. Paul's Road, Tottenham, London N17, United Kingdom

Sri Lankan, born 30 March 1961. Membership secretary of the National Anti-vivisection Society. Educated in Sri Lanka and United Kingdom; B.A. (Archaeology) from University of London in 1986.

This project aims to survey an underwater archaeological reef site off Colombo, Sri Lanka. The survey will test previous hypotheses that older sites are buried beneath the coral or debris by measuring debris/rock accumulation. In particular, archaeological survival on the seaward and shore sides of the reef will be compared and measured. Archaeological remains indicate the existence of 17th century shipwrecks.

Kyrenia II – Greece to Cyprus

Ian Meadows

18 Doreion Street, Ayios Andreas, 163 Nicosia, Cyprus

British, born 24 January 1933. Writer and Producer. Educated in United Kingdom and France; external course (Modern Languages) at the Université de Rennes from 1951–1953.

This project – which is being undertaken in collaboration with the Hellenic Institute for the Preservation of Nautical Tradition, Athens – aims to make a 55-minute documentary video on the history and construction of a fully sea-going replica of the *Kyrenia*. This vessel was a merchantman dating from the 6th century BC which was sunk off the north coast of Cyprus in the time of Alexander the Great.

Sunken boats in the Dead Sea and the Sea of Galilee

Zvi Ben-Avraham

Tel-Aviv University, Raymond and Beverly Sackler Faculty of Exact Sciences, Department of Geophysics and Planetary Sciences, Ramat Aviv, 69978 Tel Aviv, Israel

Israeli, born 16 November 1941. Professor and Chairman. Educated in Israel and United States; Ph. D. (Marine Geophysics) from Massachusetts Institute of Technology in 1973.

This project aims to locate and recover the wrecks of two iron boats that sank in the Dead Sea and the Sea of Galilee in 1918. The Dead Sea is a highly saline body of water with almost no oxygen, while the Sea of Galilee is a body of fresh water. Much will be learnt about the events in the Middle East during this period, and about the preservation of wrecks in both hypersaline and fresh water.

Operation Selva

Jean Luc Sanchez

Expédition Selva, Le Béguinage, Appt. 34, 10, route de Dourdan, 91650 Breuillet-Village, France

French, born 30 April 1954. Head Police Inspector. Educated in France; attended the Ecole Nationale Supérieure de Police, Cannes, in 1976–1977.

This project will undertake a single-handed expedition to the Peruvian Amazon under absolute survival conditions with, as sole companion, a dog. A study will be made of human behaviour and man/dog relationships in a hostile environment. The media impact of the project will be used to: expand medical assistance to a small Indian community; create public awareness of the danger of massive forest clearing, etc.

Pygmy hippos and early man in the Mediterranean: Prehistoric over-exploitation

Alan Henri Simmons

Quaternary Sciences Center, Desert Research Institute, 7010 Dandini Boulevard, P. O. Box 60220, Reno, Nevada 89512, United States

American, born 15 April 1950. Associate Research Professor. Educated in United States and Canada; Ph. D. (Anthropology) from Southern Methodist University in 1968.

Excavation at Akrotiri-Aetokremnos, Cyprus, has led to the conclusion that man may have been responsible for the extinction of the endemic pygmy hippopotamus and pygmy elephant. Findings also show that this site dates some 2,000 years earlier than any other documented occurrence on any of the eastern Mediterranean Islands and have challenged many notions of early human adaptations in the area.

Exploring the lives and communication system of Atlantic spotted dolphins, *Stenella plagiodon*, in the wild

Denise Lore Herzing

Wild Dolphin Project, 537 West Kalmia Drive #2, Lake Park, Florida 33403, United States

American, born 4 September 1956. Research Director for the Wild Dolphin Project. Educated in United States; B. S. (Marine Zoology) from Oregon State University in 1979.

This project is exploring the social habits and communication system of free-ranging spotted dolphins *(Stenella plagiodon)*. It ineracts with a group of dolphins and records their underwater behaviour and sounds in the wild in order to: document individual dolphins; record their social communication signals; and document the psychological and physiological effects of dolphin contacts on humans.

Ancient and modern techniques of building ships in bottles

Eduardo Raffaelli

Autolatina Argentina S. A., Virrey Olaguer y Feliú 2690, 1426 Buenos Aires, Argentina

Argentine, born 4 October 1954. Investment planning and control specialist at Autolatina Argentina S. A. Educated in Argentina, United Kingdom and Federal Republic of Germany; studied (Public Accountancy) at Universidad de Belgrano from 1978 to 1988.

This project aims to investigate the history of ships in bottles, by visiting museums, private collections and other possible sources throughout the world, by compiling a full photographic record containing each of the relevant models in existence and, finally, by recreating the original techniques plus new and advanced ones. The results will be published in a three-volume encyclopaedic work.

Bayeux tapestries

Bernadette Guyot-Jullien

1 rue du Canal, 91160 Longjumeau, France

French, born 20 January 1940. Sales agent for Air Inter. Educated in Algeria; studied for the first section of the Baccalauréat.

This project has studied the Bayeux Tapestry and now intends to demonstrate that the actual Bayeux Tapestry is not, in fact, an original document, but rather an adaptation, composed around 1105, of the history of the conquest of England, which has been put together from elements contained in the original tapestry. Therefore, it is a replica which is similar in appearance to the original but not in its fundamental spirit.

Trekking along the Rift Valley – for the sake of the future

Diana Joyce Moe

P. O. Box 329, Mbabane, Swaziland

American, born 23 May 1959. Science and mathematics teacher and head of both departments at St. Joseph's High School, Mzimpofu. Educated in United States; M. S. (Natural Science) from University of Wyoming in 1986.

This project plans a 1,500-km trek along the Rift Valley from the Ethiopian/Kenyan border at Lake Turkana to the southern shore of Lake Victoria in Tanzania. The trek team will comprise archaeologists, a photo-journalist, a photographer and a school curriculum designer. The team will write several articles, create a slide presentation, and pursue the development of ecological educational resources.

Ancient monument of the Andean civilization of Chavin-Peru

Tiberio Petro-León

Avenida Javier Prado (Este) 1712, Lima 27, Peru

Peruvian, born 11 August 1945. Energy-source substitution investigator. Educated in Peru; studied Business Administration at the Universidad Técnica de Piura in 1967–1968.

The Chavin is widely considered the cradle of Andean culture; however, the ancient monument of this Andean civilization in Chavin de Huantar remains an enigma. This project has studied the monument and proposes to produce a publication which will provide an overall description, and point to the most effective approaches to the architectural, sculptural, and iconographic aspects.

A Renaissance cargo cult on Easter Island

Dragos Gheorghiu

Str. Valea Rosie No 9, BL. Z5, Ap. 47, Sect. 6, Bucharest, Romania

Romanian, born 27 June 1953. Industrial designer and essayist. Educated in Romania; B.A. (Architecture) from the Institute of Architecture "Ion Mincu", Bucharest, in 1979.

This project aims to demonstrate the similarity between the statues on Easter Island and late 16th century European art, resulting from the impact that the first circumnavigators had upon the natives of the most remote island of Polynesia. It is hoped to produce a half-documentary, half-fiction film about Easter Island, with actors in Spanish period costumes and portraying the building of a 16th century galleon.

Pharmacological potential of the Cape Verde Island opisthobranchs

Jesus Angel Ortea Rato

Laboratory of Zoology, Faculty of Biology, Oviedo University, Jesus Arias de Velasco s/n, 33005 Oviedo, Spain

Spanish, born 21 January 1951. Professor in Animal Biology, Oviedo University. Educated in Spain and Netherlands; doctorate in Biology from Oviedo University in 1977.

The opisthobranch molluscs are a major source of raw materials for natural pharmacological substances but are difficult to gather in quantities in nature. This project has identified the Cape Verde Islands as an ideal location for collecting these molluscs, with a wide range of species available in large quantities. A zoological expedition will be organized to collect the molluscs and study their biochemistry.

Underwater photography of the Nile crocodile

Michel Roggo

Brugerastrasse 1, 3186 Düdingen, Switzerland

Swiss, born 13 September 1951. Free-lance photographer and writer. Educated in Switzerland; Diploma in Sciences from the University of Fribourg in 1974.

This project aims to produce a documentary based on underwater photographs of the daily life of the Nile crocodile *(Crocodylus niloticus)* in its natural environment in the Okvango Delta, Botswana, showing its behaviour under or on the water at different seasons and age phases. A special underwater camera with remote control and through-the-lens video control will be used.

A family exploration and discovery of the southern seas

Sophie Anne Marie Labruhe

c/o Luizáo, Rua 15 de Novembro, 1560, 17300 Dois Corregos, S. P., Brazil

French, born 22 July 1951. Housewife, educator and yacht project worker. Educated in France; Masters Degree (History of Art) from Sorbonne, Paris, in 1976.

On the basis of 320,000 km of previous sailing experience, this project is designing and building a sailing boat for the southern seas. It will offer the owners' children and anyone interested in studying the southern seas and lands (scientific research, surveys, etc.) an outstanding exploration vehicle. The boat will navigate the southern seas and be the first to sail to the South Sandwich Islands since the time of Captain Cook.

The Dakhleh Oasis Project

Anthony John Mills

Watergate House, St. Mabyn, Bodmin, Cornwall PL30 3BQ, United Kingdom

Canadian, born 8 September 1937. Research Archaeologist specializing in Egypt. Educated in United Kingdom and Canada; B. A. (General Arts) from McMaster University in 1959.

This project has been making a multi-disciplinary, long-term archaeological study of the relationship between environmental changes and human activity in the 2,000 km² region of the Dakhleh Oasis in Egypt's Western Desert. All human activity, from mid-Pleistocene Old Stone Age man to present day inhabitants, has been included. Information is being collected on site distribution and environmental history.

Yorkshire challenger for the British land speed record

Malcolm Brian Pittwood

11 Fieldside, Edenthorpe, Doncaster, South Yorkshire DN3 2JS, United Kingdom

British, born 12 August 1952. Senior Fuel Technologist for British Coal Corporation. Educated in United Kingdom; B. Sc. (Fuel and Combustion Engineering) from the University of Leeds in 1974.

"Project 275 UK" is the title of a project to raise the British land speed record above 275 miles per hour (440 km/h) for the "flying mile" distance. If successful, it will also become the world's fastest steam-powered vehicle, the world's fastest vehicle on sand and produce the fastest speed in Britain. The team will design and build the streamlined, rocket-powered vehicle, and attempt the record in Wales.

The dinosaurs of darkness

Thomas Hewitt Rich

Curator of Vertebrate Palaeontology, Museum of Victoria, 285–321 Russell Street, Melbourne, 3000 Victoria, Australia

Australian, born 30 May 1941. Curator of Vertebrate Palaeontology, Museum of Victoria. Educated in the United States; Ph. D. from Columbia University, New York, in 1973.

Dinosaurs and the terrestrial vertebrates that lived along side them are less well known in Australia than in any other continent except Antarctica. This project has discovered a dinosaur site and has recovered a small collection of dinosaur remains. The work has been carried out by volunteers but the difficulties of tunnelling are now such that qualified miners and mining engineers are needed.

Heat generation and accumulation in mammal and human large intestine

Jambalyn Shagj

House No. 40, Flat No 21, 19th. Residential Area, Ulaanbaatar, Mongolia

Mongolian, born 27 October 1935. Senior lecturer, Ulaanbaater Medical Institute. Educated in Mongolia and the Soviet Union; entered the Sanitary-Hygienic Medical Institute of Leningrad in 1959.

This project has discovered a heat generation and accumulation phenomenon in the large intestine of mammals and humans; it is caused by interaction between normal microflora and indigestible food remnants. Theories, rules and inventions elaborated on the basis of this discovery offer a possibility of increasing active life span by preventing intestinal infections and curing some somatic diseases.

Discovery and exploration of Maya sacred caves

James Brady

24231 Tama Lane, Laguna Niguel, California 92656, United States

American, born 20 June 1948. Archaeological researcher. Educated in United States; Ph. D. from University of Texas, Austin, in 1975.

Caves are a major focus of prehispanic Maya religion. Reports from speleologists and this project's earlier findings at Naj Tunich demonstrate that large caves with monumental architecture, which may have been pilgrimage or cult centres, do exist. It is now proposed to establish an exploratory project to discover several major caves in an unlooted condition which will shed light on Maya ritual cave use.

Unveiling one of Leonardo da Vinci's enigmas: Ultrashort sleep

Claudio Stampi

Via Loreta 13, Bologna 40138, Italy

Italian, born 19 June 1953. Founder and President of La Barca Laboratorio Research Foundation. Educated in Brazil, Italy and Switzerland; M. D. from the University of Bologna in 1977.

Leonardo da Vinci adopted ultrashort sleep patterns to enhance productivity. This project aims to replicate and optimize the sleep schedule attributed to Leonardo, and to study its effects by means of state-of-the-art methodology. Careful historical investigation into Leonardo's manuscripts will also be undertaken. Such strategies might become feasible and powerful tools to control fatigue and enhance efficiency.

Canadian shipwreck archaeology project

Bessel Jan VandenHazel

288 Rancier Street, North Bay, Ontario, Canada P1B 8M4

Canadian, born 3 May 1927. Founder and Director of the Canadian Shipwreck Archaeology and Conservation Institute. Educated in United Kingdom, Netherlands, Canada and United States; M. Sc. (Outdoor and Environmental Education) from Northern Illinois University, DeKalb, in 1969.

This project proposes to set up a Shipwreck Archaeology Centre to interpret the construction and uses of the schooner-freighters, schooner-warships and the early steamboats that sailed the Great Lakes during the early and middle 1800s. The Shipwreck Centre will permit visitors to experience the conditions that led to the wrecking of a ship and explore the remains of ships on a simulated, but dry, lake bottom.

A replica of the Zheng He treasure ship

Li Bang-Yan

No. 9 Lane 1192 (Avenue), Beijing Road (West), 200040 Shanghai, People's Republic of China

Chinese, born 25 February 1926. Senior Engineer. Educated in People's Republic of China; graduated from Shanghai Chiao-Tung University (Marine Administration Department) in 1947.

This project has researched the Silk Road on the land and sea, and has, in particular, studied the design of historic Chinese sailing vessels with special reference to the sails of these vessels. On the basis of an excavated rudder post and historical documents, an attempt is being made to reconstitute the plans of the Zheng He treasure ship. A model of the treasure ship, 1.50 m in length will be constructed.

Preserving traditional African music

Walter Edwin O. Ominde

P. O. Box 43167, Lower Kabete, Nairobi, Kenya

Kenyan, born 20 April 1943. Project Director for Planning Systems Services. Educated in United Kingdom and Kenya; Diploma in Building Technology from the Polytechnic of South Bank, London, in 1970.

This project aims to preserve traditional African music through the church. It seeks not only to inspire and entertain people through the singing of newly composed African sacred music, but also to ensure that the original African melodies, so unique in their rhythm, tone and performance, are permanently preserved. Rhythm patterns, moods, feelings and physical movements of the music have been studied.

1989 Mekong River Geological Research Expedition, Yunnan, China

Peter S. Winn

Earth Science Expeditions, 202 North Avenue # 102, Grand Junction, Colorado 81501, United States

American, born 17 November 1948. Mine geologist and Founding Director/Vice President of Win-Eldrich Gold Inc. Educated in United States; M. S. (Geology) from University of Utah, Salt Lake City, in 1982.

The Mekong River geological expedition aims to: facilitate scientific and cultural exchange between the United States and China; and obtain geological data to aid geoscientists study active fault zones with a long history of deformation. The study area is located in western Yunnan, along the eastern margin of the Himalaya Mountains, in a region noted for frequent large earthquakes.

Studying and filming the "Great red fish" in Lake Kanasu, People's Republic of China

Shigetaka Tomotoshi

Kasumigaoka-Haitu 105, 2–6-1, Kasumigaoka, Chikusa-ku, Aichi Prefecture, Nagoya City, 460 Japan

Japanese, born 12 March 1949. Planning Director at Shito Tsushin Co., Ltd. Educated in Japan; joined the Takenaka Graphic Design Study Centre in 1968.

In July 1985, a gigantic fish (the "Great red fish"), 12-15 m in length, was observed at Lake Kanasu, in the Xinjiang Uygur Autonomous Region of the People's Republic of China. In collaboration with the Toba Aquarium, this project has studied the ecology of this fish and, on 1 September 1988, signed an agreement with the Institute of Zoology of the Academia Sinica for a full-scale investigation.

Cataloguing Muslim instruments, machinery and industrial art in the Iberian Peninsula

Luis Javier Rodriguez y Silva

Avenida de Andalucía No 22 (10), 29007 Malaga, Spain

Spanish, born 9 April 1962. Student. Educated in Spain; currently studying Law at University of Malaga.

This project is investigating and cataloguing instruments, machinery and industrial artifacts which were introduced by the Muslims into the Iberian Peninsula over a period of eight centuries. The object of the project is to demonstrate that the art of the Muslims is still alive in the Iberian Peninsula in such fields as pottery, leatherwork, filigrane, bronzeware, weaving, etc.

Interdisciplinary study of aquatic settlements in northeast Poland

Michaił Domaiński

Buszczyińskich 9a m.45, 87–100 Toruiń, Poland

Polish, born 17 October 1962. Student. Educated in Poland; currently studying Archaeology at the N. Copernicus University, Toruiń.

This project proposes a programme of comprehensive interdisciplinary research on the aquatic settlements discovered in the Masurian district of northeast Poland at the end of the 19th and beginning of the 20th centuries – and of which only a small number have been adequately researched. The main focus of interest will be to determine the chronology of the settlements, and their economic and cultural background.

Exploring the Malay peninsula for evidence of early man *en route* to Java

Zuraina Majid

University Sains Malaysia, Minden, Penang 11800, Malaysia

Malaysian, born 5 October 1944. Associate Professor and Director of Project Archaeology Malaysia. Educated in United States and United Kingdom; Ph. D. (Anthropology) from Yale University in 1978.

This project is excavating and analyzing a prehistoric stone-tool-making site in north Malaya, and exploring for evidence in the Malay peninsula of hominids on their migratory route to Asia from Africa. The peninsula represents the most stable of the proposed "bridges" between Africa and Asia. Using a database of archaeological knowledge of the peninsula, the project will explore for stone tools and fossil bones.

Comparative painted essay: Art of the African Ndebele and Southwestern American Indian

Rebecca Ann Covalt

Covalt Designs, P. O. Box 26653, Albuquerque, New Mexico 87125, United States

American, born 19 December 1951. Artist and President of Covalt Designs. Educated in United States; B. A. from University of New Mexico, Albuquerque, in 1973.

Artists have an instinctual respect for the creativity of other artists. This project will attempt to create a painted record comparing the art of the African Ndebele tribe of South Africa and the North American Southwestern Pueblo Indian. It will embrace the regions of Ndebeleland, Transvaal, South Africa, and the American Indian tribes of the Navajo, Santo Domingo, Hopi, Zuni, and Taos of the Southwest.

Philippines, underground

Antonio De Vivo

Via Caboto 7, 35100 Padua, Italy

Italian, born 16 October 1958. Professor of Physical Education. Educated in United States and Italy; graduated from the Superior Institute for Physical Education, Bologna, in 1981.

The aim of this project is to develop a comprehensive picture of the major karst areas of the Philippine archipelago. Four surveys have already been carried out and have provided topographical, hydrogeological and anthropological data together with iconographic material. Particular attention will be devoted to a study of the interaction of man and the caves in a karstic environment from a symbolic point of view.

The Jupiter wreck project – free-enterprise shipwreck recovery

Dominic Anthony Addario, Jr.

Jupiter Hills Enterprises Inc., 18261 US Highway 1, Jupiter, Florida 33469, United States

American, born 10 May 1949. Captain / Master Mariner. Educated in the United States; B. S. in Education and Economics from Northeastern University in 1964.

This project aims to recover a 330-year-old shipwreck that changed the development of the New World and Europe. It is also the scene of conflict between state regulation and bureaucracy and enterprising individuals, and the project sees the *Jupiter* Wreck story as an international testing ground between the contrasting "Rewards System Approach" and the punitive approach of the US Abandoned Shipwreck Act of 1987.

Hydrobiology, fish and fishery exploration in the Korup rain forest, Cameroon

Gordon McGregor Reid

Natural History Department, Horniman Museum, London Road, Forest Hill, London SE23 3PQ, United Kingdom

British, born 9 February 1948. Head, Natural History Department, Horniman Museum. Educated in United Kingdom; Ph. D. (Fish Systematics) from University of London in 1978.

Korup is the best example of unspoiled tropical rainforest in West Africa. This project has carried out a baseline study on the nature and identity of Korup fishes, their economic importance, local relevance, distribution, abundance, ecology and the hydrobiological characteristics of the major aquatic habitats and inland water systems. It now plans further investigations in natural resources management there.

The earliest human settlement of Wales

H. Stephen Green

Department of Archaeology and Numismatics, National Museum of Wales, Cardiff CF1 3NP, United Kingdom

British, born 11 September 1945. Keeper, Department of Archaeology and Numismatics, National Museum of Wales. Educated in United Kingdom; Ph. D. (Wales) in 1978.

This project is researching the site of Pontnewydd Cave in Clwyd, Wales which has yielded the fragmentary human remains of at least three, probably four, individuals. The individuals represented are probably early Neanderthals and are dated to around 250,000 years ago. More complete, and therefore diagnostic, remains of these early Neanderthals are almost certainly preserved in the cave.

A photographic portrait of Sumba Island and its islanders

Sandro Roberto Scarioni

Via Manzoni 10, 20091 Bresso, Milano, Italy

Italian, born 13 January 1950. Free-lance photographer. Educated in Italy; Diploma in Indonesian Culture and Language from Istituto per il Medio e l'Estremo Oriente in 1982.

The aim of this project is to achieve, through photography, a better understanding of the natural, historical and cultural heritage of Sumba Island, Indonesia. The study will cover: geography and nature; economic and social issues; and megalithic art and ancient history of the island. Documentational research will be followed by field work based on direct observation and brief interviews.

Walking the beaches of Ecuador: A study of the Ecuadorian coast and its people

José-Germán Cárdenas

c/o Fulbright Commission, P. O. Box 826-A, Quito, Ecuador

Ecuadorian, born 11 October 1947. Economic Analyst and International Business Consultant. Educated in United States; M. A. (Economics) from the University of Maryland, College Park, in 1973.

This project aims to expand knowledge of the history, archaeology, geography, economics, environmental resources, popular culture and folklore of the Ecuadorian coastal region. The project team has already covered, on foot, Ecuador's wide-open beaches (832 km), and 1,920 km have been covered by small plane and canoe. A book, *Walking the Beaches of Ecuador*, has been published.

Acrypot – a new approach to pottery-ceramic work

Crisologo Ondoy

Penthouse Arts and Frames, D-71 Narra Avenue, Capitol Shopping Center, Bacolod City 6001, Negros Occidental, Philippines

Filipino, born 24 November 1947. Professional photographer and artist/designer. Educated in Philippines; B. Sc. (Commerce) from La Consolación College, Bacolod City, in 1974.

This project has established a livelihood-generation industry based on a pioneering pottery-ceramic product called Acrypot. The project is creating jobs for at least 1,000 unemployed. Intensive skills-training workshops will be provided free of charge to candidates who, after graduation, will be helped to start up a livelihood-type activity involving the production of Acrypot products.

Behavioural study of the great white shark off southern Africa

Marie Christine Levine

1 Top Circle, St. Winifreds, 4126 Kingsburgh, South Africa

American, born 4 August 1940. Journalist. Educated in United States; B. A. and B. F. A. degrees from Mundelein College, Chicago, from 1958 to 1962.

The great white shark (*Carcharodon carcharias*) is responsible for the majority of attacks on humans in southern African waters and, possibly, throughout the world. However, this shark is difficult to study because it does not survive in captivity. For the past two years, this project has been studying the behaviour of great white sharks off the southern tip of Africa and has tagged a free-swimming shark.

The Environment

The projects described in this section were submitted under the category "The Environment" which was defined in the Official Application Form for The Rolex Awards for Enterprise 1990 as follows:

Projects in this category will be concerned primarily with our environment and should seek to protect and preserve, or to improve, the world around us.

Seals for underwater search, recovery and rescue

Michael I. Sandlofer

North Wind Undersea Institute, c/o North Wind Museum, 610 City Island Avenue, Bronx, New York 10464, United States

American, born 4 March 1948. Executive Director of North Wind Undersea Institute. Educated in United States; graduated from the Divers Institute of Technology, Seattle, in 1971.

The concept of a Seal Search and Recovery Team was developed in the 1970s by Captain Michael Sandlofer when he was working as a commercial diver. Weighed down on the ocean floor by heavy, cumbersome diving gear, he admired the speed and agility with which curious seals and sea lions moved around their aquatic environment, and he began thinking how marine mammals might be trained to aid divers underwater. Subsequently, after he had established the North Wind Undersea Institute, for public education, marine mammal preservation and environmental conservation, he was contacted by the New England Aquarium and offered the opportunity of acquiring three harbour seal pups which had been found sick and abandoned and which could not at that time be re-released to the wild.

Ten months later, the first step was taken in the development of the Seal Search and Recovery Team with an eight-week programme designed to explore the training potential of harbour seals. At that time, it was not known whether harbour seals would be good candidates for training. Most pinniped training is done with larger sea lions which are more agile on land where they tend to spend most of their time. Harbour seals, on the other hand, are more evolved towards an aquatic environment. One of their greatest assets is the dexterity of their front flippers.

A seal rescuing training programme

The goals for the programme were to train seals to: take directions, respond to simple commands and know their own name; carry objects in their mouths to and from their trainer; conduct an underwater search and communicate the results; search for and retrieve objects underwater; enter a submerged diving bell and breathe fresh air; locate human bodies underwater; attach a grabber to bodies underwater and release a signal float; release a seat belt underwater; work routinely with a human partner as part of an underwater search and recovery team; be deployed from a beach, pier, boat or aircraft.

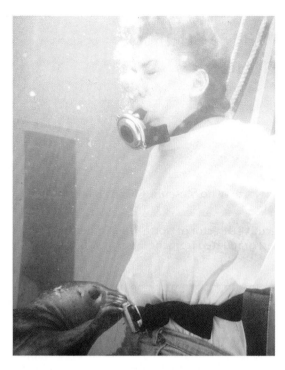

The seal understands his task and begins to scratch at the seat-belt, demonstrating the great dexterity of his front flippers.

While these goals were ambitious, the three seals proved to be willing, able students. Within 30 hours of training, they had been taught to react to their individual names, accept human handling and touch and to respond to a target and hold position on command. They were also at this point able to retrieve objects from the floor of their tanks. Another 30 hours of training strengthened their learning and their ability to perform tasks. They were soon able to rendez-vous in a diving bell to share breathable air with a diver and thus increase their bottom time. The seals soon became adept at carrying all kinds of objects from the trainer on deck to a diver underwater; tools, emergency air bottles, clip-boards, etc.

To teach a seal how to open a seat belt was an ambitious project. However, after sessions first on land and then underwater, the seals learned to "search" for a submerged person, then release the person's seat belt as quickly as possible. Work was also done on discriminating between whether or not a body was present in an underwater site and teaching the seals to attach a grabber to a submerged victim to permit rescue.

Further developing the seal's potential

To fully exploit the seal's potential in this field, however, we plan to build a larger training pool to accommodate the maturing animals, and to be able to simulate other air/sea disasters; commence open-water training in a natural, free-ocean environment; develop a more efficient grabber; simulate air/sea disasters using a submerged aircraft or automobile cockpit; institute a captive-breeding programme for the three seals; and investigate their abilities in real-life search and rescue, recovery and exploration assignments.

In our opinion, the Seal Search and Recovery Team offers the world an unequalled example of how all earth's species are interdependent. Just as canine and equine species have contributed to the development of civilization, a humane partnership of mutual respect between man and seal can offer a new dimension to humankind's interaction with other species. Given the growing environmental crisis that the world now faces, "different but equally important" may soon become the watchword of wildlife preservationists.

We believe that seals can offer a safe and environmentally clean way to harvest ocean resources, to save lives and to recover underwater objects, for example by: assisting divers to locate accident victims underwater; to act as lifeguard assistants on public beaches and as shepherds or farming assistants in aquaculture; and to explore and photograph historic shipwrecks, bridge supports and ship hulls.

The future of human-seal partnership

The possibilities of these intelligent animals as partners to humans are exciting and unlimited. Although much research and data have been compiled already, much still remains to be done. North Wind has already invested four years on this project, but anticipates another five years of training, captive breeding and research before the first Seal Search and Recovery Team is ready to be safely deployed. Beyond that, it is hoped that the concept of Seal Search and Recovery will be utilized throughout the world. Just as dogs are used to guide the blind, locate earthquake and avalanche victims, search for the missing, aid police, search for drugs and help fight crime, seals may one day become natural and invaluable partners in saving lives and enriching our world.

The seal's natural curiosity and trust in his trainer and diver-partner allow him to make use of the diving bell to breathe underwater.

Brazil – the new Minamata: Mercury pollution from river gold mining

Adonai Rocha

SQS 203-B-104, 70233 Brasilia, DF, Brazil

Brazilian, born 17 August 1958. Independent photographer, journalist and film-maker. Educated in Brazil, United States and United Kingdom; studied Gemmology at GIA-Gemmological Institute of America, Santa Monica, in 1987 and 1988.

There are two main methods for the extraction of gold from ore. These are the processes of amalgamation and cyanidation. The process of amalgamation is based on the ability of gold to alloy with metallic mercury to form amalgams of varying consistencies, from solid to liquid. The gold can be removed from the amalgam fairly easily by distilling off the mercury. In internal amalgamation, the gold is separated from the crushing apparatus at the same time as the ore is crushed. The amalgam removed from the apparatus is washed free of any admixtures with water in special bowls. Then the remaining mercury is pressed out of the amalgam. In external amalgamation, the gold is separated outside the crushing apparatus, in amalgamators or sluices. Before the amalgam is removed, fresh mercury is added for disintegration. The purified and washed amalgam is then pressed. In both processes the mercury is removed from the amalgam by distillation.

The occupational and environmental hazards of mercury

In the mercury extraction of gold, workers may be exposed to airborne mercury concentrations when mercury is placed in or removed from the sluices, when the amalgam is purified or pressed, and when the mercury is distilled off. Mercury poisoning has been reported among amalgamation and distillation workers. Under normal circumstances, strict precautions are taken to ensure that mercury does not come into contact with the workers' skin and, wherever possible, the jobs are mechanized to prevent physical contact with the hazardous substances.

A major problem is also the large quantities of waste mercury that may escape from the gold processing equipment; this may seep into the ground and affect the subterranean water table or enter the water courses and produce generalized environmental hazards for the surrounding population. Mercury may also be absorbed by nearby, or even distantly located, animals and fish. As a result, mercury concentrations build up inside the animals and, when they are caught and consumed by humans, cases of severe, chronic, or even acute mercury poisoning may occur.

326

Access to the gold ore is achieved by burrowing into the ground and cutting terraces from which the workers can progress in their excavations.

Persons suffering from mercury poisoning have digestive and neurological disorders and the signs and symptoms they display may include hysteria, neurasthenia and tremors. A number of years ago, public opinion was shocked by reports of cases of mass mercury poisoning in Minamata, Japan, in which large numbers of the population were affected by the consumption of fish and seafood containing dangerously high levels of mercury.

Creating awareness of the mercury hazard in Brazil

In Brazil, many of the major river basins have been polluted with mercury coming from gold mining operations located in the Amazon tropical forest and the Cerrados areas. Our objective is to educate gold miners in north central Brazil about the hazards of the methods they are using and to increase public awareness about the dangerous effects of mercury pollution on the environment and about the human contamination risk. This project will produce a film and audiovisual educational materials for use in the mining areas and the towns covered by the project. The miners' ignorance about the effects of mercury is terrifying. The men, women and children, usually of low educational level and in many cases illiterate, have to confront a lack of social services, high rates of violence and juvenile prostitution.

The Brazilian Government seems unable to solve the mercury pollution problem, and provide protection for the remaining Brazilian tropical forest. This project aims to be instrumental in focusing world attention on the critical need to develop new technical support to stop excessive mercury pollution in Brazil's rivers. It includes: the production of a l6-mm colour film of approximately 15–20 minutes' duration, in English, describing gold mining in the Tapajos and Araguaia Rivers, to be released on video-tapes (VHS) to scientific, educational and ecological institutions and the development of educational materials and, in particular, 35-mm slides for use in local schools, churches and other community centres in mining areas, providing environmental education and presenting basic procedures to reduce mercury contamination and its risk to the gold miners' community.

The project will donate a slide projector and sets of slides with printed commentaries for public presentation to each city hall office in a number of major areas. It will also offer local television stations, in the main mining areas, a 15–30 second video-clip putting over an anti-mercury-pollution message.

The most suitable educational medium

The use of visual aids in the campaign against mercury pollution was chosen as the most effective medium to reach the gold miners scattered around the Araguaia and Tapajos River basins. The production of the audiovisual educational materials will last two months; the establishment of arrangements for the expedition crew, transportation, filming equipment, audiovisual projectors and location sets, one month; location work in gold mines, towns, indian tribes, rivers, six months; and post-production work, film editing, sound tracking, video copying, three months; i.e. a total duration of 12 months. The project will apply for technical support from the Brazilian Amazon Research Institute, the Brazilian Mineral Research Institute and the University of Brasilia.

Working in atrocious conditions without the minimum of protective equipment, workers stand knee-deep in water while pumping takes place.

328

Remote sensing survey and ecological monitoring of arrow bamboo to save the giant panda

Li Xiaowen

Honourable Mention
The Rolex Awards for Enterprise – 1990

Institute of Remote Sensing Application, Academia Sinica, P. O. Box 775,
100012 Beijing, People's Republic of China

Chinese, born 2 March 1947. Associate Professor. Educated in People's Republic
of China and United States; Ph. D. (Geography) from University of California,
Santa Barbara, in 1985.

The giant panda is an endangered species and, according to a survey in the
1970's, only about 1,000 were still in existence. Pandas feed almost exclusively on
different kinds of bamboo. This woody plant has a peculiarity: after a long
vegetative growth that can last from 20 to 100 years depending on the species, it
suddenly blooms, produces its seeds, and dies. However, since all the bamboo in
one region blooms at one time, hundreds of hectares disappear all at once. The
pandas roam around searching for food in vain, and eventually die of hunger.

Statistics show that the situation has become a serious one. For example, in
Pingwu county, a major habitat for the panda, following the 1973–1976 bamboo
blooming, 64 dead bodies and 23 weak animals were found. What is required is a
survey of the location and extent of the bamboo plants so that bloomings can be
identified and pandas brought to the area. A complete field survey is almost
impossible due to the vast areas involved (thousands of kilometres) and the
rugged terrain.

The aim of the project is to locate the areas in bloom on satellite pictures so that
the pandas can be moved to a region where the bamboo is still green. But
spotting bamboo from the sky is very difficult because it is sheltered by conifers.
The aerial photographs taken so far have been completely useless because the
spaces between the trees are so tiny that it is practically impossible to see what is
hidden underneath.

An approach to bamboo localization

Our objective is to develop the necessary "gap frequency" models to permit
computer analysis of the remote sensing data from satellite photographs to
determine spatial distribution of arrow bamboo and monitor the ecological
change of bamboo so as to: help in the planning of bamboo planting and rescue
activities; find out why large areas of bamboo bloom simultaneously; and predict
and counter impending disasters.

A giant panda (Ailuropoda melanoleuca) at the Wolong Nature Reserve. Li Xiaowen hopes his project will ensure regular supplies of bamboo for these animals (Photo: WWF/GEO/ Tim Rautert/BLC).

However, satellite observations do not speak for themselves: the satellite, which observes the ground in several ranges of electromagnetic frequencies, transmits raw data to earth stations. In order for a particular element to show up (trees, grass, diseases, the quality of water, etc.), a mathematical analysis must then be done of the measurements made on different frequencies. This procedure will reveal whatever information is required. To achieve this, the applicant and his former teacher, Professor A. H. Strahler of the University of Boston, have developed a number of gap-frequency and remote-sensing models which will form the basis for very sophisticated methods of analysis to detect what is hidden under trees and especially between conifers.

The models deal with the relation between the three-dimensional structure of the coniferous forest and remotely sensed signals and the gap frequency, i.e. the probability of a pencil-like beam of light reaching the ground or lower branch levels without being absorbed or reflected by tree crowns or trunks. Once the density, size, and shape of the conifers have been determined and various calculations made, it will be possible to distinguish bamboo from other bushes and offer ecologists and biologists a great deal of information.

Project plan and current status

It is planned to proceed in two stages: use aerial photographs to analyze the terrain and its vegetable covering, and then work out how it is possible to locate ordinary and blooming bamboo by the special characteristic of the light reflected from them. First, together with the Senior Engineer and Deputy Director of the Ecological Laboratory, Sichuan Academy of Forestry, Chengdu, I will map out the forest and its structure so that we can calculate the spacing of the conifers and the light reflectance from any given direction. According to the research schedule, this map of bamboo sheltered by conifers should be completed by the end of 1989. During 1989, measurements will also be made on the light reflected from the ground so as to determine what kind of light bamboo absorbs and reflects (this is known as the bamboo's "fingerprint") and, in this way, distinguish it from other kinds of plants not eaten by pandas.

In the second phase, which will not start until 1991, we will use satellite remote-sensing data, such as that from the SPOT satellite and the Shuttle Imaging Device, third generation (SIR-C), that will be carried aboard the US space shuttle.

This project is currently being supported by the Chinese National Foundation of Natural Sciences through two basic research projects in which I am the principal investigator. The Sichuan Academy of Forestry is collaborating in this project by an agreement signed with the Director of its Ecological Laboratory, who has offered to help in ground data collection, consulting in ecology and biology, and service in the Wanglong research station in Pingwu county.

Bamboo in bloom, Wolong Nature Reserve. (Photo: WWF, G.B. Schaller)

OUR (Orbiting Unification Ring) – Space Peace Sculpture

Arthur Ray Woods

Orbiting Unification Ring Satellite, P. O. Box 180, Im Grund 21, 8424 Embrach, Switzerland

American, born 26 March 1948. President of the OURS Foundation. Educated in United States; B. A. from Mercer University, Macon, in 1970.

As the year 2000 draws nearer, we are becoming increasingly aware of our place in the universe and of the earth as a living entity. There is a growing awareness of the interdependence of the human family and the interrelationship of all life. Our communications, our economies, our politics as well as our problems have become global processes. We know that it would now be technically possible to eradicate most diseases, to overcome hunger, to reduce pollution and to eliminate nuclear weapons, if these issues could be addressed from a planetary perspective. Furthermore, we have been creating new technologies to explore and develop the immensity of outer space and to spread the seed of life to other parts of our immediate universe.

Though we may have arrived on the threshold of the greatest age in human history, we know that we are still a danger to ourselves and to the rest of life on our planet. Any consideration of having "Peace on earth" may now depend on our species making "Peace with earth". Thus, the challenge of our time is to find new ways of working together that transcend our differences, solve our problems, restore our environment and transform our lethal technologies in order to ensure the success, the survival and the future of all life on earth.

Man in a space environment

Recent developments concerning the commercial use of outer space have made it possible for cultural events to take place in the space environment which can be seen and experienced by much of the world's population. This opportunity to communicate to the global audience as well as to add a cultural dimension to the development of outer space may have much bearing on how we articulate the future goals of our civilization. Therefore, the first of these "cultural space events" may become a valuable way for our planet to speak to itself about its future. Furthermore, their process of realization may serve as a highly visible example of how international co-operation on an individual and organizational level can be focused into an expression of planetary well-being. The first such

The 1992 deployment of the OUR-Space Peace Sculpture from the Soviet MIR space station will be televised to the world audience. Its message: "Peace on Earth – Peace with Earth."

event to take place in the space environment may occur during the year 1991 with the realization of the Orbiting Unification Ring (OUR) – Space Peace Sculpture as a symbol of and a call for world peace – peace with ourselves and peace with the whole planet.

In 1984, I initiated a project which was submitted to the 1987 Rolex Awards for Enterprise and which proposed to celebrate our passage into the next millennium with a "circle in the sky" symbolizing planetary unity, wholeness and peace. It is a global art work that is dedicated to helping create a better, safer and healthier world. This project supplies the context and the background for the realization of the OUR-Space Peace Sculpture.

An enormous space sculpture

The OURS will be an enormous space sculpture in the form of a ring with a diameter of more than one kilometre. Its mirror-like surface will be painted with artistic expressions by artists representing every nation and culture. In the year 2000, this globally created monument is to be placed into orbit around our planet. Illuminated by sunlight, it will appear as a circle in the early morning or evening sky and its symbolic message will be known to the entire population of the world. At a pre-designated time the OURS will suddenly become a brilliant star that will slowly disappear from our skies as it leaves the earth's orbit, propelled by the solar wind, to travel and to remain in space forever – a gift from our time to future generations.

Three possible technical designs have been suggested for the OURS of the year 2000. They consist of: trusswork as a structural backbone; a centrifugally stabilized solar sail ring; and a rigidized toroidal ring. Environmental concerns in relation to mass efficiency and visibility have favoured the toroidal ring configuration. Visibility calculations indicate that a ring sculpture constructed out of a

333

highly reflective material, having a diameter of one kilometre and placed in a 500 km polar orbit, would be visible to the entire population of the planet by appearing as a circle or an ellipse in the sky approximately one-quarter the size of the moon. Visibility would occur approximately ten minutes before sunrise or ten minutes after sunset once a month anywhere on the planet.

A sculpture with a purpose

The purpose of the OUR – Space Peace Sculptures is to symbolically celebrate the peaceful development of outer space and the opportunity for international co-operation that this activity offers the nations of our planet. To the whole world, they will communicate the message that: peace on earth ultimately means making peace with earth. Their form, a ring with a cross in the centre, is the ancient symbol of peace and unity that is being defined in the technology of tomorrow. The word "peace" expressed in the languages of the planet will be painted on their reflective surfaces.

On 13 January 1988, proposals were sent to the space agencies of the United States and the Soviet Union for the space flight of the OUR-Space Peace Sculptures. On 25 February 1988 at Space Commerce '88, held in Montreux, Switzerland, the OURS project signed an agreement with officials from Glavcosmos, the Soviet space agency, for the space transport and deployment of the first sculpture. As the United States has now resumed its manned space activities, it is hoped that they too will agree to send a "ring of peace" around the planet. This could take place either simultaneously or during the 1992 International Space Year.

Members of the public are invited to add their energy to the project by helping to paint the "Public Painting" during exhibitions.

The evolution of a meat-type of water buffalo – the "Buffalypso"

Stephen Penlyn Bennett

"Glamorgan", Gordon Street, Curepe, Trinidad, Trinidad and Tobago

Citizen of Trinidad and Tobago, born 18 January 1922. Consultant and part-time livestock farmer. Educated in Trinidad and Tobago, Canada and United States; Degree in Veterinary Medicine from Colorado State College, Fort Collins, in 1948.

On returning to my native home, the island of Trinidad in the Caribbean in 1948, having qualified as a veterinarian in the United States of America, I was immediately employed by a multinational sugar company as the company's veterinary officer, on a part-time basis, to take care of the livestock which were an integral part of the company's extensive local sugar cane and sugar manufacturing operations.

The livestock inventory included approximately 200 hack horses, 500 large American mules, 200 Holstein dairy cows and last, but not least, a herd of some 500 water buffalo used as beasts of burden. It was for these water buffaloes that my heart went out, because although the other livestock enjoyed a satisfactory form of husbandry, these poor animals were abused, misused, underfed, overworked and penned at night in totally unacceptable conditions.

A versatile but maltreated animal

Water buffaloes were introduced from India into Trinidad around 1906, as work animals on the sugar plantations to replace the Bosindicus cattle or Zebu more commonly referred to nowadays as "Brahim cattle". The Zebu cattle were succumbing at a rate of about 80% to tuberculosis under the existing environment, and it was believed that the water buffalo was immune to tuberculosis. I had a grim determination that I would not stand by and see these animals so harshly and brutally treated as they were then. Many of the working herd animals had been blinded from being beaten by sticks to steer them in their work, as no harness was ever used on them – only a simple wooden yoke put over their necks, by which they pulled the carts. They were fed only with sugar cane tops, which had little feeding value and were spread on dirt floors as a soiling crop, to manufacture the valuable "pen manure" to fertilize the cane fields, since artificial fertilizers were not yet a true reality in Trinidad. The pens had no automated or adequate water supply and malnutrition was evident.

A small herd of young Buffalypso bulls raised by Stephen Bennett.

Many of the animals also had abscesses on their necks caused by the yokes and on their hind quarters from the beatings these hungry and tired animals received when they were mercilessly driven onwards. When these abscesses were opened they appeared to be tubercular, so I decided to test the herd, and to everyone's amazement over 30% of the entire herd were positive reactors. A tuberculosis eradication plan was put into operation and ten years later we had completely eradicated the disease.

Fortunately, soon after I began my plan for improving the lot of the water buffaloes with particular emphasis on the breeding herd, a local brewery was built within about 5 km of our breeding herd and, as there were no provisions at the time for drying the wet brewers' grains, the brewery was happy to give this material to our company provided we paid the transport; so this by-product was dumped at the breeding pens and fed to the animals. This feed was magic, the calves grew and fattened like pigs – the cows all got into good flesh and this opened my eyes as large as two soup plates! The animals, if given half a chance, should develop into wonderful meat-type animals for the tropics.

A plan for breeding a "Buffalypso"

We already knew water buffaloes were hardy, disease-resistant, very resistant to ticks and tick-born diseases and resistant to internal parasites; they also had a great ability to get by on marginal pasture, poor roughage and poor-quality grasses high in cellulose content – their digestive capabilities had to be better than those of cattle!

It was in 1950 that I began to select bulls of a type that would resemble conventional beef-type breeds of cattle; I was fortunate to have been well trained in judging livestock at the Ontario Agricultural College, in Guelph, Ontario, Canada, where I graduated in 1941 in animal husbandry. I set a standard of perfection in my mind: to select bulls that would have the straightest top line, with the widest, broadest and strongest loins, and carry lots of rump and meat down to the twists, or hocks, and also have refined heads.

My idea was to metamorphose the animal by selection, to put the meat in the right places, i. e. to emphasize and develop the expensive cuts in the carcass – loin and rump. After years of selection, I eventually accomplished this, and have produced the first meat-type water buffalo in the world. Our island of Trinidad has been known as the "land of the calypso", after the music which originated here in Trinidad, so I thought I would blend our calypso with the buffalo and call our new breed the "Buffalypso".

The "Buffalypso" ready for the world market

There are about 150 million water buffaloes in the world used as beasts of burden and for milk production, but the "Buffalypso" has been selected specifically as a meat-type animal. Its meat has been proven to be very palatable and acceptable, and is indistinguishable from beef. This work was first done here in Trinidad in 1961, and subsequently confirmed in Malaysia and Australia. These animals are able to digest roughages better than cattle, they are far more resistant to diseases and more adaptable to adverse conditions; they can do almost anything that cattle will do in the tropics – and do it easier and cheaper. In Italy and South America, cheese is made from water buffalo milk which, in general, has almost 300% more butterfat than cows milk; it is also higher in solids and therefore takes less milk to make a kilogramme of cheese.

In 1965, the first shipment of "Buffalypsoes" was exported to Colombia, South America; subsequently, exports have gone to 13 other countries, i. e. Cayenne, Guyana, Suriname, Venezuela, Barbados, Cuba, Ecuador, Costa Rica, Panama, Honduras, Belize, Guatemala and the United States of America. The "Buffalypso" breeds true to conformation but comes in two acceptable colours, brown and black, and a small percentage are off-white or albinoid in type; this colour we disqualify, not because they do not fatten and grow as well but because, probably, if they were encouraged they might develop a tendency to sunburn.

"Shergas", a four-year old Buffalypso herd sire at the Circle B Ranch.

Biological control of the tropical water weed salvinia

Peter Michael Room

Honourable Mention
The Rolex Awards for Enterprise – 1990

CSIRO, Division of Entomology, Private Bag No. 3, Indooroopilly,
4060 Queensland, Australia

Australian, born 3 July 1947. Senior Principal Research Scientist, Division of
Entomology, Commonwealth Scientific and Industrial Research Organization of
Australia. Educated in UK; Ph. D. (external) from University of London in 1971.

Salvinia (*Salvinia molesta*) is a floating fern from South America which is having
devastating effects on freshwaters in many tropical countries by forming mats up
to a metre thick which completely blanket water surfaces. No light penetrates
these mats so that submerged plants die, the water becomes anaerobic and most
other organisms including fish die or move away if they are able to do so. Salvinia
mats halt all but the biggest boats, clog irrigation systems, blanket rice paddies,
harbour the vectors of diseases such as filariasis, and cause damage to bridges,
fences and buildings when swept along by floods. Despite several studies, no
economic uses for salvinia have been found. Most of the countries infested have
large rural populations and salvinia causes considerable human suffering.

An international problem

Problems caused by salvinia were first reported from Sri Lanka in the 1940s, from
Africa in the 1960s, from India, Australia, Malaysia, Papua New Guinea and
Indonesia in the 1970s, and the Philippines in 1987. The plant is unusual and all
dispersal between countries has been by man. Stationary or slow-moving freshwaters at low elevations throughout the tropics are at risk of infestation. Salvinia
is very difficult and expensive to control by physical removal or with herbicides.
Under favourable conditions, plants double in size in a mere 2.2 days and, in large
infestations, massive operations are needed to kill the weed faster than it is
growing. Application of herbicide to Lake Moondarra in Australia using a hovercraft and helicopter was abandoned in 1978 after A$160,000 had been spent,
when it was realized that the weed was growing faster than it was being killed.
Herbicidal control has also been abandoned in other countries because of prohibitive costs and because of concern over water pollution.

Biological control

When carried far from their places of origin, many animals and plants increase to
pestilential levels of abundance and have devastating effects on the environ-

Caption 1:
The salvinia weevil
(Cyrtobagous salviniae) used
for biological control of
salvinia. The insect is 3 mm
long, and is resting on the
upper surface of a salvinia
leaf.

ment. A common reason is that the predators or parasites which keep their numbers in check in their native ranges are absent from other geographic regions.

Biological control involves finding the natural enemies which control a pest in its native range and introducing them into places where the pest has escaped from their influence. Major components of the work involve screening potential control agents for their specificity to the pest, so that agents do not become pests in their own right, and ensuring that diseases and parasites of agents are not introduced as contaminants because they would reduce the effectiveness of the control agents. Biological control is an attractive technique for controlling weeds because it results in none of the unwanted side-effects of mechanical or herbicidal methods. In addition, it is self-perpetuating and needs none of the continuing costly inputs of energy, trained manpower and chemicals required by other methods.

A weevil to attack salvinia

A survey in Brazil, where *S. molesta* originated, identified a weevil, later named *C. salviniae*, which thrived on *S. molesta*, causing severe damage to the plant. This weevil was first used for control of *S. molesta* at Lake Moondarra and the result was spectacularly successful. Within a year, hundreds of weevils had multiplied into tens of millions and destroyed 40,000–50,000 tonnes of salvinia, returning the surface of the lake to open water. The dead weed sank to the bottom and decayed slowly so that there was no sudden release of nutrients to pollute the water. The great bulk of the weevils died of starvation once the weed was gone and there were no cases of weevils attacking other plants. Widespread distribution of the weevil has resulted in control of all major salvinia infestations in Australia.

At a later date, salvinia control operations were organized in the remote Sepik River floodplain in northern Papua New Guinea where salvinia had infested 500 km^2 of lakes and channels and caused food shortages because people could not fish or use their canoes to collect their staple diet of sago palm. By late 1984, redistributions of weevils at densities above the critical level had been made to 130 salvinia-infested lakes and, by late 1985, all major infestations had been destroyed. At late 1988, salvinia remained a minor component of the vegetation amongst reeds fringing the lakes, held in check by small numbers of weevils. The CSIRO salvinia research team was awarded the 1985 UNESCO Science Prize for its role in assisting Papua New Guinea to control salvinia.

Extending the weevil's range of operation

Subsequently, weevils and technical collaboration were given to Botswana and India (Kerala) in the mid-1980s, and salvinia is now under control in both countries. Collaboration is currently under way with scientists in Sri Lanka where approximately half of the very numerous infestations of salvinia have been destroyed, removing a serious threat to the very large Mahaweli hydropower and irrigation project. Plans are being made to start work with Malaysian scientists in 1989; Kenya, Côte d'Ivoire, Indonesia, the Philippines and Fiji are known to have salvinia infestations and our plan is to extend the project to those countries before too long.

Typical plants of the floating fern salvinia (Salvinia molesta), in the absence of attack by the salvinia weevil (palm of hand), and when the plant has reached equilibrium with the salvinia weevil (index finger).

Assuring the future of the African wild dog, *Lycaon pictus*: science, education and policy

Joshua Ross Ginsberg

Department of Zoology, University of Oxford, South Parks Road, Oxford, Oxon OX1 3PS, United Kingdom

American, born 15 January 1959. Researcher, Faculty of Zoology of the University of Oxford. Educated in United Kingdom and United States; Ph.D. (Biology) from Princeton University in 1987.

In the 1970s and early 1980s, populations of the wild dog (*Lycaon pictus*) declined throughout Africa for reasons that are not well understood, although hypotheses as to the critical factor regulating wild dog populations include: hunting by humans; prey availability; interspecific competition at kills; and disease, particularly canine distemper, rabies and anthrax. The African wild dog is now considered among the most highly endangered of the world's 35 canid species.

The conservation status and population numbers of wild dogs varies greatly throughout Africa. In some countries, e.g. Botswana, they are still treated as vermin, while in other countries, e.g. Kenya, wild dogs are completely protected. Tanzania has recently banned professional hunting of the species. In Zimbabwe, wild dogs have only recently received any form of protection. Local extinction may have some economic consequences through declining tourism. Furthermore, wild dogs may be critical in controlling certain prey species.

Several issues are critical to developing a general strategy for biological conservation including: the need to develop and test models of disease transmission, to measure disease prevalence and to determine the susceptibility of both wild and captive populations to various diseases; an understanding of population genetics and its relationship to conservation; the need to create conservation strategies which both include local and regional involvement and, in particular, address the potential conflicts between wildlife and other land uses outside of protected areas.

Studying wild dogs in Zimbabwe

The present study of the African wild dog in Hwange National Park, Zimbabwe, incorporates elements of each of the above concerns and will develop a conservation strategy for wild dogs in the region. As for most species of wild mammals, little is known about the prevalence of either disease or parasite infections.

Despite their relatively small size (30 kg), the wild dogs have an intricate social system which allows them to hunt prey very much larger than themselves. They will even occasionally stalk and prey zebra.

Nothing is known about the relationship between these factors and social behaviour and organization (ranging movements, pack size, hunting behaviour, etc.).

The levels of heterozygosity in wild populations that have been investigated have been derived from a limited number of samples (eight of which are from one pack of Serengeti dogs). No information linking genetics, disease and population regulation is available. Because the project is one of the first studies which simultaneously addresses questions of genetics, disease, and the influence of a species' social behaviour on its interaction with game and domestic stock outside the park, the results of this research will have a great impact on developing a general strategy for wildlife conservation.

The study will provide information which relates population dynamics (and individual pack reproductive success) to: disease and parasite prevalence; levels of inbreeding within and between packs; prey abundance and availability; competition from sympatric carnivores; and hunting of dogs outside the park. Furthermore, the causes of pack movement outside the park, and the interaction between wild dogs and the local population will be assessed. These data will allow development of a conservation plan in which the risk of extinction from each variable can be balanced against the cost of either active intervention (e.g. inoculation, excluding other predators from an area, translocating individuals to increase heterozygosity) or passive non-intervention (compensation schemes, opening ranches to tourism, etc.).

Developing a public education programme

Another important aim of the project is education. The project emphasizes co-operation with local groups responsible for management, and stresses education of those nationals involved with the day-to-day operation of Hwange Park, the people residing adjacent to this conservation area, and of Zimbabweans in other

A vigilant wild dog bitch.

parts of the country where wild dogs are still extant. Members of the project will work with local farmers to air their views of the problems and threats posed by all wildlife, and discuss the benefits (both real and potential) of including wildlife as a productive part of a farm or communal ranch.

The project will also train several Zimbabwean scientists and several park managers. The educational opportunities and facilities in Zimbabwe are among the best in Africa; the opportunities for field research and training in conservation biology are, however, few. Although the project will certainly make only a small contribution to training in a country as large as Zimbabwe, we hope that the net effect of training local people, who will then train others, will be somewhat greater.

Training and education will be undertaken at two levels: local and regional. Experience gained in local educational efforts will be used to develop and implement a regional education campaign to save the wild dog in Eastern and Southern Africa.

Using experience gained in Zimbabwe, I will use the material we have developed to sponsor educational efforts in countries in which viable populations of the African wild dog still exist (e.g. Botswana, Zambia, Tanzania, Kenya, Ethiopia). I plan to make liaisons between this project and established, effective educational groups in other countries (e.g. wildlife clubs, Pied Crow, East African Wildlife Society).

Light umbrella project to protect fragile archaeological sites

André Stevens

138 Brusselsesteenweg, 3009 Winksele, Belgium

Belgian, born 15 September 1945. Architect. Educated in Italy and Belgium; qualified as a Graduate Engineer Architect from the Catholic University of Louvain, in 1970.

Many buildings of antiquity were made from unbaked brick which proves to be a very friable material if it is not protected, in some way or another, from the weather. Much the same applies to certain types of baked-brick and pisé structures.

A sad view

An archaeological excavation that brings to light several millenia of old brick remains, may at the same time be contributing to their accelerated destruction. When confronted with archaeological constructions where the roofing has totally disappeared, but with thick walls that are sometimes remarkably preserved, the local authorities attend to the most urgent things first. They either completely reconstruct – where the building appears new, plaster the remaining structure with a waterproof protective coating, or roof over certain areas with second-hand material such as corrugated iron, a metal framework, wood, etc., without any concern for the aesthetics. Often the temporary solution becomes a definitive one and offers the visitor the sad view of a ruin covered by another "ruin", completely degrading any serious appreciation of the original remains.

Archaeological sites involving unbaked brick structures (e.g. Mari in Syria and Babylon in Iraq) are rarely spectacular, with the exception of the very small minority of those that have been entirely reconstructed. The visitor always seems disappointed, since it is difficult for a non-specialist to find his or her way through such a maze of walls, digging surfaces and rubble piles. Visual appeal is lacking, even though, in the case of Mesopotamian or Indus sites, the findings date back over 4,000 years and are pregnant with history. The approach that I have put forward at meetings of the International Council for Monuments and Sites is that of a light but durable protective structure that can be erected relatively easily over an archaeological site so as to protect it from the weather but at the same time not detract from the site's visual appeal. The solution enlivens the site with visual landmarks highlighting a privileged area – an "attraction". The construc-

In the field of site preservation, audacity and novelty are not in any way lacking in the respect due to the past. The realization of such a bold project would be tangible but remediable proof of this. This photo shows a montage of André Steven's light umbrella concept on the site of Mohenjo-Daro in Pakistan: an archaeological site on the World Heritage List.

tion material – the unbaked brick – or the part of a ruined wall then lose their sordid aspect. The spaces and forms, emerging from the new aerial structure, are protected from the rain and the sun. The canopy may also constitute a new roof to a building which has lost its original one. The site becomes a "precious treasure", which can be visited in comfort.

Heritage and modernity

Only a tensile, tent-like protective structure, which can have an extremely large span, will meet all the criteria for such an application. Since the anchoring points can be located outside the local zone, the shelter does not really touch the archaeological remains. Moreover, it can reflect the plan of the building itself, mirroring the importance of the covered spaces and casting light or shade where appropriate. Starting in 1980, I began to make contacts with the German builder Stromeyer, famous for the structures that he erected in Montreal, Canada, in 1967 and, more recently, in Riyad, Saudi Arabia (diplomats' club). A design was produced on the basis of a case study: the Ishtar Temple in Babylon. Another example is the tensile structure designed by a group of American architects for the new Jidda terminal, which received the Aga Khan architectural award in 1983.

Our cultural heritage: Mohenjo-Daro on the Silk Road

In 1979, at the invitation of the Iraqi Antiquities Service, I carried out an in-depth study on several sites in the Tigris Valley, and it was proposed that a tensile structure should be built to protect the Ishtar of Agade Temple in Babylon. However, the war with Iran put an end to this project. Other sites, throughout the world, could lend themselves to such an experiment, such as, for example, the dead city of Ebla in Syria, the tombs of the Assassif Valley in Egypt, the site of Chan-Chan in Peru, Pendjikent in the Samarkand area of the USSR, the dead cities of Chinese Xinjiang in the Turfan oasis, and last, but not least, Mohenjo-Daro in Pakistan.

Mohenjo-Daro figures on the list of endangered world heritage sites and is today the object of an international preservation campaign since several groups of the buildings it comprises need to be sheltered from the sporadic but heavy rainfalls. My proposal is that a tension canopy structure be installed at this site within the framework of the UNESCO Silk Roads Programme.

Cultural patronage/sponsoring/assistance

Such a project would be possible only with adequate sponsorship. The project brings together the use of modern technologies and the creation of a visible object which preserves, with its plastic and environmental aspect, the original character of the ruins. The local authorities are highly concerned with the deterioration of these monuments of the past, and such a project would contribute to revitalizing the site and opening up opportunities for a range of cultural events: festivals, exhibitions, processions, concerts, etc., in ways similar to what has been done at Carthage, Babylon, etc. The 21st-century nature of this construction would provoke an international media reaction and almost certainly raise diverging passions. It would afterwards be submitted to regular controls, and, if the experiment is successful, the proposed system could be applied to any other cultural site, with improvements only possible by testing the actual designs and structures *in situ*. Furthermore, interest in and knowledge about unbaked brick monuments and their conservation would be stimulated by the publication of my book *Terra Incognita* which will give an overview of the history of monumental unbaked brick architecture in past civilizations.

In the field of site preservation, the audacity and novelty of the concept that I am putting forward are in no way lacking in due respect for the past and our archaeological heritage. The realization of this bold project would be a tangible but never irremediable proof of that fact.

The ruins of Chan-Chan, Peru, now inscribed on the World Heritage List – a potential site for the "light umbrella project" to be installed.

Gene banks for giant clams

Gerald Allen Heslinga

Honourable Mention
The Rolex Awards for Enterprise – 1990

Micronesian Mariculture Demonstration Center, P. O. Box 359, Koror, Caroline Islands 96940, Republic of Palau

American, born 13 August 1953. Manager, Micronesian Mariculture Demonstration Centre. Educated in USA; B. A. (Biology, Hons.) from Harvard University in 1976.

Giant Tridacna clams, which may reach over a metre in length and weigh hundreds of kilogrammes, have long been an important part of the diet of Indo-Pacific peoples, but in recent years they have been harvested at an unprecedented rate, both by Asian poachers and by local subsistence fishermen. The entire flesh of the clams is consumed, either raw, cooked, dried or pickled in vinegar. The shells of the giant clam are used locally for a variety of purposes, and they are often fashioned into handicrafts for sale to local or international markets. Recent extinctions of giant clams are known to have occurred on many islands of Micronesia and near-extinction has occurred across vast regions of the Philippines, Indonesia and Papua New Guinea.

Recent advances in giant clam mariculture technology

During the past ten years, research and development work under my direction at the Micronesian Mariculture Demonstration Centre (MMDC) in the Republic of Palau has shown that Tridacna clams can be grown in captivity using simple low-technology methods. The MMDC's most significant contribution has been the development and demonstration of methods for mass cultivation of clam "seed", and for the husbanding of these seed to maturity in shallow coral reef farms.

The giant clams are uniquely appropriate for cultivation by man because they do not require feeding as they house billions of tiny, single-celled algae – the zooxanthellae – in their exposed mantle tissues. Carbon compounds such as glycerol and glucose are produced by the algae and released directly into the bloodstream of the host clam, thereby eliminating the need for filter feeding. This symbiotic relationship allows giant clam to grow faster and larger than many other molluscs. There is now a need to begin building a mariculture industry based on the giant clam. To do this, we must combine research and development with training, technology transfer, and commerce. True domestication of the Tridacna clams is within reach if the necessary technical and genetic information can be made widely available in the Indo-Pacific region.

Giant clams are unique among farm animals because they produce their own food. This is accomplished by photosynthetic algae living symbiotically in the colourful mantle tissues. Sugars released by the algae nourish the clams.

Giant clam mariculture training and technology transfer

Over a period of five years, the MMDC Giant Clam Hatchery has begun training Asians and Pacific islanders in clam mariculture methods. To date about 50 individuals have been trained. Each has been given 1,000 baby clams to take to his or her home country for planting on local reefs. The programme has worked well and we are continuing to pursue it as a primary means of transferring mariculture technology from Palau to other nations of the Indo-Pacific. To date some 12 Pacific nations have received baby giant clams from the MMDC. In recent years we have begun to see a proliferation of giant clam hatcheries, nearly all of which are modeled to a greater or lesser degree on the MMDC.

One of the most serious constraints, however, is a lack of high-quality breeding stock. What is needed is a giant clam gene bank, and only the MMDC laboratory has the broodstock, the international shipping experience, and the regional network of contacts necessary to implement a successful giant clam gene bank programme. During the past three years I have visited 12 Indo-Pacific nations. With few exceptions, I have found keen interest in expanding giant clam cultivation programmes, but before this can be done the genetic resource – that is, the giant clam breeding stock – must be transferred to those desiring to establish hatcheries and ocean farms. I would like to devote 25% of my time during the next four years to solving this problem.

Spreading the genetic resources

Over the past five years, I have identified at least eight individuals and institutions in the Pacific region that have both the interest and the capability to maintain giant clam broodstock in protected areas. The best way to guarantee successful maintenance of giant clam genetic diversity is to spread the genetic resource around to a wide variety of people, institutions and islands. By establishing eight repositories of genetic information between the Philippines and Samoa, the chances are excellent that at least some of the participating individuals and institutions will be successful in maintaining long-term Tridacna breeding programmes.

The MMDC is in a unique position to distribute this genetic resource to broodstock-deficient countries in the region. Methods for air-freighting giant clams of all sizes have been developed and demonstrated by the MMDC, such that the technical aspects of transferring the large clams will not be a constraint. The technology is now at hand to halt the decline in numbers of giant clams, to restore their importance in the coral reef community and to form an industry of potentially great nutritional and commercial relevance. Success in this endeavour will bring tangible benefits to coastal peoples in at least six Indo-Pacific nations. It will prove that a positive, constructive, long-term approach to the biological diversity problem can produce far-reaching impacts.

Giant clams require about five years to reach sexual maturity. A practical way to help conserve natural populations is to establish international "gene banks" which can function as sanctuaries for giant clam breeding stock.

The return of the monkeys – a primate conservation project

Anwaruddin Choudhury

c/o Mr. Alauddin Choudhury, Near Gate No 1 of Nehru Stadium, Islampur Road, Guwahati 781 007, Assam, India

Indian, born 25 October 1958. Deputy Director of the Department of Welfare of Plains Tribes. Educated in India; M. A. (Geography) from Guwahati University, in 1985.

Assam and six other states of northeast India, i. e. Arunachal Pradesh, Nagaland, Manipur, Mizoram, Tripura and Meghalaya, are very rich in primate resources. Ten out of 15 known species of Indian primates are found in this region. Although the study of non-human primates has excited much interest in the past few decades, northeast India has remained virtually unstudied. A detailed research survey in the region is long overdue since many species have already, or soon will, become locally extinct.

Numerous primate species at risk

Primates found in the region include the: slow loris (*Nycticebus coucang*), stump-tailed macaque (*Macaca arctoides*), Assamese macaque (*M. assamensis*), rhesus monkey (*M. mulatta*), pigtailed macaque (*M. nemestrina*), hanuman langur (*Presbytis entellus*), golden langur (*P. geei*), Phayre's leaf monkey (*P. phayrei*), capped langur (*P. pileatus*), hoolock gibbon (*Hylobates hoolock*) and silvered leaf monkey (*P. cristatus*).

With the exception of the rhesus monkey, all the primates in the region are essentially forest dwellers, and their survival depends on the continued existence of their forest habitat. However, habitat destruction is the major threat to primate survival in this region. The main reasons for forest destruction are agricultural expansion, slash-and-burn shifting cultivation, tree felling for commercial use and various developmental activities such as the construction of hydroelectric installations and large paper mills. In Assam alone, 200–250 km² of forest are destroyed each year. Forest conversion for agricultural purposes is the single most important cause of forest destruction, and is ultimately attributable to very rapid population growth.

Skulls of primates killed for food by tribals in Assam's North Cachar Hills District.

Hunting of primates for food is the next most important threat to their survival in this region. Various hill tribes such as the Nagas, Kukis and Mizos relish primate meat; they possess old-fashioned and in some cases modern firearms, and the primates are frequently stalked and killed.

A ten-year research and conservation programme

In February 1986, against this disturbing background, I launched a ten-year project to study and investigate the distribution, habitat and status of various species of primates. At present, my study area is confined mainly to Assam, but I propose to extend it to the other states of northeast India when resources are available. On the basis of the first three years' work, I have submitted a Ph.D. dissertation entitled *Primates of Assam: their distribution, habitat and status* to the University of Gauhati.

My discovery of specimens of Phayre's leaf monkey (*Presbytis phayrei*), which was previously unknown in Assam, is a significant find of this study. The study also revealed that the silvered leaf monkey (*P. cristatus*) may also occur in Assam and Mizoram. A total of 13 new areas have been identified as potential conservation areas of primate importance. The study also showed that all species except the rhesus monkey were in need of conservation.

A public educations programme on monkey conservation

At present, besides surveying various forests, the prime method I am using to promote conservation and discourage the hunting of primates is by writing articles in local newspapers and by holding informal talks at village levels; in many cases, I have obtained encouraging results. Many poachers and regular hunters have become keen observers, and their hunting has been reduced from the "regular" to the "occasional" level. Even local forest officials who were not aware of the importance of the primates and their status in their areas, are now keeping a watch on primate hunting – especially hunting of the rarer species such as the hoolock gibbon.

A female stump tailed macaque, one of the rarest primates of India, photographed in the North Cachar Hills District.

The Danube Delta: A European paradise preserved

Anne Katherine Tagge

Susan Lee Campbell Institute, 37 Avon Road, Wellesley, Massachusetts 02181, United States

American, born 20 October 1954. President, Susan Lee Campbell Institute. Educated in Japan, Cyprus, Italy, Romania and United States; B.A. (History) from Wellesley College in 1977.

The Delta of the river Danube which enters the Black Sea in Romania is one of the largest expanses of reed beds in the world, the largest wetland left in Europe, an unrivalled avian migratory crossroads, a refuge for numerous endangered species of flora and fauna.

A region of exceptional natural riches

The wealth of the Delta takes many forms. There are: unequalled reed patches; vast fisheries (including, for instance, sturgeon for prize caviar); an enormous teeming wetland serving as a busy hub for migrating birds from many nations and continents; a nesting area for vanishing species; a wildlife wilderness with numerous examples which are now extinct or rare in the rest of Europe (such as for example wolf, boar, lynx); a luxuriant profusion of flora; an ever changing hydrological maze of hundreds of lakes, meanders, willows and water; a living ethnographic museum (the Lipovans).

The abundance of landscape types is startling, for amidst all this water are mini-deserts with Skeleton Coast-like sand dunes. Danger lurks at every turn in the shape of treacherous snakes, entwining plants and vicious insects. Unlike many parts of the world where lighthouses tumble into the sea, here the sea has abandoned them and fled. Because the land is growing, they are stranded farther and farther inland from the dolphins who frolic offshore.

Beneath one's feet, archaeological treasures from every conceivable epoch await exploration. According to Apollonius' *Argonautica*, Jason passed through the Delta *en route* home after capturing the Golden Fleece. Languishing in exile just south of the Delta in Constanta, the famous Roman poet Ovid poured his woes into the *Tristia* and *Ex Ponto*. North of the Delta are the remains of Trajan's Wall, similar to Hadrian's in Great Britain. Nearby lies Histria, where Suleiman the Magnificent camped.

353

*The Delta of the river
Danube is a vital part of the
migratory patterns of many
species of birds.*

The Danube Delta was until December, 1989 under a death threat. A number of unsustainable projects had already been launched only to be proven spectacular economic and environmental failures. Irrational schemes to drain the Delta had been proposed, and threatend to doom a splendid wilderness. The Delta's tremendous economic potential, which could have been developed without destroying human and wildlife habitats (e.g. native fish and reed harvesting, tourism, etc.), was being ruined. Pollution, public health concerns, water supply problems, soil erosion, and animal extinction were just the tip of the iceberg of an ever widening litany of ecological disasters affecting the entire region.

Now, the new Romanian political situation offers an opportunity to save the Delta's ecological soundness for the future welfare of all forms of life.

A collaborative quest

My interests in the Danube Delta were significantly shaped by my years in Romania as a Fulbright Scholar. I was inspired to found a non-profit organization, the Susan Lee Campbell Institute. Its mission is to enthusiastically and creatively develop broad applications of the following themes: environmental improvement; technological investigation and progress; promotion of world peace, prosperity, and respect of the indivudal by tying nations together through co-operation on practical levels – the spirit of internationalism and idealistic care for life. The concept of debt-for-nature swaps has been developed in order to utilize international debt resources held by the Western banking system. A proportion of the debt is cancelled in return for work being done locally on nature conservancy activities.

354

I have now gained considerable and valuable experience in this area of international financial arrangements since only recently I negotiated on behalf of the Susan Lee Campbell Institute with the banking community for the organization, structuring and implementation of the first debt-for-nature exchange in Europe. This programme will involve a donation of Polish debt by Bankers Trust, a leading New York merchant bank; this debt will be used in the campaign to clean up the heavily polluted Utata (literally in Polish, «Lost») River which flows by the revered cultural site of Chopin's birthplace at Zelazowa Wola. The agreement was concluded with the Polish Fund of External Debt Service and the responsibility for the implementation of this significant and ground-breaking international effort is being co-ordinated by the Vistula Programme which has as one of its key purposes the resurrection of Poland's endangered water resources.

I very recently met in Bucharest with a varied range of persons in leading roles in the field of environmental planning. Romanian realities will shape the specifics of components such as financing mechanisms. Consultations with the requisite scientific experts are being enhanced by a more open political and economic climate including involvement of youth, and increased integration of Romania into global society.

The country beyond the fog

The advent of a new government in Romania dedicated to wise use of the country's heritage, resources and biological diversity, combined with a new co-operative relationship between Romania and the rest of the world will promote the realization of this project. The ideal plan for the Danube Delta ecosystem will provide for the needs of man and nature to be met, thus ensuring preservation of this paradise for Romania and all the world.

The resources of the Danube Delata support a unique indigenous culture.

Rolex Laureate – The Rolex Awards for Enterprise – 1990

Suryo Wardhoyo Prawiroatmodjo

Suryo Wardhoyo Prawiroatmodjo, a qualified veterinary surgeon from Indonesia, has been developing the environmental educational facilities of the Green Indonesian Foundation. He has now set out to establish Indonesia's first Environmental Education Centre with programmes that, he hopes, will bring about a radical change in ecological attitudes in Indonesia.

The first Indonesian environmental education centre

Suryo Wardhoyo Prawiroatmodjo

Rolex Laureate
The Rolex Awards for Enterprise – 1990
Jl. Undaan Kulon 43, Surabaya 60274, Indonesia

Indonesian, born 22 June 1956. Head, Environmental Education Centre. Educated in Indonesia; graduated from the Faculty of Veterinary Medicine, Airlangga University, in 1982.

Although the general public in Indonesia is still largely lacking in awareness of conservation problems, there has been a noticeable increase in recent years in the younger generation's interest in conservation and environmental issues. This can be seen from the participants who attend the various conservation education programmes organized by Yayasan Indonesia Hijau (Green Indonesian Foundation), the Indonesian Environmental Forum (Walhi), Skephi, and other groups. Yayasan Indonesian Hijau (YIH) has been involved in public conservation education since 1978. With funds raised from local and foreign sources, it visits schools, participates in exhibitions, conducts field study courses, and provides a forum for young people concerned about their environment. Better facilities are now needed to serve as a centre for these operations.

In 1985, Dr. Suryo W. Prawiroatmodjo started various regional activities for YIH in Surabaya, East Java and, in 1986, he had the opportunity to attend a conservation and wildlife management course at the Smithsonian Institute in the United States. On that occasion, he submitted to the WWF-USA a proposal for the establishment of an environmental education centre. Subsequently, his proposal was accepted, and WWF International gave him a contract for 125,000 Swiss Francs, agreeing to subsidize both the purchase of 3.5 hectares of land located at the edge of the tropical forest on the slopes of the sacred Penanggunan volcano, and the construction of Indonesia's first Environmental Education Centre.

An ambitious development and action plan

The site is ideal and meets the criteria for the perfect location for an environmental education centre. In particular, it contains a range of natural ecosystems, is accessible from nearby cities, is situated in a calm, quiet atmosphere, with beautiful scenery of mountains, forest and rice fields; it is also close to the villages, so that it can motivate the villagers to a better, healthier style of ecological living.

The lecture theatre and the canteen-cum-restaurant at the Environmental Education Centre being built by Suryo Prawiroatmodjo.

Putting the Centre's education programme into action

Several courses of instruction will be held on such topics as soil, water and air conservation, and the preservation of balanced ecosystems; slide-shows, films, practical demonstrations, simple experiments and field observations will be used during the residential or day courses. Special attention will also be paid to encouraging the development of regional core groups which can be used to spread conservation awareness in the outer regions of Indonesia.

We already have experience in producing support materials for development programmes aimed at rural communities living on the edge of national parks and nature reserves. As sufficient land becomes available, demonstration plots of crops suitable for buffer zones will be created. Fruit and vegetables produced on these plots will be used for consumption by course participants, staff and visitors. We are fully aware that the Centre should become self-supporting if its activities are to flourish in the long term. Income is expected from the services provided by a guest-house and restaurant and from some special courses.

The essential components of the Centre will consist of: a main building with offices, auditorium, library, slide repository, dark room, visitors' centre and other facilities; accommodation for permanent staff and visitors; auxiliary buildings and structures to accommodate plant nurseries, renewable energy projects, etc.; and about 3 hectares of surrounding land.

The objectives of the project have been clearly defined. It will promote effective conservation education in Indonesia by providing a permanent focal point for operations with supporting facilities (office space, field study centre, etc.). It will provide a model for similar conservation education centres to be established in other parts of the country, and increase the efficiency and effectiveness of YIH conservation education programmes. The Centre will offer facilities for the implementation of eco-development techniques and conservation activities such as: medicinal and commercially useful plant nurseries, new and renewable energy projects, optimization of rural/urban gardens, endangered bird species breeding, etc. Finally, it will contain a training environment for teachers and educators in conservation, promote Indonesian national parks and nature reserves by encouraging well-guided tourism to these areas and generate income to sustain these objectives through the exploitation of a commercially run guesthouse.

A model for development elsewhere

The final product will be a functioning Conservation Education Centre operating an exclusive conservation education programme on environmental problems, wildlife conservation, plant conservation, new sources of energy, etc. The Centre will stimulate an awareness of conservation problems among Indonesians, particularly the younger generation, and constitute an example to be followed in expanding and extending conservation education to other parts of Indonesia and Southeast Asia.

Secondary school students experimenting in a laboratory at the Environmental Education Centre. Hands-on experience is one of the Centre's prime objectives.

359

The Kelly Legend Country

Lorna Merle Chick

P. O. Box 637, Wangaratta, 3677 Victoria, Australia

Australian, born 18 August 1922. Owner and manager of a "hobby farm", and painter. Educated in Australia; attended the Wangaratta Technical School from 1962 to 1966.

I am a water diviner – a person who, given a length of good steel fencing wire, can find an underground stream of water and then mark a definite spot at which the farmer should dig a well in order to get a water supply. Just think what this can do for any environment. This gift, linked with my decision to learn to paint landscapes in oils, goes to explain just why I think people should realize how important it is to start appreciating the beauty of their environment and to do all they have in their power to preserve it and keep it beautiful. Water divining is a gift that I learnt whilst travelling around Kelly Country with my husband who, with his brother, had been divining water and digging wells for farmers for a living for many years.

I live on what is classed in Australia as a "hobby farm". This covers 40 hectares of the land originally left to me by my husband when he died ten years ago; the rest I have given to my two sons.

A financial need to paint

It was after my husband had a nasty tractor accident that I started attending a course given for farmers' wives at Dookie Agricultural College. After day classes we went, at night, to films on art appreciation and I became very interested in this subject.

The trips around the district on water divining projects provided lots of stunning landscapes, and I could not wait to have a go at putting them on canvas. My two sons, Marcus and Louis, and myself went to night classes to learn painting at the Wangaratta Technical School.

When my husband died, I at first received a widow's pension but, after the local authorities had decided to classify my land as a potential urban development area, my widow's pension was cancelled since it was considered that this land constituted a future asset; no actual plans for development have materialized so

360

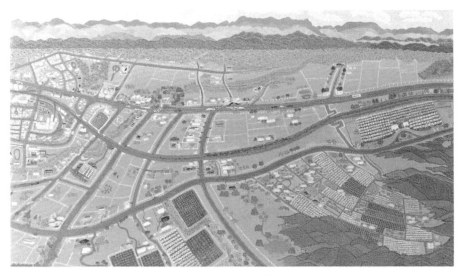

Lorna Chick's painting entitled Glenrowan and the Kelly Legend Country *(3.6×1.5 m).*

far. Consequently, since the farm could support only 25 steers, painting became a financial necessity for me.

I live at the foot of a range of mountains – an area which has now been taken over as a national park and what I can see from my windows is an ideal background for a painter. Just across the Ned Kelly Legend Country in which I live is the town of Glenrowan – about 12 km from where I have my farm. Glenrowan has developed into quite a tourist centre and earns big money from the visitors' trade – especially at Easter time when they organize the well publicized Northeast Winery Walk About. I saw here an outlet for my paintings – not the small pictures you normally find in art shops but large murals of Glenrowan and Kelly Legend Country, measuring typically 130 cm by 100 cm in size.

Painting to help conservation

Between water divining trips and painting I began to realize that the spreading towns were slowly creeping out into the country but that most of the people who bought small farms proved to be very environment minded, built nice houses and planted native trees and made the landscape even more beautiful than before.

By painting landscapes I hope to let people see just how beautiful our Kelly Country really is and how the northeast of Victoria, Australia, has realized that Wangaratta is a central town for tourists to make their holiday headquarters and tour the northeast in one-day trips.

Glenrowan Town, Beechworth (an old gold town), Rutherglen (ten wineries), Myrtleford (miles of tobacco fields), Yarrowanga (weir, boats and water sports) are sources of inspiration for me; they are all places of beauty and I want them to remain that way. The tourist trade to the Australian alps in winter through here is now terrific, but the tourist committee has realized the enormous amount of

361

financial gain involved and are at last not going to let anything spoil the environment. It is too much of an asset. So I am sending along a few photos of my paintings, hoping the rest of the world will wake up to the beauty of their countries and do what our tourist and environmental people are doing to protect our natural heritage.

My paintings attract a wider audience

Gradually my naive paintings have begun to attract a wider and wider audience. I have held exhibitions and was delighted at the reception my work received. I was very proud indeed when four of my paintings were purchased for hanging in the Parliament House in Canberra and another five in the Australian National Gallery in the same city. My favorite painting though, *Wild flowers of the Warby Range*, is now hanging in the Shepparton Art Gallery. I also had a painting published on the cover of the local telephone directory and another as a poster by the forest conservation authority promoting the reduction of soil salinity in order to protect our agricultural land. Many newspapers and journals have carried articles about me and the pictures that I paint. I have even been included in the *World Encyclopaedia of Naive Art.*

For the first time in my life now, I am getting more time to paint and I am looking forward to painting all those scenes that are long overdue on account of family commitments. Also I am looking forward to turning out some much better work – without being interrupted all the time. Thanks for your interest and encouragement. I will try even harder!

Detail of Glenrowan and the Kelly Legend Country *painted by Lorna Chick.*

Protecting the birds of French Polynesia

Guy Chabot

Segonzac, Vabres L'Abbaye, 12400 St. Affrique, France

French, born 8 December 1937. Retired military officer now a small farm owner breeding Icelandic horses. Educated in France; attended the Ecole Militaire Préparatoire, Tulle, until 1955.

The bird population of Oceania includes varieties of pigeons and parrots which are to be found in abundance in the west; however, these birds decrease in number the farther east one travels until, arriving at French Polynesia, they are almost non-existent. Whole species of multi-coloured budgerigars disappeared at the end of the last century from Tahiti and Raiatea and, if measures are not taken immediately, other species will become extinct in future years. A landscape without birds, devoid of all living creatures, provides a lifeless picture which very soon becomes one of desolation.

Apart from certain imported and often undesirable breeds, such as the moliques blackbird and the red-vented bull-bull, there are about 20 endemic species of pigeons and parrots. Tragically, their existence is seriously threatened with extinction. They continue to survive on some islands spread over five archipelagos. A few dozen birds are all that are left of certain species, found on a remote islet, where previously they colonized the whole territory. Their disappearance is due to the impact of man's activities on their site or to the introduction of new species of wildlife, which have led to great upheavals in their environment.

Endangered species

The species that are under threat include parrots, pigeons and turtle doves. There are five similar species to be found in Polynesia and three of these can be seen in French Polynesia: *Lori vini ultramarina* (Marquises Islands); *Lori vini peruviana* (Tuamotu Island); *Lori vini kuhlii* (South Island); *Lori vini stephenii* (Pitcairn Island); and *Lori vini Australis* (Fiji and Samoa Islands). These names incorporate the designation *vini* because they are Polynesian and *lori* because they are nectarivores.

The ultramarine lory *Lori vini ultramarina* was originally present on the archipelago situated 1,500 km to the north of Tahiti. It has been disappearing

363

The Lori vini peruviana *photographed by Guy Chabot in the Tuamotu Islands.*

very rapidly since the beginning of the century; an in-depth field study carried out suggests that there are only 20–30 individuals left in the lower part of the island. Today the name *Lori vini peruviana*, the Tahiti blue lory, is nothing more than a sweet reminder of the past. Formerly found in Tahiti, it also disappeared in Bora-Bora during the first half of the century. Since that time, it has been found only to the west of the Tuamotu Islands on certain islets of the atoll of Rangirora and on other small atolls in the area; I now estimate the population at 200–300 individuals in 1987.

Lori vini kuhlhii, the "Kuhl's lory", was formerly found in four out of five of the Southern Islands, and there are still a few in Tubuai but they have not been found at Rimatara since the Americans seized them and transported them to the islands of Fanning and Washington. The *Ptilinopus purpuratus* is rare in certain places (e.g. Va-Huk) whilst it is abundant in others (e.g. Va-Pou). Given its extreme rarity, there is great cause for alarm there as well. The striped turtle dove (*Geopalia streata*) has been imported from Hawaii for the last two decades, whereas *Gallicolumba rubiscens* was sighted in 1920 on the almost inaccessible island of Fatu-Huka in the Marquises. Nobody else has been able to claim witness to its presence or its survival today.

Birds hunted and captured

Laws exist against the capturing of birds but tragically these are not enforced. The local people have been made aware of the problem and are co-operative now that they realize that such natural riches are part of their heritage. Nevertheless, certain people have been caught red-handed. Examples of piracy are too numerous to cite. The authorities must be made more aware of such thefts from their territories. No serious long-term study of the problem has been carried out before; although some English and American associations have shown an interest in the matter. They advise the raising in captivity of different varieties of birds which could then be released back into the wild should the species suffer any harm in its natural surroundings. I have now obtained the support of the Head of the National Parks for the creation of a protected bird park of this type.

The project

In Tahiti there is a botanic garden covering several hectares and open to the public. I introduced the territorial government to my plan for a bird park during a conference at Papete in 1988. The opening of a bird garden in the midst of the botanic garden would be of great scientific interest, not to mention its value as a tourist attraction. About 20 varieties of budgerigars, pigeons and turtle doves, all endemic to the territory, could be gathered there. Jobs would be created. In this way the birds' descendants would be protected if the species were to die out due to unforeseen changes in nature. The raising of birds would allow them to be ringed and then released into an area free from infection. This would allow more detailed observation of their habits.

Unfortunately, the territorial government, after having warmly received the project, lost its initial enthusiasm and is concentrating on other matters. I there-fore turned to the private sector and contacted Marlon Brando, owner of the Tetiaroa Atoll and an ardent defender of the environment, who is acutely aware of the immediate dangers faced by the bird population in the territory. Sadly, he will not be returning to Polynesia in the near future. I then went to Bora-Bora where I spent a week with Paul Emile Victor who has proposed his islet as a site. This will not be possible because the installation of aviaries demands a lot of time and space. Nevertheless, Paul Emile Victor remains an ardent supporter of the plan to create this park in Polynesia.

*A pigeon (*Ducula galeata*) photographed by Guy Chabot in the Marquises Islands.*

Waste utilization – the aesthetic dimension

Nek Chand Saini

Honourable Mention
The Rolex Awards for Enterprise – 1990
88 Sector 27-A, Chandigarh 160019, India

Indian, born 15 December 1924. Creator-director of the Rock Garden – A Fantasy, Chandigarh. Educated in India; no formal education beyond High School.

The city of Chandigarh, built by the visionary Swiss architect, Le Corbusier, is the capital of the north western provincial state of Punjab (India). In one corner of the city, a unique sculpture/fantasy garden has been created by me, an untutored former road worker, entirely out of discarded city debris, industrial waste and natural fossil rocks collected from the nearby Himalayan foothills. Work on the garden started almost 30 years ago. The forms of Le Corbusier's geometry have an antipole in my works – an exercise in free flight for a space-free emotional environment, where the only constraint is man's own feelings. To uplift man I have given a bend to the structural inflexibility of modern architectural planned and measured vision. Until the mid-1970s my work remained largely unknown, having been carried out in stealth on land owned by the city Government. As more and more people stumbled upon it, word about this fantasy kingdom gradually spread. With that came national and international recognition.

An enchanted garden

The garden presently covers over 4 hectares and is divided into a number of enclosures. Each enclosure is a kind of "sculpted space" to enable the viewer to go through a different experience. Each section is different, with an element of surprise, and yet each is thematically linked.

It is difficult to reduce to words a proposal for the pursuit of an artistic vision, which is a soul soother, an uplifter of man to Godly realms – a vision, the pursuit of which requires the skills of an architect, a landscaper, a gardener, a sculptor and an artist rolled into one. The raw materials of this vision are the discarded debris of a high-energy and material-consuming civilization – concrete poles, bitumen drums, cast-off pots, crockery, cycle tyres, cycle parts, rags, electrical fixtures, bits of porcelain, plumbing, whitewash waste, industrial slag, junked steel furniture, pebbles, natural stone fossil rocks and a hundred other bits and pieces no one has use for. The vision takes the shape of a landscaped fantasy kingdom which, in its imaginative sweep, its romantic, slightly whimsical, gran-

Nek Chand's collection of natural rockforms is estimated at 20,000 pieces or so. This is one of the objets d'art sculpted by the uncanny forces of nature. It has a remarkable resemblance to some of the sculpture done by Rodin.

deur, has compelled viewers to draw comparisons with the Taj Mahal, Picasso, Noguchi, Miró, Max Ernst, Gaudi, without being able to do justice to the magic of the place. This particular project envisions the use of "waste" for a creative, aesthetic purpose – a purpose which deserves some elaboration.

A garden with a range of objectives

The principal objective is to demonstrate the aesthetic harmony between man-made scrap/waste and nature. It is my belief that any conflict between nature's will and man's design is bound to lead to an overall destruction. The dimensions of the essential harmony between man and nature can be economic, social, political and aesthetic. My own effort is to explore the aesthetic dimension. The natural environment – trees, water, soil, birds, rocks – are the major participants in my work.

In a consumer society, most creative artists are reduced to becoming, in a certain sense, producers of artistic objects, artifacts, "products" for sale to consumers of art. The project range may vary – a book, a painting, a sculpture, a performance. The consumer may belong to an elite, be a member of the working class, be young or old, rich or poor. The relationship, however, is essentially that of a producer and a consumer. I aim to demonstrate the possibility of a different kind of relationship – one in which the creator and his creations engage the viewer in heightening his inspirational awareness of his environment, his sense of wonder, his playfulness and his own spirit of creativity.

The project may, in fact, be called one of environmental education. The educational process involves in this instance the creation of a unique environment –

367

through a kind of total mythic landscape planning. The mythic power of the created "enviroscape" is such that every viewer must undergo a unique learning experience. It is impossible not to react. At one level it is simply the magical transformation of city junk, broken, disused artifacts of daily use, natural rocks, into works of art sometimes whimsical, sometimes profound, sometimes primitive, sometimes distinctly modern and sometimes all and yet none of these.

At another level is the audacity of man, imitating God – nowhere else except in this garden kingdom does a man set out with a grand design to create mountains, waterfalls, armies, populations, palaces, courtyards and anything else that his fancy turns to. At still another level it is the astonishing complexity of the relationship between man and nature, man and man-made objects which emerges from a creative dialogue.

At which ever level one responds, the net impact is of developing a new respect for environmental alteration on one's concept of beauty in which everything produced by nature or man is a thing of beauty because it embodies creative labour.

Reinvesting waste with aesthetic appeal

In sum, the project proposes to achieve the following objectives: demonstrate that industrial and city waste, as much as natural objects, can be used so that they are reinvested with an aesthetic value, even as they lose their economic value; forge a relationship between the creative artist and his fellow human beings which comes from sharing an intense aesthetic experience rather than based on the exchange of goods and services for money; create a landscaped space, an environment, which reinforces in every viewer, the bond between man and nature, man and the objects he has discarded and thus teach him to have a new respect for his environment.

These fascinating animals have been sculpted by Nek Chand Saini from a selection of urban and industrial waste.

Global cheetah project

Paule Gros Philippot

University of Michigan, Evolution and Human Behavior Program, 1524 Rackham Building, Ann Arbor, Michigan 48109, United States

French, born 7 June 1963. Graduate Research Assistant at the University of Michigan. Educated in France; Diplôme d'Etudes Universitaires Générales (Biology) from University of Montpellier in 1983.

Cheetahs are highly endangered and the world population is estimated at no more than 5,000 individuals. Moreover, substantial changes have occurred in countries were they were numerous only 15 years ago; for example, erection of wildlife fences in Botswana, persecution on farmland in Namibia and Zimbabwe and civil war in Ethiopia and Somalia have all taken their toll.

However, in order to determine the measures necessary to remove the dangers threatening cheetahs, but also to develop an effective policy of protection and a coherent strategy for making and improving reserves, it is essential to have accurate data on the numbers of cheetahs living in the world, their habitats, their natural predators, and the available preys as well as their own predators other than cheetahs. Furthermore, in order to reintroduce captive animals into their natural environment, new reproduction techniques require thorough knowledge of the factors affecting the viability of the species in the wild.

Estimating the world cheetah population and distribution

I and four collaborators propose to employ three methods to estimate cheetah populations in each country where they still exist. First, we will correspond with a wide range of contacts (scientists, park directors, officials, etc.) to obtain a broad picture of current distributions in each country. Second, we will launch a national questionnaire survey to a wider audience (farmers, veterinarians, hunters, etc.) from conservation organizations in each capital. Third, on the basis of this information we will visit particularly promising regions to assess cheetah numbers more accurately through direct observation, ground and aerial counts of ungulates, and discussion with local officials. A campaign of interviews will be undertaken to check on problems raised by the questionnaire, fill in the missing gaps and to follow up particularly fruitful contacts.

An exhaustive review of studies in several ecosystems has shown that the biomass of the cheetah's principal prey in an area is a good predictor of its

Families of cheetahs like the one pictured here are becoming increasingly rare as the cheetah's range recedes in the face of habitat destruction.

numbers. We will use prey biomass as an indirect estimate of cheetah numbers in regions where prey densities are known but where little other information is available.

In collaboration with Global Ecological Monitoring Systems (GEMS), we will map cheetah distributions to detailed vegetation maps, and refine these analyses through field work by recording factors that are important for cheetah reproduction: degree of cover, water in the dry season, incidence of fires, and availability of safe areas for raising cubs. Since cheetah density depends on the available prey, cheetah distribution will be matched to the known distribution of medium and small-sized ungulates in conjunction with the IUCN Sahel Project. The presence and density of other predators will be examined to determine whether, across populations, cheetah densities are low when large predators are numerous.

Evaluating human threats to cheetahs

The chief human pressure on cheetahs is the reduction in their habitat brought about by increased agricultural practice and deforestation. However, direct hunting of their prey, their persecution as livestock predators, and limited poaching all pose additional threats to their existence. To assess these pressures in more detail we will: map cheetah distributions obtained from questionnaires on to human use patterns; visit two to three of the areas in each country where cheetahs and people co-exist; visit local markets to determine if there is a trade in cheetah skins and whether it poses a threat to cheetahs in the area; and study regional plans for tourist development and the pressure these may exert on wildlife. Results of this field work will be used as the basis for a conservation strategy involving local people and their activities.

A relic population of a different subspecies of cheetah (*Acinonyx jubatus venaticus*) still survives in Iran, and perhaps in Turkmenistan and northwestern Afghanistan. Optimistic reports put numbers at no more than 200 animals widely scattered over a large area and locally threatened by recent rises in uncontrolled hunting of the cheetah's prey and invasion of their range by cattle. We want to stimulate the existing concern for cheetahs in Iran and USSR by providing wildlife scientists in both countries with outside interest and support. In conjunction with local teams, we hope to be able to arrive at a population estimate and make recommendations for more effective conservation.

Heightening public awareness about the cheetah

We intend to make recommendations to individual governments to set up reserves that will protect cheetahs and to strengthen existing park structures to ensure better protection. Where creating new reserves is realistic, we will advise on park design based on our knowledge of cheetah ranging patterns and prey movements in that area. In protected areas already in existence, we will advise on management techniques best adapted to cheetah survival and reproduction on the basis of the existing facilities.

We also plan to mount an education campaign to promote public awareness both locally and internationally through radio programmes and slide shows arranged in the countries we visit, focusing on the importance of the cheetah as a national heritage and symbol of conservation, on its importance in the wildlife community, the need to maintain natural ecosystems, and on its impact on livestock and human settlement. The programmes will conclude with possible solutions to some of the conflicts encountered.

Very few cheetah cubs, such as this ten week old youngster, manage to survive to adulthood. The main causes of mortality are predation by other carnivores, abandonment by their mothers and possibly disease.

Saving the biological diversity of Pinta Island, Galapagos – the home of "Lonesome George"

Ole Jørgen Hamann

Botanical Laboratory, University of Copenhagen, Gothersgade 140, 1123 Copenhagen K, Denmark

Danish, born 4 February 1944. Senior lecturer at the Botanical Laboratory of the University of Copenhagen. Educated in Denmark; Doctor of Science from the University of Copenhagen, in 1981.

No other archipelago in the world is at the same time so isolated, so extensive and so little altered by man as the Galapagos. The islands and their surrounding waters contribute notably to the diversity of species and ecosystems of the world, through their geographic and evolutionary history. These *isleas de los galapagos* – islands of the tortoises – straddle the equator some 1,000 km west of South America. Sixteen large and numerous smaller islands cover about 8,000 km², of which more than 90% is uninhabited national park. The islands are volcanically very active, and are true oceanic islands which never have been connected to any larger land mass.

However, by the early 1930s it was realized that the islands were coming under threat – the original biological isolation had been broken by man. Today the consequences are grave: original ecosystems are destroyed, endemic plants and animals are faced with the threat of extinction and the balance of nature is changed. This is the background on which we are working to conserve the unique World Heritage Site of Galapagos.

The Island of Pinta

Pinta is one of the northern islands in the archipelago, rarely visited by scientists and not at all by tourists. It covers about 59 km² and reaches an altitude of 650 m. There is a great variety in habitats, several vegetation zones can be distinguished corresponding to the local variation in climatic conditions, and the diversity of plants and animals is exceptionally high compared with other islands in the archipelago.

Numerous indigenous and endemic land birds live on Pinta, and the three native taxa of reptiles on the island are all Pinta endemics, viz. the giant tortoise *(Geochelone elephantopus abingdoni)*, the marine iguana *(Amblyrhyncus cristatus sielmanni)* and the lava lizard *(Tropidurus pacificus)*. There are no native land mammals on Pinta, but goats were introduced in 1959, and have since

372

"Lonesome George" on Pinta Island in March 1972, on the day when park wardens had caught him. The next day he was sailed to Santa Cruz Island, where he since has been kept in a special enclosure (Photo: O. Hamann).

caused serious problems. The flora of Pinta is remarkably rich. With only 59 km^2 Pinta covers about 0.75% of the total land surface of the archipelago, but is has 32% of the native land plants.

Tortoises and goats on Pinta

The Pinta giant tortoise is today very close to extinction. Only one individual is known to be alive, the now famous "Lonesome George", kept at the Charles Darwin Research Station on Santa Cruz, where he has been since he was caught on Pinta in 1972. "Lonesome George" is the last of his kind, which presumably numbered hundreds or thousands of individuals in former times. During the 17th, 18th and 19th centuries buccaneers and whalers took a heavy toll on the tortoises of Galapagos.

Following the introduction of goats in 1959, the situation on Pinta deteriorated rapidly during the 1960s and 1970s. Originally one male and two female goats were set ashore, presumably by a local fisherman, but in a few years the goat population grew dramatically. In the early 1970s it was estimated that about 10,000 goats were present on Pinta! The goats had a very destructive impact on the ecosystems and a major goat eradication campaign was initiated, which has continued until today. In total the park wardens have shot about 40,000 goats during the almost 20 years of effort, and are now close to eliminating the goats completely from the island.

The general objective of the project is to save the biological and ecological diversity of Pinta Island, Galapagos, through a comprehensive project including elements of research, conservation and management. Specifically the project aims at: ensuring eradication of the last handful of feral goats on Pinta; saving the genes of "Lonesome George" in any possible way; and reintroducing giant tortoises to Pinta as soon as feral goats have been eliminated. The main conservation and management components will comprise goat eradication, building up a stock of giant tortoises suitable for reintroduction, making the introduction, and monitoring the progress over a fairly long period of time.

Preserving the genes of "Lonesome George"

Attempts have been made to mate "Lonesome George" with females of other subspecies of Galapagos giant tortoises, but so far without luck. However, building on the experience gained through the successful breeding programme, a careful analysis will be made in order to enhance the possibility of using "Lonesome George" in a breeding programme. The morphologically closest subspecies, *Geochelone elephantopus becki* from Volcan Wolf, Isabela Island, has been suggested as a possible taxon for breeding with "Lonesome George". Another analysis will be made on the possibility of extracting semen from "Lonesome George" with a view to preserving it in freeze-storage for use in an artificial insemination programme.

In summary, it is of the greatest importance that giant tortoises be reintroduced to Pinta as soon as possible, and the only prerequisite initially is that the first reintroduction consists of a known set of animals. The eventual outcome of the breeding programme and the introgressive hybridization programme involving "Lonesome George" will then determine how to proceed in the future.

Restoration of the natural ecological balance of Pinta will allow ecological processes to continue on a track as similar as possible to the original, i.e. as they were before man broke the biological isolation of the island. Pinta will again be one of the few, larger islands in the Galapagos where the indigenous and endemic biota would not be threatened by extinction through human-induced changes. If breeding "Lonesome George", or the preservation of his semen and subsequent breeding, or both, prove successful, there is a possibility for preserving his genes in a future population of giant tortoises on Pinta.

Pinta sunflower tree, (Scalesia baurii ssp. hopkinsii). The genus Scalesia is endemic to the Galapagos and comprises 21 taxa of shrubs and trees. In spite of being a small tree, the Pinta sunflower tree does not get to be more than 14–15 years old (Photo: O. Hamann).

Resuscitation of Navajo Indian culture through economics and mythology

James Alfred Mischke

Honourable Mention
The Rolex Awards for Enterprise – 1990

143 East North Street, Cortez, Colorado 81321, United States

American, born 2 April 1944. Professor of Social Work and Social Sciences, Navajo Community College.

The Navajo Indians are the largest Indian tribe in the United States. In 1868, following the "Navajo War" in the early 1860's, the population had fallen to some 12,000; it has now grown to 200,000, is one of the fastest growing populations on the planet and shows no sign of slowing. Arid as their land may often be, the Navajo people have throughout American history amassed a huge land base. The Navajo Indian Reservation is larger in area than the American state of West Virginia, and the Navajo people have been able to develop a tribal governmental structure which stands as an undisputed prototype among such Native American phenomena. The Navajo Tribe, a body recognized by the US Government as retaining internal sovereignty, has in fact developed the early stages of an autonomous society, at least in the areas of law enforcement, social services, soil conservation and agriculture, research and higher education. The Navajo people have developed the rudimentary forms of a culturally unique society.

In the early 1860s, Navajoland saw one of the most brutal US army campaigns in American history. The "Navajo War", as it was called, evolved into a scorched-earth campaign. The core refuge of the Navajo people was a beautiful, scenic, deep canyon known as Canyon de Chelly. The invasion and destruction of Canyon de Chelly under Colonel Kit Carson broke the back of the Navajo military resistance and resulted in the virtual extermination of the Navajo nation. The Canyon de Chelly was at that time a vast Navajo agricultural development, and Carson ordered the destruction of all Navajo property within the canyon – including the 5,000 peach trees that were the pride of the Navajo people. Subsequently, the irrigation system deteriorated progressively and erosion has made the damage even worse.

Replanting the Navajo peach trees

This form of agriculture was extremely viable and was not rendered unserviceable until the destruction of the peach trees and the forced mass exodus of the Navajo Indians. The Canyon de Chelly was in reality a fruit basket and much of the

Planting trees on Navajo land.

Navajo Reservation is considered by experts as highly suited to the cultivation of fruit trees. My project consists in planting fruit trees on the 65,000 km² of the Navajo Indian Reservation in Arizona in the hope that it will revive the culture, myths and environment of the Navajo. Together with two of my friends, who organize educational programmes in two Colorado junior high schools, I was trying to find ideas for field trips that would give schoolchildren the opportunity to be of service and, at the same time, make them aware of foreign cultures. At the request of a Navajo woman, I decided to replant different species of fruit trees which, for the natives, are both mythological symbols and a means of subsistence.

Experts in desert agriculture and orchard owners in the region warned me that the undertaking would probably end in failure if I did not ensure that the Indians would take care of the young trees once they were planted. But I still decided to take the chance and, in 1986, 23 schoolchildren and students together with six adults took 2,000 fruit trees to Chinle, a Navajo town in Arizona. We planted 700 of them and gave the Indians the rest for their private use. The Indians were not very enthusiastic about the project and were even slightly suspicious because they did not believe that this team of Americans would really do anything for them on a purely voluntary basis. Some 40% of the trees nevertheless survived and the programme's relative success gave the Indians the incentive to start building diversion dams and repair the original irrigation network. The following year, the Indians and Americans planted 1,000 trees together and this collaborative planting has continued. Finally, by June 1988, the irrigation system had been installed and some of the earliest trees were already bearing fruit. Moreover, the supervisor of the Apache county of Arizona had set his people the target of planting 10,000 trees in their part of the reservation.

Orchards of a fruitful future

I intend to persevere in this project and the fundraising campaigns begun in 1986 have already borne fruit. Different foundations, firms and 350 individuals have offered financial aid. I submitted a request for a total of US$ 10,000 in aid from the US West Foundation, the Gates Foundation and the Taylor Foundation for 1989 or 1990. The Adolph Coors Company has promised that it will contribute US$ 2,500 a year as long as it continues to like the project. The Bureau of Indian Affairs and the Navajo Tribal Council do not back this type of project but the Council would like to see trees planted in each of the 110 political units in the region.

One further thought! At a time when forests in Brazil are being destroyed, the act of tree planting would seem, on both the planes of symbolism and actuality, to constitute one of the sanest and most loving activities that the race can make manifest in the interest of its survival. It is my hope that our activity will serve in turn as a pilot project for other intraplanetary activities as the fruit trees which rightfully belong to Navajo Indians continue to produce topsoil and the stability thereof. The trees will be necessary to produce a more diversified and enhanced subterranean water level, particularly in the face of the water-based coal slurry pipelines so commonly and tragically used by the power plant interests on the reservation. The trees hold out a hope of providing a habitat for wild birds, as well as embodying an ever-growing matrix for the production and proliferation of seeds and fresh air. It is even possible that a regional climatic change of sorts may be facilitated. The implication of the creation of a new source of planetary oxygen supply in the form of a human planted forest is perhaps unimaginable. Yet, an army of potential caretakers for this forest stands waiting.

Three years of trees in the canyon floor.

A book and two travelling exhibits for the blind and sighted

Paul Bartlett Ré

10533 Sierra Bonita Avenue NE, Albuquerque, New Mexico 87111, United States

American, born 18 April 1950. Artist. Educated in USA; B. Sc. (Physics, Hons.) from California Institute of Technology in 1972.

There are between 28 and 42 million blind persons in the world, of which an estimated 8 million are totally blind; for most of these persons, direct perception of the visual arts is impossible. Since 1979, I have been translating my drawings and paintings into raised-line embossings and bas-reliefs which are not only visually pleasing, but can be appreciated tactually by the blind. From these, I have made both a handmade art-book and a travelling exhibit of "Touchable art". My project consists of publishing my art-book for worldwide distribution; continuing to circulate my travelling exhibit of "Touchable art", which has had 13 showings and an audience of about 50,000; and making a second travelling exhibit of touchable art entitled "Inspired by nature" which is completely distinct from the first and is dedicated to both the visually impaired and nature conservation.

The development of my embossings

The new idea of making embossings for the blind came to me while I was sitting quietly with a page of 60 basic shapes. During my youth, Helen Keller's life and writings had made a powerful impression on me, and I remember blindfolding myself for long periods to find out how well I could manoeuvre without seeing. When making sculptures, I do the final smoothing and polishing with my eyes closed.

My basic shapes have the following unifying geometric properties. First, they are all derived from one or more curves, with possibly one or more line segments removed. Second, all line intersections are of three types: X-intersections; T-intersections; or V-intersections. Knowledge of these properties is helpful in reading the embossings. The derivation of my basic shapes from closed curves is significant; it symbolizes the interconnectedness of everything in existence. In sociology, it corresponds to the peaceful, constructive interaction of human beings. In ecology, it represents the dynamic interdependence of all species, including man. Finally, it expresses the hope that mankind will use thoughtfully the physical and spiritual bounty of nature. I emphasize these ideas in all my exhibits and writings. When mankind adopts a philosophy of reverence for nature, it will have a profound influence on human actions.

During the development work on my embossings, I was aided by a person who had been blind for over 50 years and who acted as a major source of feedback. Her innate sensitivity and appreciation of art made her an excellent tester. She has been able to read all of the 45 shapes completed to date easily, accurately identifying the number and the kinds of intersections, the approximate angles between branches, and the number of regions, their approximate shapes and relative sizes.

Deer and Reflection. A pencil drawing on paper by Paul Bartlett Ré.

Embrace. An acrylic painting by Paul Bartlett Ré.

Putting my art into a travelling exhibition

In 1981, my drawings, paintings and raised-line embossings were exhibited at Caltech's Baxter Art Gallery. The introduction to the tactile portion of the show, and the labels identifying each of the 19 embossings, were presented in both print and braille. Inspired by the response to the Caltech show, I reworked my embossings into a travelling exhibit: I added extra explanatory material, photo-graphs of the 19 visual works translated, and a professionally recorded introductory tape combined with my own compositions for classical guitar. These sooth-ing compositions, also based structurally on closed curves, are particularly com-plementary to the embossings. My travelling exhibit has been shown 13 times in the United States.

Subsequently, in 1983 I produced a handmade book which contains 29 raised line basic shape embossings that are vacuum thermo-formed in plastic. Explana-tory material is given in braille and print. I consider this book a prototype for a second expanded and machine-made edition, which I hope to retail for about US$ 30. For that edition, I envisage the following changes: a full-page reproduc-tion of the 29 visual works from which the embossings are translated; this would include 15 colour plates of paintings and 14 black-and-white reproductions of drawings; the embossings would be reproduced on a heavy white paper with the raised line laminated with a gold-coloured foil (at present, paper embossings are easier to mass-produce than plastic ones, and the gold-coloured foil will el-egantly strengthen the raised line); and an expanded introduction in braille and large print that would guide the viewer through a step-by-step appreciation for each of the works.

This book will be intended for both the blind and sighted, as I am trying to make bridges between these two communities. Both have much to offer the other. For example, the concentration needed as a blind person to read braille and function without eyesight would be valuable to all persons. Furthermore, many of these books will reach blind persons through their sighted friends, and I am hopeful that the blind and sighted will interact while exploring this book.

My travelling exhibit is shown primarily in large or medium sized cities, and my artbook will be available for purchase at those showings. But unlike the exhibit, the artbook can reach the blind who live in rural areas. Eventually, I hope that an inexpensive, abridged edition of my book would be available.

A new travelling exhibit

My new travelling exhibit, "Inspired by nature", will be completely distinct from my first and will contain four introductory panels in large print and braille, 16 large photographs of my pencil drawings, and their corresponding tactual trans-lations. Approximately 30 metres of running wall space will be required for the exhibit, which I hope to have ready for circulation by mid-1990.

"Inspired by nature" is dedicated to the visually impaired and to nature conser-vation. Developing a reverence for nature, and realizing how dependent we are on it, will help in protecting the environment for future generations. May my life-work contribute to a greater environmental awareness, and may all viewers find it a peaceful oasis.

Argentina: Its ecologic reality

Ulises Serafin Maria Gagliardo

Agro Palermo Foundation, Sarmiento 1183, 6° P., 1041 Buenos Aires, Argentina

Argentine, born 31 March 1936. President of the Agro Palermo Foundation. Educated in Argentina; graduated from Navy Military School, Buenos Aires, in 1956.

Throughout my life, from my earliest youth, I have developed my culture on the basis of the humanistic education I was given at home, in the schools I attended and in the libraries I frequented. I grew up in the conviction that there is no greater justification for our existence than that which is achieved for the benefit of mankind.

My studies on agro-ecology have convinced me that Argentina is one of nature's ecological miracles with a food production capacity so large that not to develop it is a crime against mankind. My project has been to create awareness of the extent to which Argentina is endowed and what it must produce for human welfare. It is my desire that my country should assume its role and place in the service of humanity all its incredible food production potential. Just the Province of Buenos Aires, by itself, could feed the whole population of Latin America.

Research on the Argentine ecosystems

I started my research in 1973 directing a team of agricultural engineers and using as a starting point the work done by Professor F. S. Papadakis who based his studies on the analysis of climates. Adopting his methodology, I published in 1982 an ecological map of Argentina together with a booklet summarizing the relevant data to make the map more readily intelligible. Following up this achievement, I launched into a more detailed study of each of the ecosystems identified in the map. I soon realized that any attempt to study ecosystems independent of political boundaries would prove fruitless since readers need to be presented with an orderly method and a comprehensive system.

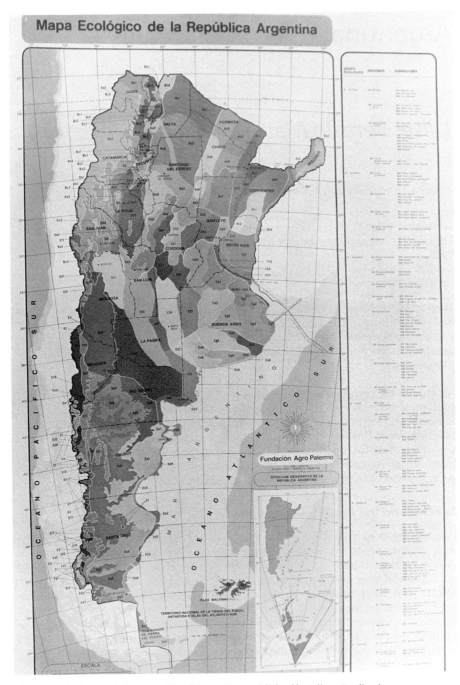

Mapa Ecológico de la República Argentina

The ecological map of the Republic of Argentina published by Ulises Gagliardo.

Manuals of ecology for each province

I therefore decided to produce an ecology manual for each of the 23 Argentine provinces and began the task with the province of Buenos Aires on which I have been working for the past five years. Countless problems have been encountered in the development of a methodology that would combine scientific excellence with a sound educational approach. I have gathered together a team of agronomists, geologists, geographers and other specialists who have together overcome numerous obstacles such as the lack of topographic surveys.

Recently I completed the manuscript on the province of Buenos Aires and am currently preparing to go to press although the cost of printing is a major barrier; in the meantime, the work is being translated into English by Andrés Pavón. This book has made the first agro-ecological analysis of the province and is intended to be read by students, scholars, producers, government officials, university staff and research centres specialized in the development of agricultural resources. I expect it to be read by the scientific, technological, political, educational, economic and financial communities in Argentina and other countries.

The next volume, which deals with the ecology of the province of Córdoba, is nearing completion and step by step we hope to complete a volume for each province in the country, which will constitute a reliable data bank on the ecology of the Argentine Republic. Each volume will analyze a single province, studying in detail each ecosystem as defined in the *Ecological Map of the Argentine Republic*. It is my aspiration to be imitated and followed by other researchers because, at 53, I do not harbour the illusion that I will see my work completed. To do so, we would require funds far above what is currently feasible.

Argentina – a food producer for the world

I also believe that the completion of a project like this would offer the educational system in my country the opportunity of developing an ecological awareness at all levels and instill in the Argentines the realization that they possess one of the richest countries in the world and that they are committed to developing those resources. They must also make themselves and these resources available to the needy of the world in order to alleviate hunger and misery in the less-privileged areas. Any objective sustaining the ideas of discovering and documenting food resources to a hungry world serves in my judgement the human cause, because "the expectations of the inhabitants of the earth converge in one point: the common welfare".

Reintroducing the Socorro dove to its island home

Luis Felipe Baptista

Honourable Mention
The Rolex Awards for Enterprise – 1990

California Academy of Sciences, Golden Gate Park, San Francisco, California
94118–9961, United States

American, born 9 August 1941. Chairman, Ornithology and Mammalogy
Department, State University of San Francisco. Educated in Hong Kong and USA;
Ph. D. (Zoology) from University of California, Berkeley, in 1971.

The three islands comprising the Revillagigedo archipelago, situated about 460
km off Cabo San Lucas, Baja California, Mexico, are the ecological counterpart of
the Galapagos Islands in the northern part of the tropical eastern Pacific Ocean.
Ten endemic land bird species live on Socorro, the largest of the islands. These
islands are thus of great importance for evolutionary biology and biodiversity
studies, and our conservation activities have thus far focused on Socorro Island.
The avifauna is threatened due to predation by introduced feral cats and destruction of the habitat from overgrazing is being brought about by feral sheep and
the resulting soil erosion. The forests are dying! Already extinct on Socorro Island
is the formerly endemic Socorro dove, *Zenaida graysoni*. Fortunately, Socorro
doves still exist in private avicultural collections, so that a well-managed captive
breeding/release programme could ensure the restoration of this striking avian
species to its former home.

As a result of our lobbying, the Commission of the Californias passed a resolution in 1988 urging its citizens to make a concerted effort to repatriate the
Socorro dove to its ancestral home. Consequently, in collaboration with Mexican
conservation biologists and concerned individuals, my colleagues and I have
begun a programme to: increase the captive population of Socorro doves
through a captive breeding programme; restore the disturbed ecosystem on
Socorro Island; and re-establish a self-sustaining wild population of Socorro
doves on their original island home.

Propagation of Socorro doves

We first began a census of breeding birds in the care of aviculturists, both in the
United States and in Germany. A similar exercise in 1978 gave us an estimate of
about 400 individuals in captivity. However, this number has probably been
halved due to waning interest amongst bird breeders since, although tame to
humans, Socorro doves in captivity can be very aggressive to each other and to
other birds. The next step will be to bring about 50 pairs to a breeding centre in

Highland forest and sheep-damaged areas. The sheep-damage is manifested by the areas of red soil exposed after the vegetation has been destroyed by sheep and erosion has set in. (Photo: Helen Horblit)

California to increase numbers and to conduct life-history studies. Aviculturists will act as "reserves" to provide us with additional birds for eventual release, and also to ensure that not all individuals are in one centre, thus minimizing the risk of losing breeding stock due to disease or natural disaster.

Studies on the genetic diversity in the captive population will also be carried out; all the captives are probably descended from very few ancestors and these studies will allow the compilation of a computerized stud book to determine the optimal pairings. Medical screening and treatment of all captives will guarantee the health of the birds to be repatriated, and a quarantine programme will ensure that no pathogens alien to Socorro Island will be introduced. Finally, the doves to be released will be housed in aviaries on a selected site on Socorro Island, to acclimatize the doves to the native vegetation.

Habitat restoration

To restore and prepare Socorro Island's unique ecosystem for the return of the Socorro dove, it will be necessary to: continue mapping and exploring the island, its vegetation and soils; construct sheep-proof fences to protect from overgrazing; collect some 2,000–3,000 feral sheep and the feral cats and ship them off the island; and reforest the sheep-damaged woods with the native forest trees described in early accounts of the island.

An extensive programme of research on the flowering characteristics of the plants and breeding characteristics of the birds will be implemented to achieve an understanding of the ecosystem structure and function, which is imperative to save both the habitat and the dove.

My field studies will concentrate on a banding/ecological study of the endemic mocking-bird and endemic parrot. Others in our team will study the other seven endemics. The mocking-bird and parrot, once abundant throughout the island, are now restricted to the highland forests. We only encountered six singing mocking-birds in the space of three week of searching by foot, vehicle and horseback. We plan to explore one last unexplored forest on the northwest side of the island to seek more mocking-birds. The remnant populations of mocking-birds may have to be captured for captive propagation. However, we wish to avoid this if at all possible.

Returning the Socorro doves to the wild

The first releases can take place once the cats and the sheep are removed, at the earliest five years from now. Annual releases of captive stock will augment the reintroduced population until a self-sustaining level has been established. Released birds will be banded (ringed) and monitored to study dispersal, survival and reproductive success. Radio-tracking of doves is planned for the initial release phase. In restoring the habitat in preparation for release of Socorro doves, we shall also be saving the other endemic bird species which cohabit the same forest stands.

One of the advisers to the project is the Governor of Socorro, Admiral M. Rodriguez. An ardent protector of nature, the Admiral is completely devoted to the project and has supported the ornithologists' previous expeditions by supplying logistics (personnel, horses, motor boats). He is now building an information centre which will explain the value of the island to its few inhabitants, something they are hardly aware of, and the behaviour they should adopt in order to preserve it.

Head of Socorro Island dove (Zenaida graysoni). This species is extinct in the wild but is being bred in captivity for eventual release in the ancestral home.

The Silverglen medicinal plant nursery

Geoffrey Richard Nichols

8 Larch Road, Morningside, 4001 Durban, South Africa

South African, born 22 October 1953. Horticulturist with the Durban Parks Department. Educated in South Africa; National Diploma in Parks and Recreation Administration by correspondence in 1980.

In Southern Africa a very high proportion of indigenous plant species have come to be valued for some specific purpose, e.g. for food or for medicinal, medico-magical or ritual purposes. In the face of demographic shifts and economic and technological changes, traditional food-plant usages have very often come to be abandoned in favour of new high-yield crop introductions. But the same has not been the case with medicinal and ritual plant utilization. More often than not, native plant species have remained in as much demand as ever for these purposes, even in the face of massive trends towards urbanization with accompanying changes in lifestyle.

Recourse to traditional healing practices constitutes a deeply rooted element in the indigenous cultures of the region, and access to Western medicine displaces these practices only partially. But the capacity of the biome to sustain its yield in this respect is continuously diminishing due to increasing demand and the loss of land to intensive agriculture.

In addition, the traditional herbalists (or *inyanga* in Zulu) are moving to the towns, and the work of collection and distribution is being left to middlemen who, since they are paid in cash according to the quantities they can deliver, have little incentive to observe the conservation practices that used to be part of the traditional healer's code. Trees that once readily healed after yielding small patches of bark now die when all their bark is stripped at once; a whole local population of a species is easily wiped out, and many species that are heavily utilized for roots or bulbs have wholly disappeared from remnant grasslands and forests. In nature reserves and conservation areas, attempts are made in management policies to allow for controlled gathering but they are quite inadequate to the level of market demand.

Conservation in these circumstances cannot, as up to now, simply be pursued by defensive measures, and protection of species by legislation and control of proclaimed reserves is merely to wish away the massive fact of the market

A bird's eye view of the Silverglen nursery and surrounding nature reserve.

demand. It was in contemplating this inescapable fact that I finally realized that if the market will pay for gathering, it should equally pay for growing. And my experience as a public amenity horticulturist specializing in the ornamental use of native Natal plants told me that nearly all the species at risk from herbalist overexploitation could quite easily be grown for sale by large-scale commercial growers, farmers, nurserymen, etc.

Moving to protect a dwindling heritage

My first move was to improve my acquaintance with leading figures in the herb trade itself, and I found that cultivation was attractive to the professional herbal practitioners because it held out the prospect both of dependable sources of supply and of stabilized prices. However, the success of a commercial cultivation hinges on having dependable supplies of high-grade propagation material grown under optimum, controlled conditions, and this necessitates the establishment of a stock nursery on the largest scale possible. The Durban Municipal Parks Department proved willing to support the concept and one of the Department's nurseries in the 220-hectare Silverglen reserve was, in January 1986, exclusively set aside for the project, and we were able to begin the work of bulking up stocks of all the native medicinal plant species we then had available. The next stage has been to build up and expand a network of seed and plant suppliers, chiefly farmers who have some of the needed plants growing wild on their land, and parks wardens stationed in nature reserves who collect for us under the auspices of their conservation agencies.

One Silverglen is not enough

The Silverglen Nursery operation extends at present over approximately one hectare of intensive seedling cultivation, running to about 120,000 plants in total. Already we have something like 120 at-risk species in cultivation, but no more than four or five have yet been propagated in quantities that enable us to start supplying commercial growers, so there is still a long way to go. Present indications are that the total number of local Natal species that are intensively utilized in herbal medicine probably runs to something over 400. Some are not especially at risk but, of the ones that are at risk, there are probably another 40 or 50 species that are a high priority for cultivation. In addition, we are probably going to have to concede that perhaps 10 to 20 species may in the end defy attempts to bring them into cultivation and will only be conserved by active protection of wild habitats.

It is plain enough already that one Silverglen is not going to be sufficient, not even as the pump-priming undertaking that it is intended to be. Seed supplies and stocks of propagation material will have to be increased to a level well beyond that which our single operation will be in a position to sustain, and climatic factors set limits in any case to what we can successfully propagate in one location. Furthermore the intrinsic scale of the environmental problem sets it beyond the legitimate scope of a single municipal Parks Department. My own Department's initial response was a recognition that Silverglen has direct relevance to management policies for nature reserves within its own jurisdiction, but the idea clearly needs to be taken up on a much wider front from now on. Not just the Silverglen plants, but also the Silverglen idea, wait to be transplanted to further minds and soils, both in South Africa and abroad, wherever there seems to be a chance that the concept could usefully put down new roots.

Muthi gatherers display
their wares.

Rolex Laureate – The Rolex Awards for Enterprise – 1990

Les Stocker

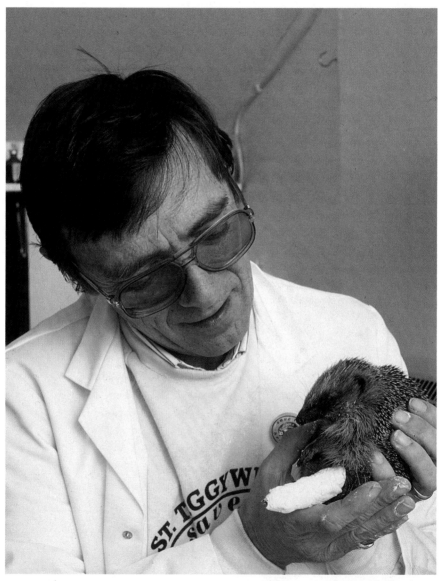

Les Stocker, a writer and photographer from the United Kingdom, has for over a decade been caring for injured wild animals at his Wildlife Hospital Trust. He now plans to establish a teaching hospital, the first in Europe, where veterinary professionals and concerned lay people can acquire the wildlife treatment skills not covered by conventional veterinary training.

Setting up Europe's first wildlife teaching hospital

Les Stocker

Rolex Laureate
The Rolex Awards for Enterprise – 1990

1 Pemberton Close, Aylesbury, Bucks HP21 7NY, United Kingdom

British, born 31 January 1943. Writer and Photographer, Director and Managing Trustee of the Wildlife Hospital Trust. Educated in United Kingdom; ACCA intermediate examination.

Every year in Britain over five million wild birds and other wild animals are injured as a direct result of their encounters with man and man's world. The majority of these are purely accidental, causing traumatic shock to the animals and often to their human counterparts. Without experienced and expert treatment, most of these casualties inevitably die, to the great consternation of all those who vainly tried to rescue them. In addition to animals that are injured, there are also many that are killed outright, including a vast number of small birds and animals slaughtered by domestic cats.

The veterinary profession in Britain and, I would think, in the countries of mainland Europe, receive no formal training in dealing with wildlife casualties. Most wild birds and other wild animals are totally different from domesticated animals and need specialized techniques in handling, medical care and husbandry. None of the conservation groups offers any support to injured wildlife, often recommending any method of slaughter, including the swinging of birds against walls, rather than offering any help.

A decade in the care of injured wildlife

Over the last 11 years I have, on a voluntary basis, succeeded in reversing the trend that every animal injured should be slaughtered. The Wildlife Hospital Trust I founded has, during that time, taken in more and more casualties and instigated methods of treatment and rehabilitation, all with increasing success. In 1988 alone, over 6,000 casualties were treated, with the vast majority being made fit enough to return to the wild.

The positive approach has shown that wild animal casualties can be rehabilitated successfully, and the welfare of individual wild animals is now being accepted as a crucial part of Britain's overall conservation strategy. The general public, who usually find the casualties, are now greatly relieved that there is help

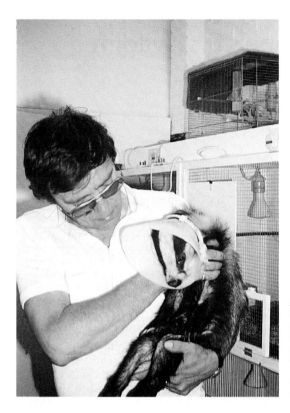

At the new teaching hospital Les Stocker shall be able to demonstrate handling techniques for dangerous wild animals like badgers. At present there are no training facilities anywhere in the United Kingdom.

available where there was none before. The individual casualty, although not consciously appreciating the help, is better off with a life to look forward to.

Even without a full veterinary and diagnostic section, the Trust has uncovered previously unknown conditions in some wild animals and has found and published many treatments. From the existing centre, in my garden, many educational projects and publications have been produced: fact sheets are issued to schools and children on various wildlife subjects, offering practical advice on preserving wildlife and its habitats; veterinary publications specifically for wildlife, notably hedgehogs and badgers, are circulated to the veterinary profession. I have also written and had published complete textbooks on hedgehogs and, soon, garden birds.

Our book, *The Complete Hedgehog*, which is an illustrated guide to every aspect of the life of the hedgehog and the care they receive at the Centre, is a best-seller and has already been translated into German, with other languages to follow. Since 1985, people have been rescuing hedgehogs injured on the roads in increasing numbers – so many in fact that the Wildlife Hospital Trust has had to create a special section for hedgehogs, St. Tiggywinkles. This is the only unit we know of that specializes in the treatment of these animals and, in 1986–1987, no fewer than 600 of them were seen by experienced veterinarians. The hospital also specializes in the care of badgers and owls. Large numbers of birds have been rescued from certain death thanks to a boat specially equipped to rescue the victims of oil spills. Moreover, we have recently instituted a telephone service offering the public information 24 hours a day.

Founding a teaching hospital for wildlife care

Obviously, the existing set-up could not cope with those five million casualties, so I have set in motion the creation of what is to be Europe's first wildlife teaching hospital. The new hospital complex will be a focal point where veterinarians, veterinary nurses, animal welfare operatives and lay members of the public can come to learn techniques for the handling, treatment and rehabilitation of wild birds and other wild animals. These delegates to the training courses will then have the knowledge and confidence to return to their localities and offer a local wildlife rescue and treatment service.

I have lived with wildlife traumas for many years. I have seen Britain's failure to support its wildlife, in particular the drastic lack of facilities to deal with oiled birds and the injured larger animals like badgers and deer. When the seal virus hit the North Sea, there was nowhere that could even take in a seal, let alone treat it. With all these things in mind, it is our intention that the new hospital will have many unique features. There will be a complete, fully staffed veterinary unit to deal with the hospital's own casualties as well as specialized referrals from other groups and veterinarians. A fully equipped diagnostic laboratory will be available for patient evaluation and diagnosis and a complete oiled bird cleaning unit and rescue network will be set up to handle some of the thousands of birds who become oiled each year; this unit will also treat sick or injured seals. Finally, intensive care units will be provided for the badgers, foxes, deer and swans together with specialized facilities for bats, amphibians, insectivores, birds of prey, etc.

Creating the human resources for tomorrow

The teaching element will constitute a major thrust in the new hospital. Over and above courses for veterinarians, veterinary nurses and lay people, it will offer facilities for involving the younger generations in practical conservation projects, including the culture of rare and endangered species and general conservation management of small areas, notably the children's own garden.

The release of rehabilitated wild animals is a new science in its own right requiring much research and education.

Conserving marine turtles in the western Indian Ocean

Bernard Bonnet

Laboratoire d'Ecophysiologie, Faculté des Sciences, Université de la Réunion, B. P. No. 5, 97490 Sainte-Clotilde, Réunion

French, born 18 October 1946. Director of a University research laboratory, Réunion. Educated in France, Réunion; Doctorate (Biological Oceanography) from Université d'Aix-Marseille in 1970.

Over the past centuries, the worldwide population of marine turtles has declined considerably due to extensive exploitation in tropical areas; with human colonization, numerous sea turtle populations have been decimated, for local consumption and for international trade. The situation has become worse during the past few decades because of demographic development, building along the coasts, overfishing, tourism and pollution; many breeding sites have been destroyed or are under threat. The International Union for Conservation of Nature has listed all the marine turtles among the endangered species and international conventions give them maximum legal protection.

Endangered marine turtles in the Indian Ocean

In the Indian Ocean, human occupation of even the most isolated coastal areas where turtles breed, traditional hunting and collecting of eggs and the introduction of new technology for large-scale and systematic exploitation of marine resources has intensified the destruction of marine turtles and their habitats. In coming years, this region will witness a further acceleration of industrial development and tourist facilities, and the time has come for a concentrated effort to preserve the few sites and wild populations still existing.

Although, following publication of the proceedings of a regional working group held in 1985 we received local financial support from the authorities of Réunion to carry out surveys on the Tromelin, Glorieuses and Comoros Islands and to train young Malagasy students, more substantial funding at an international level is required. At the same time, we are convinced that after more than ten years of field experience, a more enterprising approach is necessary: our ambition with the project is to mobilize, in a relatively short time and in a delimited area, financial, material, intellectual and human resources which will permit all of the countries to find adjustable and co-ordinated solutions for the conservation of marine turtles and their environment.

The green turtle, here on a nesting beach of the isolated island of Tromelin (Indian Ocean), is representative of the seven world species of marine turtles, long-distance oceanic migrating reptiles, all of which are endangered.

Partners in the defence of marine turtles

This project has set itself the following objectives: to establish and/or enforce a network of private and public partners that will provide technical and financial support, and launch an international association to manage the resources made available; to train at least one young student in the Mascareignes Islands, Seychelles Islands, Comoros Archipelago, Madagascar, and on the east coast of Africa and the coasts of the Gulf of Eden and the Red Sea; and to collect information required for biological evaluation and conservation strategies, with special attention being paid to the human and economic conditions of each island or territory.

To implement the project and the scholastic and public education activities it entails, we plan to take leave from our present University responsibilities either partially or totally for one or two years. This will allow us to supplement the various activities with local interventions of an educational nature (public information, production of documents, etc.).

A training programme for turtle conservation

The objective of the training programme will be for each country to have its own specialist in marine turtle research and conservation. To achieve this we plan to: select a suitable student or students capable of carrying out this scientific role in a manner responsive to natural, human and economic realities; appoint an established scientist of international repute to help in training and following up each

395

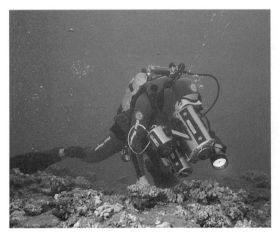

Underwater exploration of marine turtle habitat in a coral reef area; photography and cinematography are used in association with other research techniques (tagging, radio-tracking, teledetection and genetic analysis) for elucidating biological cycles of these species.

student; establish a student study programme on biological, ethnographical and economical aspects of marine use and conservation; and provide access to adequate information resources, research facilities and study grants.

In this way, we will collect the data we need for conservation activities, train local students and integrate them into the international scientific community. With this information network in place we would be able to expand our knowledge in marine turtle biology and, in particular, in their migration and homing behaviour, making use of the latest available technology.

For instance, we would organize a series of expeditions by ship to follow the reptiles as they migrate. Divers would observe them in the water and explore their underwater habitat. They would even tag some specimens to track them by radio. Ultimately, we would also hope to use satellite observation to fully chart the turtles' migration patterns.

All this will, we hope, focus more attention on these unique and endangered marine reptiles and stimulate the type of international solidarity and co-operation we feel to be the best approach to conserving these cyclical and long-distance migratory species.

Conserving Gangetic dolphins in the Karnali River of Nepal

Tej Kumar Shrestha

Royal Nepal Academy of Science and Technology, New Baneshore, P.O. Box 3323, Kathmandu, Nepal

Nepalese, born 11 February 1948. Associate Member of the Royal Nepal Academy of Science and Technology and teacher of Zoology at the Tribhuvan University. Educated in Nepal; Ph.D. (Zoology) from Tribhuvan University, Kathmandu, in 1976.

Man has long been intrigued by dolphins and has built fantasies and myths around them. Scientific interest in dolphins has increased dramatically since they were first reared in aquaria for public display in Europe around the turn of the 19th century. Scientifically, these animals offer a particularly interesting subject area for studies of behaviour. The fresh-water Gangetic dolphins deserve special attention from conservationists. These are the most primitive fresh water cetaceans, and are of intrinsic academic and aesthetic value.

An understanding of the lives of wild Gangetic dolphins in their natural environment is becoming increasingly important to the animals themselves as human contact becomes more frequent and potentially detrimental. There is a need to know how Gangetic dolphin populations are structured in terms of ranges, composition, dynamics and social systems. Such baseline information is critical to predict and mitigate potentially adverse impact from human activities.

The dolphin community of the Karnali River

Repeated observation of Gangetic dolphins in the wild can be difficult given the ephemeral nature of their appearance above the surface of the water, their lack of distinctive markings, their large territorial range and their migratory tendencies. Most of the dolphin's private life takes place in secret under the water. The problem with dolphins is further magnified by an inability to accurately assess the sex and age of many individuals strictly through direct observations.

The Karnali River in western Nepal has a resident and migratory community of some 30 dolphins of all ages and sexes. My project aims to: study the reproductive ecology, behaviour, sex, age and body condition of the Gangetic dolphin; and apply the information to academic research and the management of the dolphin

A Gangetic dolphin in its natural environment.

in semi-natural reserves, fish parks, dolphin parks, etc. The Gangetic dolphin is near the point of extinction. The Nepalese Government has already put it in the list of endangered mammals of Nepal. It is also included in the IUCN Red Data Book and in CITES Appendix I.

Fresh ground for research

I will carry out ecological and behavioural studies and will undertake a capture, mark and release programme. The specific objectives of the programme include: conducting an ecological survey of the Karnali River of Nepal; determining the seasonal hydrobiological factors in the riverine ecosystem; elucidating the dolphin's reproductive ecology, behaviour and migration habits; and drawing up management recommendations to save the wild dolphin population before the creation of the Karnali High Dam.

Three field-sampling stations will be established along the Karnali River. It is suspected that hydrobiological conditions induce and trigger the migration of dolphins. Therefore, to identify critical hydrobiological conditions, water quality tests as well as qualitative and quantitative studies of plankton will be made in high, low and mid-water flows of water. Temperature, current velocity, river level changes and turbidity measurements will be carried out using standard techniques. Attempts will be made to capture four to six dolphins using gill nets and drift nets. They will be stretched across the upriver and downriver sections of the Karnali River.

Any captured dolphins will be transported to the bank of the river by putting them in a specially constructed wet stretcher and then released soon afterwards once biometrical records have been made. For this study, weight, length, circumference, number of teeth and length of snout measurements will be taken. Radio-transmitters or a harness will be attached to the base of the dorsal fin or at the base of the tail fluke for biotelemetric studies. In this way the dolphins' movements will be monitored and population dynamics studied. Temporary or permanent marking methods such as the use of paint and coloured plastic markers will be tried on additional dolphins. Also, the use of natural marks and fin notching may be a feasible method of marking the dorsal fin of the dolphins. Radio-transmitters and visual spottings will be tried out for tracking the movements of individual dolphins. A spatial census and photo-identification technique will be used to estimate dolphin populations. In this way, estimates of population in a given time and space will be determined. The estimation will be based on visual counts. Medium-sized power boats will be utilized. They will be rowed or motored upstream and downstream for counting purposes. Counts will be made at intervals of a fortnight.

The establishment of river parks

One way of reducing the environmental impact on the river dolphin is to establish semi-natural river parks for existing populations. Basic ecological and behavioural data will provide the knowledge of habitat needs required to help design captive environments that permit a full range of dolphin activities, including successful reproduction. By gaining a knowledge of typical patterns of school composition in the wild, the sex and age structure of the semi-captive community can be managed to permit naturally occurring combinations of particular sex and age classes.

Knowledge of reproductive behaviour can be used to facilitate captive breeding and calf-rearing programmes, and help to optimalize the dolphin nursery and rearing programme. Data and information on seasonal variations in physiological status can be used to help monitor the dolphins' health and well-being. Further knowledge on the mother-calf relation can be helpful in the selection process during capture, and improve the chances of survival in captivity. Information on disease and parasites and frequency of occurrence of pathogens in the dolphin can help in the treatment of illness in captivity.

Tej Kumar Shrestha capturing a Gangetic dolphin on film.

Self-help project for the culturally marginalized Aetas of Zambales

GGisela Nass

University of Maryland – Asian Division, Box 98, US Naval Station, APO San Francisco, California 96651, United States

American, born 20 January 1939. Teacher for the University of Maryland – Asian Division. Educated in United States; Ph. D. (Anthropology) from University of Wisconsin, Madison, in 1979.

The Aetas of Zambales are descendants of the original inhabitants of the Philippine islands. They belong to a larger group of people who are collectively called "Negrito", and who are spread over most of the islands. Today, they form part of over eight million people (roughly 14% of the country's population) who are referred to as "cultural communities". The Aetas have always lived in the jungle as hunters and gatherers and, in some cases, have practised swidden culture. As a semi-nomadic people, the Negritos owned few material possessions, and utilized mainly plant materials for clothing and shelter. During the past several centuries, the original populations steadily lost forest lands to logging and lumber companies, miners, farmers, land speculators, and US military installations. Today, most Negritos are destitute, living on marginal lands that render few resources for survival.

Loss of traditional lands

The Aetas of Zambales lost their traditional lands to emigrating Malaysian, Spanish and Chinese groups, and, since the turn of the century, to Americans. It has only been since around 1909, that the Aetas of Zambales began to settle in scattered villages in this mountainous region. Their present politico-socio-economic status is more depressed than that of many other so-called minority groups in the country. Unlike the more aggressive Muslim groups in the south, or the tourist-attracting Ifulao of north-central Luzon, the Aetas never received help from the now defunct PANAMIN (Presidential Assistance for National Minorities), whose purported function it was to provide financial and technical aid to such groups.

This project is intended to help the Aetas not only to improve their current dismal socio-economic situation, but also to gain equal social rights commensurate with the "lowlander Filipino" populations of the eastern coastal areas of Zambales Province on Luzon Island. Since my first introduction to the Aetas some seven years ago, I have on many occasions, and unsuccessfully so, tried to find

400

Aetas pursuing their marginal agricultural practices.

financial support from national and international agencies to eliminate some of their many social, economic and legal rights difficulties.

I suggested to the chieftains of four villages to establish a self-help programme in the form of a non-profit, non-stock organization. I wrote the articles, bye-laws, modus operandi to everyone's satisfaction, and in November of 1986 our organization was legally registered with the Security and Exchange Commission in Manila as "Aetas of Zambales Development Organization, Inc.". The incorporators are three acting chieftains of local resettled villages, one retired chieftain, the mother of five children (who is attending college), and myself.

Our principal aim is the procurement of legal channels for the people in order to enable them to apply for land stewardships, and for financial support from funding agencies for the following areas of development: primary, secondary, tertiary, vocational and technical education for all children and young adults; development of agriculture and production of cash crops; health care facilities for primary and maternal/infant health care, and family planning; and establishment of village technology and small businesses.

Goals of our self-help programme

There is a great need to grow less water-intensive crops (i.e. rice) and produce protein-rich crops for local consumption and trading. This has required the introduction of a variety of crop plants and trees as food and industrial resources (i.e. soybeans, Jojoba, and Ibl Ibl trees) and plants for soil preservation. Because of extreme annual fluctuations in water supply, we are in immediate need of an irrigation system. The lack of the educational facilities has maintained a high illiteracy among the Aetas. Nevertheless, the people realize the importance of education for their children. Therefore, most donations so far have been used to pay children's tuition and school related costs. This year, we have 15 children enrolled in secondary education, and four young people attend college.

We are trying to improve the health of the people who suffer a great deal from malaria, tuberculosis, upper respiratory and parasitic diseases, and malnutrition.

401

My particular concern is the lack of maternal/infant health care and family planning. We need a local clinic and professional staff (i.e. trained Aetas mid-wives) to provide primary health care needs, education in family planning and the dispensation of free birth control materials.

Our final goal is the establishment of village technology and small businesses, i.e. a cottage industry. We are in the process of establishing a training programme for the production of traditional Aetas handicraft (an art forgotten by many Aetas). We need training programmes for the production of new articles and materials, and, indeed, have found an American sponsoring group to teach the manufacture of quilts.

Significance of the project

Many Aetas left their depleted forests years ago and either settled on lands, provided for by the government, or as unwelcome squatters on lands to which they have no legal claim. They are without legal resources, and the new constitution of the Aquino government contains no specific provisions for socio-economic advancement of minorities. Their status parallels that of many marginal societies who have remained within non-technological cultural traditions, and who are now threatened by twentieth century expansion.

It is hoped that our development project within the microcosm of a small rural population, that has barely exited the traditions of a hunting-gathering culture, will provide useful baseline data for other similar projects in applied anthropology. Further, it is suggested that continual progress assessment will furnish information on the needs of the participants, and the socio-economic changes brought about by the development. This information should be useful for large-scale planning in rural development.

Aetas inhabitants of the village of Carabassa.

402

Audio-visual education programme to prevent the disastrous effects of volcanic eruptions

Maurice Paul Krafft

Honourable Mention
The Rolex Awards for Enterprise – 1990

Centre de Volcanologie Vulcain, B. P. 5, 68700 Cernay, France

French, born 25 March 1946. Director, Centre de Volcanologie Vulcain. Educated in France; M. Sc. (Earth Science) from University of Besançon and Strasbourg in 1971.

For more than 20 years, my wife Katia, and myself have observed, studied, filmed and photographed over 100 volcanic eruptions throughout the world. In 1968, we set up the *Centre de Volcanologie Vulcain* in France, which is one of the world's best-documented centres on volcanic eruptions, with 100,000 photographs, over 500 hours of 16-mm film and an extensive library. Katia and I have already written 17 books on volcanoes and volcanic eruptions in such countries as: Italy, Hawaii, Japan, Martinique, Guadeloupe, Réunion, New Zealand, etc.

Twenty years of volcano research

For the first ten years, we viewed these eruptions merely as awesome natural phenomena, the most wonderful sight to be seen on mother Earth. Our experience was, at that stage, related mainly to basaltic eruptions which, although destructive, very seldom kill people. But our view of active volcanoes as merely awesome sights changed after the enormous explosive eruption of Mount St. Helens in the United States in 1980 and even more so after we had witnessed the Chichón explosion in Mexico in 1982 (3,500 victims), the Nevado del Ruiz mud flows in Colombia (more than 22,000 victims) in 1985 and many other eruptions.

We rapidly became convinced that, when people around volcanoes die as the result of an explosive eruption, it is mainly for two reasons: first, we the volcanologists, are not convincing enough when we draft and present our reports on the volcanic risks of a specific volcano, that may erupt any time, to government and local officials. A written report full of scientific terminology which is difficult to understand by non-specialists in vulcanology presented to a high-ranking government official in the country's capital or embassy is not the most effective way of alerting people to a poorly perceived danger.

The tragedy of Nevado del Ruiz in 1985 in which more than 22,000 people were killed in mudflows, is the most terrible demonstration of this fact. It was obvious to any volcanologist days before the tragedy that mudflows would come down

A volcanic explosion. The photographic exposure captures the traces of the material projected into the air.

the volcano, flooding cities like Armero (which had already been destroyed by the same kind of volcanic hazard in 1845); however, the reports presented by the vulcanologists were too scientific for officials that had never had any experience with volcanic eruptions.

A second point is that people living near volcanoes that are only rarely active are not aware of the volcanic hazards they will have to face in case of a crisis. There is nobody in these – usually developing – countries and no international organization that is responsible for educating people living in the danger zones, to inform them of what to do and what not to do in the event of a violent volcanic eruption. The populations at risk very often die out of ignorance of volcanic phenomena.

Volcano-hazard educational aids

It is for these reasons that I, as a responsible scientist, concerned by humanitarian problems, have decided to devote part of my time to producing two 25-minute volcanic hazard videotapes (3/4 inch BVU Pal). These will be based entirely on my collection of 500 hours of 16-mm colour movie stock shots on volcanic hazards (drawn from more than 100 eruptions that my wife and I have witnessed), and I will make them available at no cost for this purpose. These two videotapes, distributed free-of-charge in at least six languages, will be used to educate officials about volcanic hazards and, if necessary, to rapidly convince them to take the necessary measures in the event of an emergency. The videotapes will also be used to inform those at risk in the vicinity of a volcano as to what they should do to survive in the face of a specific volcanic eruption.

The first videotape will illustrate one by one, with case histories I have witnessed, the different kinds of volcanic hazards (lava flows, mud flows, pyroclastic flows, ash falls, etc.) and what to do to survive in each case. In emergency situations, only the volcanic hazards that may concern the area at risk will be shown to the officials and, where necessary, broadcast on television to inform the populations.

The second videotape will contain illustrated basic steps on prevention of the disastrous effects of volcanic eruptions, namely, the preparation of hazard maps, volcano monitoring and the development of tried and tested emergency response plans. It will be produced from footage of film that I have taken on this subject around the world over the past 20 years and will be intended mainly to convince officials to implement preventive measures on their volcanoes.

Honouring a twin objective

For four years now, I have been promoting this project amongst members of the scientific community in the conviction that it will save many lives during future major eruptions and mitigate the effect of violent environment on man. A scientist has responsibilities not only to pure science but also to humankind. This is my way of honouring this twin objective.

The vulcanologist, Maurice Krafft, measuring the temperature of a gas jet on the highly dangerous Merapi Volcano.

Reforestation of the Jacaré-Pepira river basin

Antonio de Pádua Bertelli

Rua Dr. Diogo de Faria, 171, 04037 São Paulo-SP, Brazil

Brazilian, born 12 June 1937. Chairman of the Department of Head and Neck Surgery of the São Joaquim Hospital. Educated in Brazil and Italy; M. D. from Universidade do Paraná, in 1960.

The Jacaré-Pepira River is formed at the foot of the Itaqueri range and flows for 174 km within the geographic centre of São Paulo State. The river crosses 13 municipal territories although the only city in which it flows within the urban limits is Brotas (246 km from São Paulo). In that city, the Jacaré-Pepira River forms falls up to 12 m in height. Formerly, in October and November of each year, hundreds of people gathered on the banks of the river to watch the spectacle of the fish fighting their way upstream to reproduce. Since 1970 this has no longer occurred.

Countering the degradation of the Jacaré-Pepira forest

Extensive forest burnings have been carried out around the Jacaré-Pepira River to obtain clearings for coffee plantations (1860–1920), then cotton (1920–1945) and, finally, sugar cane plantations (1960–1980). Moreover, from 1920 to 1960, nearly 1 million trees were cut to produce charcoal. The environmental decay was further aggravated in 1980, with the introduction of orange growing in the fertile lands of the river banks. I own property in the Jacaré-Pepira River area and I early became aware of the need for conservation action. However, until 1980, when the first sounds of environmental movements began to reach this area of São Paulo State, our efforts bore no fruit. Subsequently, 13 of the local 15 cities decided to set up committees for the preservation of the forest; in 1984, the mayors of all of the cities joined together in an overall conservation committee with the aim of restoring the ecosystems of the river banks by the year 2000.

The main aspects of the programme were: reforestation; recovery of the river bank soil; construction of dams to conserve such fish as the dourado, pacu, piapara, corimbata and pintado; reorganization of the bird management installations to breed endangered wild birds such as the macuco, ema, jao, mutum and jacutinga. The programme's successes have aroused considerable interest in the media and have attracted the attention of various international institutions.

A view of the last Jacaranda tree taken in 1980. A total of 640 individual trees have been derived from this sole survivor.

Over a period of 15 years, the number of land owners supporting the programme has increased and the riverside ecosystem has improved.

Original composition of the primitive forest

It is estimated that the Jacaré-Pepira river bank forest contains some 3 million large trees, and attempts have been made to determine the various species that made up the primitive forest by studies on forest remnants and the existence of birds dependent on the seeds of specific trees. I organized, starting in 1979, several expeditions along the Jacaré-Pepira River together with botanists from the Bauru, São Carlos and Campinas Universities, to record remnants of the primitive forest. Only six small groups of the original trees were found, whereas scattered specimens at the Jacaré-Pepira river banks accounted for a great percentage of the primitive species. A sole adult jacaranda was found in August 1980 and it was bearing fruit. We collected its seeds; these gave us 640 seedlings which were replanted in 1988.

Of the findings we made, 13 species or subspecies of tree could not be identified; theses are being studied at Unicamp in São Paulo. It has been observed that only on a few occasions did adult trees have daughter-trees in the range of 50 m. Most of the limit areas within the Jacaré-Pepira hydrographic basin had been occupied by eucalyptuses (*Eucalyptus australianus*), as of 1910. Besides the eucalyptuses, pine trees (*Pinus elliot*, etc.), were introduced for cellulose pulp and, by 1860, they occupied large areas. The secondary forest, which emerged as substitution, was represented by the macuva palm tree, which is presently spreading throughout the marginal areas.

Reforestation

From 1979 to 1982, the author bought 5,600 seedlings of the species to be found at the government plant nurseries in São Paulo, Bauru and Pederneiras. They were planted at random, below the Peixe River – one of Jacaré-Pepira River's tributaries – on both the left and right banks; some plantings were also concen-

407

trated on streams within 1,000 m of the main river bank. These concentrations of 100 to 150 trees contained at least ten of the varieties. News of this programme stimulated a positive reaction amongst other communities which have since set up their own plant nurseries with the seeds obtained from the expeditions.

A travelling educational exhibition visited all the cities, and in particular promoted contests for school children to search for rare seed specimens. Some cities launched commercial programmes to obtain seedlings from fruit trees existing in backyards, old houses and small rural properties. A booming trade in seedlings from the original species sprang up alongside the highways. By December 1988, 45,000 trees had been planted in the cities in the Jacaré-Pepira basin and forestry associations began to be formed to benefit from fiscal incentives accorded by the government.

By the end of 1988, the reserves of seedlings obtained from seeds or transplantations had risen to 100,000 in the plant nurseries sponsored by the municipal authorities and 1 million in the plant nurseries of the state universities. All these seedlings are available to the Jacaré-Pepira River Protection Consortium. It is expected that at least 150,000 new seedlings will be planted on the Jacaré-Pepira River banks in 1989.

Experience in the reforestation of the Jacaré-Pepira River demonstrates the feasibility of planting at least 2 million new trees by the year 2000. Certain existing concepts of plant behaviour and development will fatally be modified and new, non-classified, species will be discovered. There is clear evidence that, if the current policy is maintained with the same level of enthusiasm, in 20 years' time, the Jacaré-Pepira River will be saved from decay, and its fauna, flora, quality of the water, etc., will have largely been restored.

Antonio de Pádua Bertelli planting a very rare Jequitibá Rosa (Cariniana legalis, Mart.) raised in a plant nursery in 1988.

408

Insect conservation in the Indonesian Archipelago

Clifford E. Hoelscher

Jl. Kuwung Kuwung No. 24, Villa Duta, Bogor 16144, Indonesia

American, born 13 January 1941. Senior Fulbright Scholar conducting research and lecturing at Institut Pertanian Bogor. Educated in United States; Ph. D. (Entomology) from Mississippi State University, in 1970.

Insect life is a vital component of our environment and fills an essential role in the production of our food chain. Indonesia has one of the most diverse, unique and abundant natural supplies of insect species in the world. However, expanding agricultural pesticide use, industrial development, destruction of tropical forests and a general disregard for conservation are having a serious impact on beneficial and rare tropical insects. In addition, a primitive industry has developed in the collection and sale of rarer insects to tourists, individual collectors and museums, which – if continued uncontrolled – will further aggravate the situation of this island nation.

An insect-based business enterprise

My project is to set up a business enterprise that will help conserve the diverse insect life of Indonesia whilst, at the same time, augmenting scientific know-ledge, creating jobs and expanding tourism. The key component in this project is the Institut Pertanian Bogor (IPB) which already has a Department of Plant Pests and Diseases with a well-trained and dedicated staff and 320 bright and eager entomology students. Bogor already has a world-famous botanical garden, the Kebun Raya Bogor located adjacent to the IPB campus.

Our proposal is that the IPB should establish a world-class centre for insect life, which – in addition to contributing to the conservation of Indonesia's diverse resources – would offer outstanding educational and research facilities in entomology and act as a major tourist attraction with the possibility of creating employment for some 5,000 people. There are long-range plans to move the current IPB campus to a location currently under construction at Darmaga, some 10 km south. This would make it possible to expand the insect life facilities at the proposed adjacent botanical garden location. IPB is interested in a proposal to develop an academic centre of excellence.

IPB will develop a knowledge base to provide the expertise required for the rearing, conservation, display, commercial production and design for sale of

409

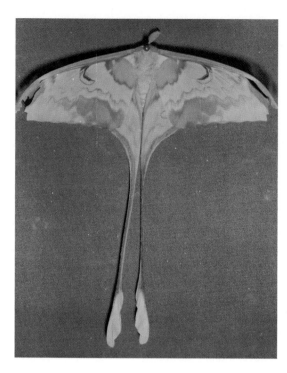

Actias isis South, *one of the Indonesian insects that Clifford Hoelscher proposes to rear and conserve in Indonesia.*

selected tropical insect life. Student involvement will be promoted and used in normal classroom training. I will develop a visitor centre on or near its property, adjacent to the world famous botanical garden at Bogor. Operating funds can come from a variety of sources including visitor centre fees and the provision of biological (integrated pest management) training programmes. Additional funds can be generated by the sale of collector photographs or specimens to tourists, foreign collectors, foreign entomology programmes and insect museums. The Institute will develop and encourage legislation which will help reduce and, hopefully, eliminate the needless over-collection and destruction of important tropical insects.

Partnership between business and higher education

The finalized programme will provide meaningful employment for approximately 5,000 citizens when the visitor centre and rearing operations are in full operation. These people will be involved in the commercial production, photography, display and approved government sale of selected tropical insect life. A carefully determined portion of each generation of reared insects will be released back into the native habitat for natural conservation. Destructive insect collection in wild habitats will, in due course, cease, except for scientific collections to support approved investigations or for private naturalists.

It will be necessary to develop a partnership between business and higher education in Indonesia which will ensure the financial success of the proposed scientific centre, the visitors' centre and employment for numerous "insect farmers". This work will be implemented through the organization of a Leadership Board selected from various groups involved in the proposed operations. Finally, it would be desirable, thereafter, to develop a co-operating visitors' centre at other tourist locations such as Bali, Manado and Ujungpandang to expand the knowledge and financial base for this enterprise.

The proposed complex will also rear and display species found in other geographical regions of the nation. Each region seems to have several types of unique species. Wild bees and beetles can be very diverse. Beneficial species are more common in the regions which produce a variety of crops and the areas which have used less insecticides. Mountain peaks in the Bogor area were found to contain very different beetle species even though they were 25 km apart. Just think what may be found on all those isolated islands. Entomologists from other countries will be encouraged to work and study at the new Bogor Centre.

Acquisition of local support

Local support is now developing rapidly. Funds generated for this idea will be used to develop the talents and skills of the Indonesian people. My interest is scientific and there are other available funds to support my future involvement in this project. The Bogor area has the trained personnel, available land, needed environment and professional desire to expand employment opportunities. In a simple market study conducted in January and February 1989 in Bogor, of the 110 tourists interviewed, 82% responded positively to the concept of a visitor centre for insects. Photographs and sample insect specimens attractively and carefully displayed were available for sale and met with eager purchasers.

The time has come for us to focus on a symbiotic relationship between insect life and business interests. A system must be constructed to enhance the natural resources of this developing nation and conserve them for future generations. Insects can be developed into a business and provide an urgently needed commodity, jobs. It took 60 to 350 million years for these insect species to evolve to their present state of existence. Why destroy the natural beauty, diversity and beneficial species it required nature so long to develop? The time has come for a new idea! Insects in the Indonesian Archipelago....

The site for the proposed visitor centre for Clifford Hoelscher's insect conservation project in Indonesia.

Saving the *Canal du Centre*

Jean-Pierre Gailliez

Honourable Mention
The Rolex Awards for Enterprise – 1990

Compagnie du Canal du Centre, Chemin de l'Apitoire 2, 7078 Le Roeulx, Belgium

Belgian, born 5 May 1944. Administrateur délégué. Educated in Belgium;
Licencié en Science de l'Education from Université Catholique de Louvain in 1969.

The *Canal du Centre*, built between 1880 and 1917, is about 20 km long. Since it goes through fairly large changes of level, it includes four boatlifts, each of which comprises a sort of metal tower 20 m high that functions on the principle of the funicular (one boat rises and another descends). These boatlifts still work the same today as when they were opened in 1917 – purely mechanically, with no gasoline engine or external electricity. All of the energy needed (e.g., for opening the gates or to counterbalance the loads moving up or down) is hydraulic, supplied by another river and a vertical accumulator.

This canal is threatened with replacement by a larger canal that conforms to the new European standards which require a capacity of 1,300 t. There was even a proposal put forward that a highway should be built on the site of the old canal and at one moment the local council decided to fill in a side branch connecting the canal with the town centre and the station. Realizing that these boatlifts were unique in the world and that the eight others existing in other places had either been dismantled or modernized (with oil-fuelled hydraulics or motors, etc.), I decided to do my best to save them from the certain destruction that would befall them after the construction of the new canal.

Organizing ourselves to save a canal

So, in 1977, I founded the *Compagnie du Canal du Centre* (CCC), a non-profit organization, to protect the canal. We rented two 300-tonne barges and then began organizing boat rides on the canal during weekends and taking people up and down in the boatlifts which also provided us with additional support for our cause. It was at this time that I realized the danger of turning the saving of the boatlifts into an objective of its own; what was necessary was an integrated campaign aimed at the much wider context of preserving a heritage of the social, economic and technical history of the area, including such aspects as immigration, industrial development, canal technology, etc.

The *Peterborough, a 300-tonne barge purchased and restored by Jean-Pierre Gailliez.*

In 1980, I took the next step: with my own money, I bought a small tugboat that could hold 25 passengers. In two years, 3,000 people had travelled on paid excursions on the barge and had gone up and down in the boatlifts; as a result of this financial breakthrough, by 1982, the CCC had sufficient funds to be able to buy a real tourist motor launch. Building on the success we had achieved, in 1983, the CCC restored an old coastguard cutter for one-day excursions and in 1986, it bought a 300-tonne barge, the *Peterborough*. The purchase of the *Peterborough* was preceded by long and tortuous discussions with the banks, but they finally agreed to grant us a mortgage loan. Soon after the purchase had been completed we started on the restoration with the help of volunteers and a number of workers paid by the Ministry of Employment as part of its policy of combating unemployment. We built in a total of ten four-berth cabins and a restaurant, and have also provided a multi-purpose room where travelling theatre companies can come to perform. Finally, in 1988, the CCC bought one last mini-steamboat with room for 125 persons, which gave the company a total transport capacity of 500 passengers.

Alongside this development, beginning in 1979, I managed to obtain from the State four abandoned houses located along the *Canal du Centre*. We then restored them and turned one into the *Canal du Centre* Museum, another into offices for the CCC, another into the CCC's technical centre, and the last into an "Exhibition Centre on the Boatlifts of the World". Each time an exhibit from a new country is put on display at the Exhibition Centre, I take the opportunity of organizing an official ceremony and send out invitations to important personalities from the countries in question requesting them to take part.

Expanding the Canal's attractions

In an attempt to preserve the historic heritage of the *Canal du Centre*, I bought in 1978 two of the last existing "clog" boats and towed them to the canal where I was able to restore them, thanks to the proceeds obtained from having been awarded the Dunhill Prize in 1983. One of them is now on dry land, in front of the Museum and its very small cabin (1.8 m by 1.6 m) has been refurnished to its original appearance. Here, young people will be able to rediscover a faraway past.

My daily association with the Canal brought me into contact with a derelict building that had been constructed to house the Italian immigrant workers employed at the local ironworks. It seemed an ideal site for a "visitors' centre" that would provide an added attraction to our canal programme. I therefore approached the Director-General of the Boel Ironworks, the building's owners, and having obtained the company's agreement, we submitted our proposals to the Minister of Labour and Employment who once again provided us with help under the job-creation scheme to restore the building and convert it into what is now known as the "Italian Canteen" and the "food centre" of our canal enterprise. Over 11,000 visitors have already been catered for to date.

Bringing fame and employment to the Canal area

Lastly, I organize festivals and rallies on "my" canal and twin my boatlifts with others in the world, enter my project in numerous competitions (it has won four awards and three large grants of support), and participate in many radio and television programmes.

At present, the CCC employs 35 people full-time and these are paid by the Ministry of Employment. The ultimate aim of all these activities is obviously to persuade the authorities to keep the *Canal du Centre* open after the new canal is finished, in six or seven years, even if it is turned into a leisure area.

La Cantine des Italiens.

The Kallindendron system to fight famine and the greenhouse effect

George Kallistratos

Faculty of Medicine, Laboratory of Nutrition Physiology, University of Ioannina, P.O. Box 1186, 45110 Ioannina, Greece

Greek, born 21 May 1927. Director, Department of Experimental Physiology, University of Ioannina. Educated in Greece, Egypt and Federal Republic of Germany; M.D. (Clinical Chemistry) from University of Hamburg in 1971.

Carbon dioxide is a "time bomb", threatening to destroy human life on our planet. It has been calculated that, if effective measures are not taken to control carbon dioxide emanations, within the next ten years, 225 billion additional tonnes of carbon dioxide will be accumulated in the earth's atmosphere and the carbon dioxide concentration in the air will have increased to 0.05% from the level of 0.03% a century ago. This would lead to dangerous changes in meteorological conditions and potential climatic collapse; increases in the earth's temperature provoking the so called "greenhouse effect" are typical of this. The prime cause of increasing carbon dioxide concentrations is fuel combustion; however, the situation is further aggravated because millions of trees are being cut down. Consequently, the capacity of our forests to regenerate oxygen from carbon dioxide is being drastically diminished. It has been estimated that by the end of this century, some 225 million hectares of forest will have been destroyed by human action. Another major negative effect of human interference with nature is to be seen in the irresistible spread of deserts throughout the world stemming also from over-population, over-grazing, etc.

One of the key measures suggested to prevent climatic collapse is the planting over the next few years of at least three billion trees at an estimated expense of US$ 450 billion. However, a practical difficulty here is the amount of irrigation water that would be required for so many new trees; estimates place the figures at between 21.6 and 43.2 billion m^3 of water per year. Innovative approaches are therefore required to reduce the water consumption of trees grown conventionally and to select new varieties of fruit and forest trees suitable for arid and desert regions, such as: almond, chestnut, mango, pear, walnut, etc.

Nature's own solution to water shortage and infertile soil

Having observed how nature, under certain conditions, permits trees to grow almost without nutrients and little moisture, I have developed the Kallidendron

415

Trees planted using the Kallidendron method on the roof of a house in Ioannina, northern Greece. These trees will contribute to the regeneration of the oxygen in this urban area.

(KALLIstratos and DENDRON = "tree" in Greek) system for planting a number of useful varieties of trees with minimal daily water requirements in sandy and rocky areas.

Following a series of experiments with selected varieties of trees such as peach, apricot, apple, plum, etc., at the Department of Experimental Physiology of the University of Ioannina in Greece, I have perfected the Kallidendron method and have gradually reduced the cost of planting materials to around US$ 1.50 per tree. Instead of planting young trees directly into the soil, the roots are first inserted into a plastic bag containing 10 litres of soil (lightened with such organic waste as manure, dry leaves, sand, etc.) mixed with 60 g of "concentrates" made up of 20 g of fertilizers (NPK enriched with magnesium, manganese, iron, molybdenum, etc.), 20 g of trace elements (containing cobalt, zinc, uranium, thorium, rare earths or lanthanides, etc.) and 20 g of a hydrogel such as Aquastore, Evergreen-500 or other water-absorbing compounds. A 50 litre bag is sufficiently large for most trees but sizes of 15–80 litres may be used depending on the tree size: studies are being carried out on bags made of biodegradable materials to replace the plastic. The roots and lower trunk are covered with 20–30 litres of the local soil, and the bottom of the bag is perforated to permit passage of the roots, the whole unit is buried in the ground and 10 l of water are added.

The Kallidendron method offers a number of advantages: a saving of some 80% on watering (due to the absorbency of the hydrogel and the physical barrier of the plastic bag); an economy of up to 95% on fertilizers (because measured quantities are mixed with the soil, and the plastic bags prevent them from being leached out); pollution of the environment by fertilizers is limited; labour requirements are reduced by more than 50%; and the salt layer formation caused by intensive irrigation is minimized.

Two proposed applications of the Kallidendron system

My project is to apply the Kallidendron system to the solution of two types of environmental problem: the reduction of smog in towns with a very high level of atmospheric pollution, such as Athens; and the planting of three billion trees in developing countries. Since an average medium-sized tree will produce at least 10 litres of oxygen a day it is calculated that, by planting 20 million trees on the roofs and balconies of buildings and at other strategic points around the city of Athens, it would be possible to regenerate 200 million litres of oxygen from carbon dioxide each day and within six months provide Athenians with a far less polluted environment. The mass planting of three billion trees in developing countries would follow a four-pronged approach depending on four different levels of water availability: along river banks; in areas of limited fresh water availability; in regions where brackish water can be obtained from wells; and in desert regions where it is possible to detect and tap underground rivers.

We will launch this vast programme and demonstrate its efficacy on a small scale by planting trees in Chad, Mali, Mauritania, Niger and the Sudan and by giving worldwide publicity to the Kallidendron system and the results that it can achieve from the technical, climate and humanitarian points of view. It is possible to save nature from the greenhouse effect by planting three billion trees in the near future with the simple, water-saving and economic Kallidendron method. The expense of the materials is estimated at US$ 4.5 billion. In addition, it is also possible to save two billion humans from starvation by means of the fruit and vegetables produced by the Kallidendron method, and thus help third world countries become self-sufficient in food in the near future.

A fruit tree planted using the Kallidendron method in Ghinda, Erythrea, Ethiopia. Irrigation water is added in carefully metered quantities, and not a drop is allowed to go to waste.

417

Chickens for children – a low-investment, high-yield poultry raising project

Alison Curtis

33 Chemin du Caudoz, 1009 Pully, Switzerland

American, born 7 October 1937. Teacher at the American School of Lausanne. Educated in United States; M. Ed. from Lesley College Graduate School, Cambridge, Massachusetts, in 1983.

The Sambaru are nomadic people who herd cattle, goats and sheep in the semi-arid area of Northern Kenya. Surface water is scarce, and these pastoralists are constantly on the move. They live as family/clan units in a manyatta within a boma (ring of thorn tree branches) for protection from wild animals. Virtually undisturbed by the trappings of the modern world, their tribal economy and way of life revolve entirely around their animals. Their food is milk, blood and occasionally meat.

No provision for the sick or disabled

Samburu traditions have no provision for the chronically ill or the disabled – apart from "local treatment". Children who have physical handicaps, a weak heart, poor lungs, limbs paralyzed from the effects of polio, limbs lost from injury by wild animals, or blindness brought about by vitamin-A deficiency, cannot herd cattle, build bomas or collect water and firewood from distances. They are an embarrassment to their families and are denied a respected place in their clan or "age set". We meet these children in the Wamba Hospital; and after their treatment they must return to their manyattas and an uncertain future.

The Wamba Hospital was started 24 years ago as a dispensary for the catholic mission in the town. Now it has more than 200 beds, a nursing school, Kenyan staff and student nurses, two resident doctors and ten ward sisters – all of whom are Italian. I began my work at the hospital after a visit to the children's ward in 1983. The doctor was concerned that the majority of the long-term patients had little to do to pass the time. After receiving a grant from the Ford Foundation, I went, in 1985, to set up a programme of physical therapy and mental stimulation for the children in the ward. The programme, after a few weeks of delays and growing pains, has become an integrated part of the patients' day and carries on in my absence under the supervision of a Samburu woman.

418

More than just an income-generating activity

Poultry is more than an income-generating activity for these children. If eggs cannot be sold because of the distance to Wamba, they can be eaten, and this is an important consideration because it means that vitamin-A is included in the family's diet. At the same time, Chickens for Children also delivers a positive environmental message. Raw egg in milk is excellent nourishment. Samburu traditionally do not have eggs in their diet; however, those with whom I have worked have been receptive to adding an egg to their milk and have had the good nature to deduce that the egg has disappeared and so the milk is milk again.

Chickens for Children provides disabled youngsters with a new lease on life. Children are accepted as useful members of their immediate clan and community; they are providing food, and/or income for the family whose health is improved with the addition of eggs to their diet. It sets an example for others to add chickens to their livestock. Chickens are easily fed, watered and relocated. Poultry raising is possible for children with heart disease, a paralyzed limb, pulmonary deficiency, loss of a limb, or blindness. It can make a significant contribution to the emotional, physical and economic environments of the children who become involved.

Chickens for Children can successfully and cost-effectively deliver self-help aid to handicapped children. The Wamba Hospital, which provides for the Northern Territory of Kenya, has the potential to be a springboard for poultry raising by disabled children other than tribal Samburu. This project involves local people directly and fosters self-reliance at low cost; it is a low-risk effort with high returns for income, health and self-worth. The foundation has been laid, the idea is a reality but only for children within a token radius of Wamba. It now needs to be transported to other geographic areas.

A fatherless family in which poultry raising and egg selling have provided for the care of the children.

Lucy and her chicken coop.

Helping the handicapped support their families

In 1985, after the terrible drought that occurred in the region, I was constantly followed by village children begging for money, or for tea or sugar for their families. There were few cattle still alive and people were "unemployed" and hungry. A boy came to me with two eggs which I bought and with the money he could buy a pen for his school work. It was then that I conceived the Chickens for Children project. The children would build chicken coops out of materials that they had available at their manyattas; I would check to ensure that the coops were in order, and then arrange for the children to purchase local hens and a rooster. When their hens were laying, I bought the eggs for the hospital's use, and the children used their income to purchase necessities for their families. There were seven children involved at the outset; three now have flocks of more than 30 chickens.

The Chickens for Children project was able to reach out further than the Wamba region when a vehicle became available. This vehicle belonged to the group of German agriculturalists who were carrying out aid work and had the equipment needed to take materials to remote areas and give logistical support. Coop construction has been done in co-ordination with the outpost school; lessons are the broadest channel for dissemination. The students raise the chickens in the school coop and take a starter flock to their manyattas when their own coop has been put together.

During the summer of 1988 I brought the Chickens for Children project to the hospital, offering the project to "elders" or "care-givers" of disabled children whom the doctor brought to my attention. The project operated under the same arrangement as for the village children. After a demonstrative, participatory, problem solving session about the child's disability, the family care-giver returns with the child to the manyatta with materials to set up as a poultry raiser.

420

The diversity and conservation of Mexican mammals

Gerardo Ceballos-Gonzalez

Honourable Mention
The Rolex Awards for Enterprise – 1990

Universidad Nacional Autónoma de Mexico, Manuel Sotelo # 421, Toluca
Mexico, 50120, Mexico

Mexican, born 3 October 1958. Professor, Centre of Ecology, Universidad
Nacional Autónomo de Mexico. Educated in Mexico, United Kingdom and United
States. Ph. D. (Ecology and Evolutionary Biology) from University of Arizona in
1988.

Over the past few centuries, human action has caused large-scale perturbation of natural ecosystems, and resulted in the extinction of many species. Extinction rates have increased dramatically in recent decades and thousands of species may become extinct before the end of the century. The effects of such losses of biodiversity on the ecology and evolution of the earth's biota are unknown, but could be catastrophic. Mexico has an extremely rich and unique flora and fauna; there are some 30,000 species of vascular plants, 500 species of mammals, 1,000 species of breeding birds, and thousands of species of reptiles, amphibians and fishes. The country boasts 450 species of land mammals and 50 marine species, and 33% of them are Mexican endemic.

Many species of mammals in Mexico are on the brink of extinction owing to habitat destruction, hunting, illegal trade or poisoning. Unfortunately, the scope of the conservation problems of Mexican mammals is not fully understood. At least seven species of mammals, including the bison (*Bison bison*), monk seal (*Monachus tropicalis*), grizzly bear (*Ursus arctos*), San Pedro Nolasco deer mouse (*Peromyscus pempertoni*), and elk (*Cervus elaphus*), have become extinct or have been extirpated from Mexico in this century. Many more species are threatened or in danger of extinction, and will become extinct if appropriate measures are not taken soon.

Establishing a database of Mexican animals

Starting in 1987, I launched a research programme to determine the conservation status of all Mexican mammals, and trends in mammalian diversity. This information will allow me to design conservation strategies for the endangered species, including an assessment of the habitats and ecosystems critical for their long-term conservation. To complete this study I need to build an extensive database about Mexican mammals and to carry out field studies on the most endangered species.

The tropical porcupine (Coendu mexicanus) is a species found in tropical wet forests.
Viable populations are still found in southern Mexico. However, it is extremely important to protect some of the remnant habitats to ensure this animal's long-term conservation.

Assessing the conservation status of all the species of Mexican mammals is a formidable task and consequently I have developed a model for conservation classification that combines information about biological vulnerability to extinction and the potential impact of human activities on mammalian populations. Currently, I am evaluating the status of each species using a set of ten criteria that measure the impact of human activities and the presence of the biological characteristics correlated to extinction. However, much work is still needed both to finish the database and to analyze the data. Thousands of records kept in foreign museums also have to be incorporated.

Preliminary results of the conservation classification model have shown, for example, that many more species of Mexican mammals face conservation problems than was previously thought. At least 46 species are considered fragile, 36 threatened, 34 endangered, and seven extinct or extirpated; the next step will be to undertake field studies about the 40 most endangered species. The study has, in particular, highlighted our lack of information about many species on the brink of extinction, such as, for example, the Mexican wolf.

A state of dwindling diversity

The second part of the project is to analyze the patterns of mammalian diversity in Mexico and determine which areas are unique for their high diversity, high endemism and high concentration of endangered species. This information is essential in order to implement conservation strategies that will protect our endangered species and preserve most, if not all, our species of mammals.

To carry out this part of my research I am using the database generated with the information about geographic ranges. So far, I have finished the analyses of the latitudinal trends of species diversity in 2×2 degree quadrants. I am working now doing the same analysis with quadrants of 20×20 km which will give me a higher resolution. Based on the results of these analyses, it will be possible to determine which areas and habitats should be protected to ensure that most of the mammalian diversity of Mexico is preserved. For example, the results of the first analysis indicate that, at the generic level, two regions are extremely important for the number of endemic genera: the transvolcanic belt of central Mexico and the tropical dry forest of western Mexico. At the species level, however, there are more endemic taxa in Baja California and the transvolcanic belt. In terms of endangered species, the most important and threatened habitat is the tropical rain forest of Chiapas and Oaxaca where the last survivors of the tapir (*Tapirus bairoii*), white lipped peccari (*Tavassu pecari*), grison (*Galictis allamandi*) and many more endangered animals are found.

A need for international collaboration

The combination of species-specific and habitat-specific conservation strategies will maximize the conservation of the biological diversity of Mexico. For example, my studies about prairie dogs, a species-specific strategy, began because of the alarming destruction of their habitat. After three years of studies it has become apparent which areas are critical for the preservation of these societies. Presently, I am collaborating with several international conservation agencies to protect some of these areas. The protection of the prairie dogs will also benefit many other mammals, including several endangered species such as the pronghorn antelope (*Antilocapra americana*).

Finally, it is important to emphasize that the conservation of the biological diversity of Mexico will not be possible with the limited financial resources of the country. The responsibility of safeguarding its unique flora and fauna should involve national and international efforts. After all, a primary goal for mankind should be to protect and maintain the biological diversity of the earth and Mexico is a key area in which to accomplish it.

The jaguar (Felis onca) is one of the most endangered species in Mexico. Jaguars are protected by international regulations, but hundreds are still killed each year for their skins, to protect cattle and other domestic animals, and as the result of substantial habitat destruction. The jaguar's chances for long-term survival appear slight.

423

Surveying the rare Abbott's duiker (*Cephalophus spadix*) and Ader's duiker (*C. adersi*) in Tanzania

Vivian John Wilson

Chipangali Wildlife Trust, P. O. Box 1057, Bulawayo, Zimbabwe

Zimbabwean, born 31 October 1932. Director of Chipangali Wildlife Trust.
Educated in South Africa and United Kingdom; M. I. Biol., Institute of Biologists,
London, in 1971.

It has become very clear from the compilation of the Antelope Specialist Group's Global Survey of Antelopes that the forest duikers are the least known group in Africa. Also, an assessment of the status of duiker species in individual countries has shown that they contain a much higher proportion of the "indeterminate" or "insufficiently known" categories than does any other group of antelopes. The duikers have received insufficient attention from wildlife researchers, especially since they are the dominant forest antelopes of Africa (at least in the terms of number and species), and constitute an important source of meat for human consumption in many African countries.

Several duiker species, along with Abbott's duiker, may be in danger of extinction, and therefore it is anticipated that the proposed Pan-African Survey of the duikers will provide the data necessary for the correct CITES and Red Data Book listing of the duikers. The primary goal of the survey is to promote the conservation of the African duikers, especially since commercial hunting for "bush-meat" is increasing, habitat destruction is widespread and some duiker populations are decreasing.

Duikers – an insufficiently documented species

A global survey of the distribution, abundance and conservation status of antelopes, which is currently being conducted by the Species Survival Commission's Antelope Specialist Group of the International Union for Conservation of Nature has highlighted that lack of information on the taxonomy, distribution, population and status of the forest duikers is the most serious deficiency in our current scientific knowledge of antelopes. In its first regional action plans for antelope conservation, the Antelope Specialist Group gave very high priority to field surveys of forest duikers and their habitats in east and northeast Africa, including various "red" duikers (*Cephalophus adersi, harveyi, natalensis, nigrifrons, weynsi* and related forms), and in particular those whose survival is believed to be under threat (e. g. Ader's and Abbott's duikers). It also called for identifica-

424

The Abbott's duiker
(Cephalophus spadix). This
animal is in captivity in
Tanzania.

tion of the most important conservation area for forest duikers in the region. An
effective conservation plan would be to: encourage the preservation of the rain
forest in the natural range of the duikers; emphasize the necessity for conservation management enabling durable utilization of the non-endangered species or
populations; and establish an effective breeding programme so as to ensure the
long-term survival of all duiker species.

An estimate of numbers of Abbott's and other rare duikers in the wild is most
unreliable since very few specimens have been observed, and little is known of
their natural history and biology. Two factors pose the greatest threat to the
survival of these species. Firstly, forest habitats are being eroded away by primitive agricultural practices and commercial exploitation. Secondly, duikers are
poached extensively for their meat and skins. Abbott's and Ader's duikers are
perhaps the rarest and least known of all the antelope of the African rain forests;
their secretive habits and the closed habitat in which they live make them very
difficult to study. These rare species could well disappear before we even know
anything of their behaviour and ecology. Considering their importance as a
source of food for many hundreds of thousands of Africans, not enough
emphasis has been placed on these forest antelopes in the past. Therefore, their
study should now be one of high priority.

Gaining an insight into the duikers' way of life

Research and field surveys are essential if the duikers are to survive. Facets of
research needing attention include distribution and status, feeding and reproductive strategies, behaviour and economic value as a protein source for the
Africans. Therefore the main objectives of the survey will be to accumulate data
which will identify critical habitats, the protection of which will ensure the

425

survival of endangered species where they occur, and to provide effective protection for large enough forest reserves in areas containing a high number of duiker species in abundant numbers.

Field work commenced in January 1985, and it is anticipated that another seven full years will be taken to cover the main study areas. Major expeditions will take place once a year and last between one and six months at a time. Each year a different region in Africa will be visited, and an essential part of each expedition will be the collection of duiker material from "bush-meat" markets. No attempt will be made to go out and collect rare or endangered duikers. Specimens collected by safari operators, subsistence and market hunters will be examined and, with time, the distribution of each species of duikers should emerge which will be correlated with the habitats and biotic zones, and the distribution of the evergreen forests.

In October 1988, I visited Tanzania to meet the Wildlife authorities in that country to discuss my planned preliminary expedition to identify major areas for research. The preliminary survey is to take place from June to August 1989, and the very detailed survey in 1990.

*The Abbott's duiker (*Cephalophus spadix*). This is one of the two known photographs in existence of this species. There is no other Abbott's duiker in captivity anywhere else in the world.*

426

Tropical mountain jungle farmers: use of hydroelectric power

Andrew Genu

Organizing Committee, Agaun Cattle Farmers' Hydroelectric Project, Anglican Church PMB, Agaun via Alotau, Milne Bay Province, Papua New Guinea

Papua New Guinean, born 1 March 1973. Committee Representative of the Agaun Cattle Farmers and Vegetable Growers Business Group Inc. Educated in Papua New Guinea; completed vocational training school in 1988.

Since 1973, Agaun farmers have been operating a beef and dairy cattle farm in the Daga Mountains of the Milne Bay province in Papua New Guinea. We obtained cattle and horses from other parts of the country; calves were flown in by a small single-engined Cessna to the airstrip (as there is no road down to the coast), and horses were walked up the rugged sides of the mountain by a track hand-cut through the rain forest.

This has provided some milk and meat to people here who are severely deficient in protein foods. At the same time, we built a small hydroelectric plant using discarded tractor wheels and a salvaged generator, which produced the first electric power in this area; this was used for lights and a small freezer unit. As a result of this effort, a farming business is now established, with fresh green vegetables being grown by some 35 young farmers. With the cash income obtained from these sales, high protein foods, tinned fish and frozen meats are flown in regularly on the chartered small planes which take the vegetables out to market.

Before this development started, cattle and horses had never been seen here; the only artificial light was from fire made in the old way by rubbing strips of bamboo across dry soft wood; and the only source of meat was from small animals hunted in the jungle.

Where do we stand today?

At present, the founders of this Agaun cattle farmers' development programme have nearly completed a larger hydroelectric plant with the help of a survey made by the University of Technology in Lae. This plant will provide 15 kWA of electric power, and is being built below the conjunction of our two closest rivers,

The concrete and stone arch cover constructed by the Agaun (Papua New Guinea) farmers to protect their water channel headrace against frequent land slips.

the Utup and the Jura. All the civil engineering work has been done by our young farmers making a weir with bags filled with clay and supported by river stones, and digging the head race water channel from the steep mountainside; in very unstable parts, they have covered the channel with an arch of stone and concrete.

They have already bought – with a bank loan – freezing and cold-room equipment, to accommodate the fresh vegetables and local or airfreighted meat; very often the planes coming to this mountain valley are prevented by cloud cover or a waterlogged airstrip. Already these activities are occupying the interest and working time of a number of young school leavers and, as they grow up and are married, they are now earning more income than ever before. This is encouraging our young men to stay in their homeland, rather than to move out to urban areas to look for other paid work.

Plans for the future

We, the new generation of farmers here in the Agaun Mountains, have completed our training and we have been elected to be in charge of future developments. Within the next few months, we will install the 15 kWA water turbine and generator, and the 3.3 MW, high-voltage power lines and transformers, and construct the freezing and cold-storage rooms and the cardamom spice heater-room – all of which have already reached the framework stage. All this past development has been paid for by our own free labour, and our village family teams' free help; on the strength of this, we have received from overseas the gift of an electric generator, a turbine, power lines and voltage control equipment. The cost of completing the cold-storage rooms and the cardamom spice heating-room equipment will now have to be found elsewhere.

We are Melanesian people, and very close to the stone age of our forefathers; but we have had some modern education, and we are putting our strength and the modern knowledge that we have been given into improving our environment, and bringing our families in this remote jungle mountain area closer to the modern world, while still maintaining our traditional agricultural background.

For the hydroelectric installation, we have already completed the weir, the silt trap and the head race over a distance of 500 m. We are now starting the settling pond, made of local materials, clay and stones and rubble, in preparation for the arrival of engineers from Sydney, Australia, who will supervise the installation of the penstock pipes, and place in position the turbine and generator and high-voltage power lines up to the farm station. Also at the farm, we are now in the process of building the utility house, which will house the voltage control panel and heater, which will provide heat for curing the cardamom spice and power for the freezer room and vegetable cold storage.

Benefit for all

All our community and local families will benefit from this project, with an increase in cash income from the cardamom heater and vegetable cold storage. In addition, there will be electric power available for lighting the station houses and street. We will be supplying lights for our small hospital, church and church community school, and also the government agriculture staff houses. However, our village family houses made of grass thatch and bamboo are a fire risk and cannot have electric wiring, so we will install street lighting along the house lines.

We have submitted our project because we will need funding to develop our work further, and also to encourage other young people in other developing countries to develop the land of their forefathers, in a clean and non-polluting way, not depleting their natural resources, but conserving the viability of their environment. We also wish to encourage our young farmers not to abandon their home lands, but to make their cash income from it, and not to be drawn to the false lights of the towns, and the drink and poverty to be found there. We want to encourage our own people to enjoy and care for the environment given to us by our Stone Age forefathers.

The Agaun hydro-electric committee, Andrew Genu (left) and Rex Wavere (right), with the experimental cardamom heating equipment and, beyond and below in the valley, the first small hydro-electric plant, showing the water supply channel and power house.

Rolex Laureate – The Rolex Awards for Enterprise – 1990

Anita Studer

Anita Studer, an ornithologist from Switzerland, has long striven to protect the forests and fauna of northeastern Brazil. She has now developed the Arco Iris (Rainbow) environmental education project to gain governmental and popular support for a long-term plan of reforestation by instituting tree-planting campaigns and by stimulating general ecological awareness.

The "Arco Iris" reforestation and environmental educational programme in Northeast Brazil

Anita Studer

Rolex Laureate
The Rolex Awards for Enterprise – 1990

19 rue Chantepoulet, 1201 Geneva, Switzerland

Swiss, born 26 February 1944. Ornithologist, Researcher, President of Association Nordeste. Educated in Switzerland and France; Diplôme d'Etudes Supérieures from University of Nancy in 1983.

During my ornithological expeditions to Northeast Brazil in search of a bird previously believed to be extinct, I made my first contacts with the Pedra Talhada in the State of Alagoas. Pedra Talhada is a decimated forest, part of a larger forested area of 30 km², which represents only 1% of its original size but still contains an enormous variety of flora and fauna. This forest helps sustain a microclimate that is more humid than the rest of the Nordeste region of Brazil, an arid and poor area. Located on the heights, its has springs that offer a supply of drinking water to five small towns with a population of 300,000, including Quebrangulo 25 km away. During my studies, I counted 150 specimens in the forest, and was alarmed by the enormous threat of extinction hanging over them. The surface area of the forest is shrinking every year, under the combined impact of erosion and the slash-and-burn agriculture. I tried to get the mayor of Quebuangulo to take emergency action to protect these last islands of greenery in the Nordeste, but was unsuccessful: the country is poverty-stricken, and the forest is the least of its worries.

Positive action to protect the Pedra Talhada forest

Back in Geneva in 1985, realizing that a solution had to be based on mutual benefit, I founded the *Association Nordeste*, the goal of which was the overall protection of the last sections of forest in the State of Alagoas. To achieve that goal, I planned to offer social aid to the inhabitants of Quebrangulo who, in exchange, would have to promise to protect their forest. The Association now has 300 members. In the meantime, following steps taken by me (particularly the creation, with the help of Prof. Vieillard, of a comprehensive dossier on the scientific and ecological value of the forest), the governor of the State of Alagoas decided to proclaim the Pedra Talhada forest of public interest. On the other hand, he could not offer any concrete aid. The mayor of Quebrangulo, for his part, agreed to sign a contract under which every inhabitant who receives some help from the *Association Nordeste* must plant a tree nearby. In return, the Association has created a 24-hour medical post, schools, a dressmaking shop, etc.

A view of one of the tree nurseries set up by Anita Studer at the edge of the Pedra Talhada forest as part of her "Arco Iris" project.

In January 1988, the "Plant Seeds" operation began. The participants, carrying saplings, followed a procession organized to mark the beginning of reforestation. The parish priest even blessed the scene, and held a mass on the site. However, it was necessary to enlist the active participation of a few large landowners who own the forest. At first they were very resistant to the idea of giving up logging in order to plant trees instead; they saw only the money they would lose in the short term, and opposed the proposal. I then organized lectures and debates. The owners finally recognized the dangers of deforestation (drought in the dry season, floods in the rainy season and erosion of arable land). They were also attracted by the advantages I described: they would not have to pay anything for reforestation, and would be able to exploit selected trees – that is, to take leaves for their livestock and fruits to make aromatic flour. On 27 May 1988, most of the owners finally agreed to the protection of the forest. They also accepted the launching by the *Association Nordeste* of a pilot project called Arco Iris (Rainbow).

The Arco Iris project takes shape

The aim of Arco Iris is to increase the surface area of the Pedra Talhada forest by joining scattered parts together and finally linking it up with another forested area into a belt of greenery 20 km long and 1 km wide that will encircle the town of Quebrangulo. On the landowners' property, the first priority will be to reforest the hilltops and the banks of streams to prevent erosion. Together with the inhabitants of Quebrangulo, I have already set up a nursery and have begun by planting four indigenous "pioneer" species that will provide the shade required by the species to be planted later. Some 80 hectares should be reforested in two years, and the first visible results are expected four years from now.

We can count on the mayor and the town priest to back the project and we have contacted local technicians who will gradually take over the project, and a Swiss agronomist will supervise the work. The five villages supplied with water from the forest are also involved. The reserves in the collection dam that give them their drinking water are drying up more every year owing to erosion. Their mayors have all been asked, therefore, to give consideration to the problem of deforestation and erosion. We have also taken the unusual step of hiring former poachers who are now paid by the Association Nordeste to work as foresters. In addition, Sampaiaó radio, paid by the Association, broadcasts a programme every day on the importance of the forest. We are also trying to get young people involved in the project. Ecological awareness, non-existent in this very poor region, will be promoted in local youth clubs, *Clubes dos Amigos das Arbores* (Friends of Trees Clubs) which will also be involved in the management of a tree nursery.

I hope that these innovations will keep the work going during my absence, because I plan to devote myself to the project fully only until 1991. Later, I will gradually withdraw, leaving it in Brazilian hands. I now have the official support of the authorities: the Environment Ministry of the State of Alagoas is very much in favour of the project, and has asked me to look for international aid to finance the planned scientific part (in particular, a hydrological study): the country has to deal with its poverty and cannot afford this luxury. If the Arco Iris project goes well, my dream is to continue the reforestation of the hilltops toward the north, to include the small remaining sections of forest. The final goal would be to create a continuous strip of forest right to the Amazon, 2,000 km away.

The project's engineer Mr. Hermogenes explains to the technicians and local workers how to plant seeds and care for the tree nursery.

Quagga experimental breeding project

Reinhold Eugen Rau

c/o South African Museum, Queen Victoria Street, 8000 Cape Town, South Africa

German, born 7 February 1932. Head of Taxidermy Department, South African Museum. Educated in Federal Republic of Germany and South Africa; obtained a Technical Certificate in Taxidermy from the Southern African Museums Association in 1962.

The quagga is an animal allied to the zebra. It was formerly encountered in vast herds on the great plains of South Africa between Cape Province and the Vaal River. It became extinct when the last individual died at the Amsterdam Zoo on 12 August 1883. The head, neck and upper parts of the body were reddish-brown in colour; they were irregularly banded and marked with dark-brown stripes which were more pronounced on the head and neck but which gradually became fainter until they disappeared entirely behind the shoulder.

The quagga, *Equus quagga quagga*, was the southernmost subspecies of the plains zebra. We believe that there were no natural barriers between the quagga and its northern relatives, the two subspecies *Equus quagga burchelli* and *Equus quagga antiquorum*.

Can the quagga be re-created?

For many years various scientists speculated on the feasibility of breeding back the extinct quagga from those southern plains zebras that show tendencies towards the quagga in their lack of stripes on the legs and in their brownish colour. However, zoologists were divided about the taxonomic status of the quagga. Some leading scientists were against such a project on the grounds that the quagga, in their opinion, was a separate species of zebra, and thus could not be "re-created". Any quagga-like animal produced would merely be a "man-made look-alike" bearing no true genetic relationship to the extinct animal.

However, it has recently been shown by three groups of scientists, all associated with the University of California, working independently and applying different molecular biochemical methods, that the quagga was so closely related to the plains zebra, that it must be regarded as no more than a subspecies of the plains zebra. This research utilized dry muscle tissue and blood which were removed from the skins and carefully collected by R. Rau during the re-mounting of four of the 23 preserved specimens of the extinct quagga – namely three at

The extinct quagga, London Zoo, circa 1870.

the Natural History Museum, Mainz, Federal Republic of Germany, and one at the South African Museum, Cape Town, South Africa. Since these studies have shown that the quagga is the same species as the plains zebra, it is possible that the genes characterizing the colouration of the quagga are not irretrievably lost but are dispersed and diluted amongst the extant populations of the plains zebra.

A breeding programme to retrieve quagga colouration genes

There is therefore scientific justification for a selected breeding programme that will attempt to retrieve the genes characterizing these colouration patterns from plains zebra. This has been started with the capture of selected individuals at the Etosha Game Reserve in northern South West Africa/Namibia during March 1987. Nine animals were transported successfully from Etosha to the Nature Conservation Station *Vrolijkheid* near Robertson, approximately 200 km northeast of Cape Town, where an initial enclosure of 80×80 m had been built for the project.

As more enclosures were completed, the group of Etosha zebras was divided into breeding groups during December 1987. A total of six enclosures, two measuring 80×40 m each and four measuring 60×40 m each are presently available; more will be built as the numbers of animals increase.

In November 1988, more zebras were added to the breeding stock with the arrival of four selected animals from Zululand, Natal. The first foal was born in December 1988. Additional zebras, already selected, will be captured and transported to the breeding venue during 1989.

A project under close scientific supervision

The project is guided by a panel of scientists qualified in museum-based taxonomy, genetics, animal husbandry, veterinary science, and nature conservation. A stud book is being maintained in which details of each animal (matings, births, etc.) are entered. As the relatively small enclosures do not provide natural grazing, the animals are being fed according to a feeding schedule that has been worked out by an animal nutritionist.

To accelerate the generation successions, artificial insemination and embryo transplantation into surrogate mares (donkeys, horses, zebras) is envisaged. At present we have four breeding groups combining an Etosha stallion, an Etosha mare, a Zululand stallion and a Zululand mare.

These animals are all of the subspecies *Equus quagga antiquorum*, according to presently accepted views. A comparison of the Zululand plains zebra population (formerly known as the subspecies *wahlbergi*) with that from Etosha reveals that Zululand zebras have the most advanced stripe-reduction, while maintaining a relatively light basic colour with fairly wide interspecies. Etosha zebras tend to have a darker basic colour, while stripe-reduction does not reach the degree of some of the Zululand animals and is less frequent.

As stated above, it is the opinion of the Quagga Experimental Breeding Committee that the quagga, or the genes responsible for the colouration characteristics of this "extinct" southernmost subspecies (or local variation of the widely distributed plains zebra), are not truly extinct. It was man's greed and short-sightedness that caused the disappearance of this zebra from the Karoo and southern Orange Free State, over 100 years ago. We view this project as a unique opportunity to rectify this tragic mistake. In this sense we see the project as comparable to the conservation of endangered species and/or the re-introduction of rare species into areas where they have become extinct.

One of the breeding stock for the quagga experiment at Vrolijkheid farm.

A marine conservation programme for the Tubbataha National Marine Park

Alan Tyler White

MCC P. O. Box 1501, Makati, Metro Manila, Philippines

American, born 4 June 1947. Technical Adviser, ASEAN-US Co-operative Programme on Marine Sciences. Educated in United States, Ecuador and Indonesia; Ph. D. (Marine Resource Management) from University of Hawaii, Honolulu, in 1984.

The Tubbataha Reefs in the Sulu Sea are a unique marine environment which constitute a source of income for subsistence fishermen from Cagayancillo and elsewhere in the Philippines. However, the reef is being destroyed and productivity diminished by over-fishing and by fishermen who use destructive fishing practices. In response to an urgent need to protect and manage this area, the reef was designated a National Marine Park in August 1988, and this designation provides the Government with the authority needed to manage this resource.

However, traditional park management methods will be costly and ineffective; because the reefs are large, they are not easily accessible and there are no permanent inhabitants. Nevertheless, even though some subsistence fishermen from Cagayancillo are part of the problem, certain local government officials and a significant number of Cagayanons are interested in marine conservation and can be mobilized to assist in managing the Park. For these reasons, it will be necessary to intimately involve residents of Cagayancillo in the day-to-day management of the Park.

Helping the Filipinos to manage their Marine Park

The project is the first phase of a programme to develop within the Department of Environment and Natural Resources (DENR) the capability of managing the Park in association with residents and local government officials. The initial project is simple and it will be possible to begin managing the Park in March 1990. The activities will respond to an urgent need for immediate action to minimize or stop destruction of this marine environment and to develop a solid base of experience for long-term management. Such experience will also be applied to similar situations in the Philippines and other parts of Southeast Asia where marine resources are being depleted.

The two major objectives of the project are to: develop and implement a programme to manage the Park; and enable subsistence and other fishermen

437

The coral reefs in Tubbataha National Marine Park, Sulu Sea, Philippines, are some of the richest and most diverse in the world. The reef crest is generally the most varied zone.

from Cagayancillo to develop alternative sources of income so as to reduce the incentive for them to fish at Tubbataha. It will be carried out in two phases, the first of which, due for implementation in 1990 and which is the subject of this project, will respond to an urgent need to prevent further damage to the Park, provide experience needed to formulate detailed guidelines and cost estimates for a park management programme and collect information needed to devise a programme to assist Cagayanons to improve the management of marine resources near Cagayancillo. The second phase will provide for the formal establishment of a systematic management programme beginning in 1991 and for the initiation of work to enable Cagayanons to improve the management and productivity of marine resources in the vicinity of the major population centres of Cagayancillo.

Several tasks need to be accomplished during 1990 to achieve the goals of the first phase, and in particular, it will be necessary to disseminate information to concerned audiences about the establishment of the Park and its management; establish an initial capability to manage the Park using a composite management team which includes staff from DENR, consultants provided by the Tubbataha Foundation and residents of Cagayancillo; assist the municipal government to develop the ability to exercise greater control over fishermen and vessels from outside Cagayancillo which receive authorization from the local government to fish in Cagayancillo and Tubbataha; identify opportunities which should be exploited to enable Cagayanons to improve the management and the productivity of the marine resources in the vicinity of the major population centre of Cagayancillo; and prepare detailed guidelines for managing the Park, a work programme and detailed cost estimates for the next phase of the project.

A foundation for marine preservation

This project will be implemented by myself in co-operation with the Tubbataha Foundation which was set up to encourage and assist fishing communities to protect and manage the marine environment and the surrounding marine life in areas such as Tubbataha, to draw attention to the problems and consequences of destruction of marine resources and to organize communities' support for enforcement of national laws relating to the environment. The Foundation prepared a reconnaissance survey of Cagayancillo in November 1988. However, aside from the preparation of this study, this project will be the first operational activity.

Overall supervision of the project will be conducted by myself and Dr. William Staub, principal officers of the Foundation, and day-to-day supervision will be performed by individuals who are engaged on a contractual basis by the Foundation. The work of the management team, the community development worker and the park management specialist will be monitored through periodic inspection visits by the principal officers from the Foundation and DENR. The cost of the work programme for phase one is estimated at US$ 50,000. The foundation is soliciting funds from several sources. DENR is expected to assist the Foundation in obtaining a modest grant from a bilateral donor. However, it is anticipated that the amount which may be obtained from this source will cover less than 25% of the amount required and there are substantial uncertainties concerning whether this financing, if offered, will be available when it is needed.

The Tubbataha Foundation installed signs on the islets in April 1989 to inform fishermen about the Park and destructive fishing. (Bird Islet).

Atlas of the breeding birds of Arabia

Michael Charles Jennings

Moonraker Cottage, 1 Eastcourt, Burbage, Marlborough, Wiltshire SN8 3AG, United Kingdom

British, born 28 April 1947. Deputy Area Civilian Staff Manager in the Ministry of Defence, Wiltshire. Educated in United Kingdom; Ordinary National Diploma (Business Studies) from Cambridge College of Arts and Technology in 1965.

Since May, 1969, when I first visited Arabia, I have been deeply interested in the birds of the peninsula. Since then, I have collected information on Arabian birds, especially breeding species, and I have written up this information in numerous publications. The databank I have built up has become an unofficial reference source on Arabian birds for ornithologists worldwide. I have visited much of the Arabian Peninsula, have been resident there for a total of five years and have led, or taken part in, at least 11 ornithological expeditions there; consequently there are few people with more field experience of Arabian birds.

Having long planned an atlas of breeding birds for Arabia similar to the atlases for western Europe, in 1984, I launched the Atlas of the Breeding Birds of Arabia project. Because of the size of Arabia and the paucity of information about its birds, the project is a long-term one. Work has already been in progress for five years and my estimate is that it will take at least eight more years prior to completion. The project was started without any financial backing but many interested individuals, societies and organizations have since helped with generally small donations.

An Atlas to provide baseline information

The aim of the project is, in simple terms, to determine the range, habitat and identification of all birds breeding in Arabia and around its shores. Although the data are intended for collation and publication in book form, they are already available in unpublished form to any ornithologist. Effectively, the project will be an inventory and archive of all historical data on Arabian birds and provide a picture of breeding birds and their distribution in the 1980s and 1990s. As such, it will be a baseline document on this important branch of Arabian biology. This is particularly relevant in view of the rapidly changing and developing face of Arabia. The Atlas, when complete, will be an important source to chronicle the development, or destruction, of avian communities and their habitats. During the data collection an annual newsletter, *The Phoenix*, is being published to keep

440

The chicks of the brown booby Sula leucogaster *are very susceptible to oil pollution. The project has identified that this bird breeds on a small number of islands in the Red Sea.*

all those interested in Arabian birds and the Atlas project up to date with ornithological developments in Arabia and give news on items of interest.

Further sub-projects have been developed to: compile and publish a definitive bibliography of the Arabian avifauna; compile a complete index of all Arabian ornithological material in museum collections; complete and publish a checklist of all Arabian bird species; and compile a complete reference source of all records of ringed birds recovered in Arabia.

The final book, apart from being a definitive statement on distribution, will also provide detailed information on the habitat requirements of each species, food, breeding details, migration, speciation and the zoological geography of this area which bridges the African, Indian and Eurasian landmasses.

The project collects data on breeding birds from four main sources: unpublished observations made by observers in Arabia; the author's own fieldwork; literature records; and museum specimens. Data are stored and processed in a structured, computer-recognizable format. Each breeding bird observation and its attendant date make up one record and, since 1984, some 16,000 records have been collected; it is anticipated that a further 25,000 records will be added before publication.

Ornithological observers in Arabia are encouraged to submit records direct on data collection forms I have developed. Since 1984, some 78 individuals have personally contributed records to the project. Observer records are an extremely important source of information as they tend to be detailed, precise and give good coverage for key areas, such as around the major towns; approximately 45% of all records collected so far are from observers in Arabia.

Since 1985, I have spent some time each year in Arabia on field work to collect Atlas records and, in particular, to visit little-known or remote parts of the peninsula; approximately 35% of all records collated by the project so far are my own observations.

There are an estimated 500 published works on Arabian birds. The project aims to identify all such material and for all information contained in these papers to be incorporated into the Atlas project; it is expected that the literature section of the data will comprise approximately 15% of the total.

Bringing the project to completion

Sponsorship has now been obtained from the National Commission for Wildlife Conservation and Development, Riyadh, Saudi Arabia, for the short atlasing surveys made by the author in Arabia, the administrative costs of the Atlas project, the salaries of a researcher and typist and eventually the cost of the publishing of the final work. However, because Arabia is such a vast region, I anticipate that I will not be able to cover the whole of the peninsula in the relatively short atlasing surveys made each year to Arabia.

I wish to obtain funds to carry out a year's fieldwork to ensure the atlasing of remote regions, examine particularly important areas at all times of the year and to look into the breeding of certain species that breed at irregular seasons.

The Namaqua dove *Oena* capensis *is a species of African origin which has exhibited a dynamic range extension in Arabia since 1975, Michael Jenning's project has plotted this remarkable distribution change.*

An optical disk reference library on venomous snakes

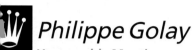

Philippe Golay

Honourable Mention
The Rolex Awards for Enterprise – 1990

8 route des Ravières, 1258 Perly, Switzerland

Swiss, born 28 January 1957. Teacher, Malagnou Business High School. Educated in Switzerland; Diplôme fédéral de maître d'éducation physique from the University of Geneva in 1982.

I first became interested in snakes when I was only 13 and it was then that I acquired my first boa (to the consternation of my parents). At the age of 20, after obtaining my school diploma, I took a year off to travel, particularly to Brazil where I met Dr. Hoge from the Instituto Butantan. When I returned to Geneva, I enrolled in the Biology Department and then subsequently at the School of Physical Education and Sport of the University of Geneva.

Never having lost my passion for reptiles, I had meanwhile, in 1980, set up – along with three amateur herpetologists – the Elapsoidea Foundation; and together we installed a private vivarium in an apartment in 1980.

By 1983, the association had already enrolled 50 members and a collection had been built up of 250 reptiles in 220 terraria. Its purpose is, among other things: to enable amateur herpetologists to combine theoretical work with practical application within a group working with specialists; and to teach the general public about snakes through exhibitions, lectures and the opening of a public vivarium.

Collecting information on *Elapidae* snakes

I was placed in charge of collecting information about the snakes we bred and, in particular, about snakes of the *Elapidae* family. We soon found that this family of venomous snakes was poorly documented and I therefore decided that, if we wanted more comprehensive documentation on this specific subject, I myself would have to prepare the necessary monographs.

The first two steps were to compile a list of all the world's elapids and to obtain copies of all documents relating to elapid snakes that had appeared since 1758, the starting-point for the use of the binomial nomenclature in zoology. Since 1982, I have spent most of my holidays in museums in Switzerland and abroad collecting data for my manuscript.

Philippe Golay observing a Naja kaouthia *(albino). This Siamese cobra has been responsible for several human deaths (Photo: Martinez).*

The monograph completed in 1985 and published under the title: *Checklist and keys to the terrestrial proteroglyphs of the world* obtained me a grant with which I was able to acquire a computer; and in 1987, I obtained from UNESCO their Computerized Documentation System/Integrated Set of Information Systems (CDS/ISIS) software. I was now ready to set up a computerized snake information system.

Widening the scope and impact of my snake database

By 1988, I had already collected 8,300 references and was preparing to start writing the *Annotated Bibliography of the Elapids*. It was at this time that a colleague was bitten by a viper; he was incorrectly treated because the physician was not sufficiently knowledgeable about this field of medicine and was unable to consult the literature. As a result of this incident, I decided to develop a more expansive Elapsoidea bibliographical database with a view to helping prevent such incidents in the future.

Nevertheless, my plan underwent some modification of emphasis when I learnt that most of the victims of such venomous snake bites were bitten by viperids (*Viperidae*) and not by elapids. The result was that I decided to: extend my bibliographical studies to all venomous snakes; make the results of this research readily accessible to as many users as possible on a 24-hour basis; and find a way to ensure high-speed dissemination of hard copy of the articles listed in the bibliography.

My solution was to store all the bibliographical data on snakes on optical disks (CD-ROMS) and then make the data available through an online database server: demand for hard copy could be met by telefax transmission of texts downloaded from the optical disks.

444

Snake information by modern communications technology

The procedure I propose is to: use available bibliographical material to build up a reference file; obtain copies of all the texts from specialized libraries; draft bibliographical entries (with particular attention being paid to species names, keywords and abbreviations); input the bibliographical records into the bibliographical database which has been loaded onto the Data-Star server. Data-Star is a London-based, very large, European database server which gives access to 160 databases worldwide. Obtaining information from Data-Star requires only a telephone line, a personal computer, a modem and the necessary communications software.

The articles collected would be input onto the optical disk by means of an image scanner that digitalizes both the text and pictures; each side of a disk can hold 20,000 pages of text and the optical disk storage and retrieval system I have selected would hold a total of 800,000 pages. Finally, any document stored on optical disk and requested through Data-Star would be sent out by telefax through a telefax card built into my computer which operates the optical disk system.

I have decided that the project should be based in Geneva, Switzerland, since this town has a plethora of libraries with zoological and botanical collections, it is the home of, or has close by, a number of major international, governmental or non-governmental organizations such as WHO, IUCN, WWF, etc., and it is conveniently situated in the centre of Europe with easy access to all major European cities and their resources.

Bothrops schlegelii (yellow colour phase), small arboreal pit viper of Central America. Its bite may be dangerous (Photo: Martinez).

Recultivating historic citrus cultivars

Wolfgang Hundbiss

Garten- und Freiraumplanung, Schützenstrasse 8, 8911 Windach, Federal Republic of Germany

German, born 8 August 1949. Engineer. Educated in Federal Republic of Germany.

One aspect of the increasing exhaustion of our environment is the distressing loss of numerous cultivated plants which can no longer satisfy the "modern" selection criteria demanded for industrial, agricultural and "consumer-friendly" marketing strategies. However, man's needs are scarcely being served by this destruction of genetic material, and the consequent loss of cultivars which have been used for centuries. It is my desire to contribute to the protection and preservation of these culturally important plants that is the driving force behind my project.

The long and fascinating history of the citrus

My particular interest in citrus cultivars stemmed from their long history. Not only are citrus plants amongst the oldest plants cultivated by man (in South China and India, *Citrus medica* was probably cultivated as early as 2,400 BC), but they also form, together with the grape, today's most cultivated fruits. Between the 15th and 18th centuries citrus plants were cultivated in enormous numbers, with cultivars being developed for both culinary and even aesthetic purposes. Only a fraction of these cultivated varieties has survived in current collections. Citrus plants are important in the history of fine arts and in the history of man's culture. In old myths and legends, they are closely linked to man's fate. The Jewish religion equates the Tree of Knowledge with the bitter orange tree. In Greek mythology, the Hesperian gardens symbolize eternal spring and eternal youth – characteristics of the lost Golden Age. This relationship with Greek mythology perhaps explains why citrus plants gained such importance in the Renaissance. Through hybridization and mutation, new cultivars were created, and travellers to the Far East brought back and introduced into Europe previously unknown species.

Documenting and collecting historic cultivars

My project started in 1987 and aims primarily at discovering and cataloguing the existing historical cultivated varieties of citrus plants. First, I studied the literature

Taking grafts of citrus plants of the collection of Villa di Castello at Sesto Fiorentino.

on historic gardens to locate orangeries past and present and, in doing so, found for example that all of the once famous collections in West Germany (one of which had, at the time, contained 3,000 plants) had disappeared.

Research on Italian gardens proved more encouraging and I found that the collections in Palermo, Naples, Florence, Sesto Fiorentino and Latte boast approximately 80 different citrus cultivars. Research continued at the orangerie of Versailles where I discovered that this unique northern European collection is threatened with total destruction due to disease, and I am currently negotiating with Ciba-Geigy SA of Switzerland in the hope that a programme of disease control can be implemented.

However, my studies to date show that a fairly large range of historic cultivars still exists, but that they are often at risk, as for instance in the Orto Botanico of Palermo, where the construction of new greenhouses has led to the destruction of several extremely rare cultivars of *Citrus medica*.

The next stage is to secure the long-term preservation of the cultivars by taking scions for grafting on to suitable bases (usually *Citrus aurantium*) to be grown into new plants, and at the same time to compile a catalogue of all known cultivars.

A nursery in Sicily specializing in citrus cultivation has been entrusted with the task; in spring 1988, 25 historic plants had been cultivated by this method, and 25 more are to follow in 1989. After the plants have grown in a favourable climate in Sicily, five or six will be taken to Germany and exhibited on the Isle of Mainau in Lake Constance, the Palmengarten in Frankfurt and the orangerie of Seehof Palace near Bamberg.

Growing hope for rediscovered citrus cultivars

The progress of the project to date has exhausted my finances but much remains to be done since I wish to build on the collection of the 50 cultivars that I have already rediscovered and recultivated to continue my work which will eventually catalogue all the cultivars still in existence and then attempt to preserve all locatable cultivars by recultivating them. In addition, I also plan to publish a book for the general public describing my achievements.

Experiences gained in Italy inspire me with the hope that a similar rich store of citrus cultivars are to be found in other Mediterranean countries and a survey of citrus growing in Southeast Asia would certainly lead to completely new insights into this genus and its cultivated varieties. If these plants can be preserved and tended in botanical gardens, etc., they will provide an invaluable genetic reservoir for future cultivation work. In addition, they will highlight a cultural desirability of preserving all kinds of plants even when current needs seem to be determined solely by considerations of cost and utility.

Citrus aurantium L., *"Fasciata"*, one of the rarest historic citrus cultivars in Naples, formerly known under the name "braghe tedesche" (striped German lansquenet trousers).

Reintroducing Père David's deer (*Elaphurus davidianus*) into China

Maria M. Boyd

Milu Ecological Research Centre, Nan Haizi Milu Reserve, Beijing, Nan Yuan, People's Republic of China

American, born 13 February 1944. Joint Head of the Research Department at the Milu Ecological Research Centre. Educated in Czechoslovakia, United States, United Kingdom and Switzerland; has attended Oxford University since 1979.

Ever since my student days at the Komensky University in Bratislava, Czechoslovakia, I have been fascinated by the Père David's deer (known as the *milu* in Chinese). I began by studying the few articles available describing them – mostly about the "romantic" story of their discovery at Nan Haizi Imperial Hunting Park outside of Beijing, their introduction into various European zoos and private collections, the search for their original habitat, their eventual extinction in China, and their preservation from total extinction by the 11th Duke of Bedford on his vast estates at Woburn Abbey Park, Bedfordshire, England.

China's desire to see the milu return

In 1979, I learned that the Chinese Government was seriously interested in reintroducing the milu into China since they regarded this deer as a national cultural and historic treasure and were eager to see it re-established in their country. The Marquis of Tavistock and my supervisor at Oxford University encouraged me to contact the appropriate Chinese officials. A small herd of milu for reintroduction was promised to me by the Marquis of Tavistock, and the Embassy of the People's Republic of China in London confirmed governmental support for the reintroduction project. In 1981, Lord Tavistock received a delegation from China enquiring formally about the possibility of the reintroduction of milu. It was after this that I contacted the relevant Chinese institutions and individuals regarding conducting further studies in China. The following three years were spent on writing proposals for financial support, developing draft feasibility studies for submission to the Chinese and on clarifying quarantine regulations – to mention only a few aspects. China, with its 5,000 years of history, is still new to the field of nature conservation and animal and plant protection. It is therefore all the more encouraging that this project has been actively endorsed from the very beginning by high-ranking officials. By 1983, I had received a formal invitation from the People's Republic of China to undertake the definitive feasibility study for the reintroduction of the milu. My first concern was to identify, from ancient Chinese literature and from fossil evidence, areas that were in the deer's

*In 1988, Père David's deer
was celebrated on a Chinese
postage stamp.*

historic range. Having received assurances of protection for the chosen site we set to work on a timetable for the reintroduction. The preliminary agreement was signed in September 1984, and work on the reintroduction site began immediately. The Chinese Government donated 80 ha of land and, in addition to this, we have received over 1 million yuan for the reconstruction of the reserve.

The milus prepare to leave their English home

Meanwhile in England, the animals were caught at Woburn Abbey Park and started their long quarantine prior to "repatriation". In June 1985, the final agreement between the Marquis of Tavistock and the Chinese Government was signed and, on 24 August 1985, the 22 deer were flown to Beijing to return to the former Imperial Hunting Park, now called Nan Haizi Milu Reserve. After several months in quarantine, they were released into the reserve on 12 November 1985, in the presence of many high-ranking Chinese officials and the Marquis of Tavistock.

The significance of this project is not only that the milu is back in China and doing well, but also that there has been a significant follow-up. As a result of newspaper, radio and television reporting, we were approached by the government of Hubei Province to establish a reserve for the milu near to the proposed Yangtze River dolphin reserve. They are donating 1,000 ha of land to us for this purpose. The second stage of the reintroduction – which entails establishing the herd in a much larger area of China – has now commenced.

A second expanded stage for the milu project

In the Nan Haizi Reserve, we are organizing a Wildlife Conservation Education Centre and plans have been drawn up for a Wildlife Research Institute. The conservation centre will have a small "pets' corner" in which city children will be able to come into close contact with animals which, in many cases, they have only seen before in a zoo or on television. For them, handling animals will be a totally new experience.

The Wildlife Research Institute will bring to China scientists from abroad to give short courses or lectures – and, in this way, students from the universities in Beijing will be able to broaden their horizons. This kind of institute is highly desirable since the Institute of Zoology of the Academia Sinica, together with many other institutes, is increasingly turning to the fields of molecular biology, genetics and bio-engineering. The current trend in China is to give greater priority to projects with a money-making potential than to conservation activities.

Projects now under way at the Nan Haizi Centre include: encouraging high-school students to put nesting boxes for birds in trees and shrubs; counselling university students to conduct short projects during the autumn and spring bird migrations or surveys of small mammals; training animal keepers; continuing observations on milu adaptation; and studying the milu's breeding behaviour, etc.

Nan Haizi is only about 25 km south of central Beijing – with its 10 million and more inhabitants – and creating a conservation centre here will bring the issue of nature conservation to the attention of a vast number of children and adults alike. Only by reaching out to the general public through the high government officials will we be able to change the often destructive attitude of people towards nature and the environment they live in.

Père David's deer that have recently been reintroduced into China as part of an international co-operative programme (Photo: C. Thouless and A. Loudon).

Coelacanths – exploring the future of an ancient fish by submersible

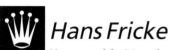

Hans Fricke

Honourable Mention
The Rolex Awards for Enterprise – 1990

Max-Planck-Institut für Verhaltensphysiologie, 8130 Seewiesen, Federal Republic of Germany

German, born 28 July 1941. Professor, Department of Zoology, University of Munich. Educated in the Federal Republic of Germany and the German Democratic Republic; Ph. D. (Zoology) from Free University of Berlin in 1968.

In December 1938, an unexpected zoological discovery made the newspapers worldwide when a strange fish was caught at 75 m depth off the South African coast. The fish was identified as a coelacanthid – a fish known only as a fossil and thought to have been extinct for 60 million years. Since 1938, some 100–200 coelacanths have been caught by native fishermen off the Comoro Islands in the West Indian Ocean; however, after surfacing, all specimens died within several hours. Anatomical and physiological examinations made on deep-frozen specimens show that coelacanths have remained unchanged anatomically for 400 million years. They must have taken refuge in a hidden habitat, undetected by science.

In 1986–1987, we launched a programme on the Comoro Islands in the Indian Ocean to: collect information from local fishermen about coelacanth catches; characterize the habitat of living coelacanths by an environmental survey; and carry out *in-situ* observations on coelacanth behaviour.

The coelacanth in its habitat

During this study – using the submersible *Geo*, which can dive to a maximum of 200 m – we were, for the first time, able to find and study coelacanths in their natural habitat. We started submersible dives off Moroni, the capital of Comoros, and the first impression of the "coelacanth habitat" was depressing: fish abundance was very low at all depths. The steep and barren larva slopes were almost empty, especially off the fishing villages. How could a piscivorous coelacanth survive in an environment with such a low prey density? After more than 20 dives, covering many kilometres along the coast-line at depths below 100 m, we finally found six different coelacanths between 117 and 198 m; we recognized the fish by their individual scale patterns. The number of observed individuals was too small to make decisions about the size of a stable breeding-population.

The coelacanth in its natural habitat.

During the next years, the fishing situation on the Comoro Islands will change. The Japanese Intergovernmental Aid programme plans to improve the fishing equipment, and local canoes will be motorized. Even remote coast areas will be reachable and coelacanths will be endangered in their last refuges. In spite of technical improvements and the increasing fishing effort, the number of coelacanths caught has not increased proportionally during the last years, and this means that the reproductive population is already declining.

Coelacanths are classified as endangered species but our investigations showed that a black market exists. Earlier, all caught individuals were registered and frozen by the Ministry for Production. However, there are no rules about the sale of these specimens and the price seems to depend of the market. One Japanese organization has already arranged four expeditions to the Comoros, and its intention is to isolate a longevity elixir from coelacanth body fluids.

First initiatives for the protection of coelacanths

After our survey, we informed the Governor of Grande Comore, the Minister of the Interior and the Minister for Education about the rarity of the coelacanths and about the necessity of immediate protective measures. We handed a memorandum to the President of the Federal Islamic Republic of the Comoros, and made an international call for immediate conservation measures and an international initiative for the protection of coelacanths.

In April 1987, we founded the Coelacanth Conservation Council (CCC) with headquarters in Moroni, Grande Comore, to co-ordinate conservation measures and the scientific investigation of coelacanths. The programme will promote coelacanth research and attempt to introduce urgent protective measures. At the moment, we are building the *Jago*, a new submersible with a maximum operational depth of 400 m. This submersible reaches the lowest depth distribution of coelacanths. It should help us to answer the many questions about the natural history and ecological requirements of the living coelacanth. First we have to know the ecology before any meaningful steps for conservation can be taken. Therefore, any financial support will go into the operation of this new submersible which is available for any coelacanth research.

The programme will also request the Government of Grande Comore to halt the trade and export of coelacanths, with a view to establishing nature reserves in remote areas, controlling fishing activity, prohibiting fishing at depths below 120 m at certain seasons, etc.

First aid for accidentally caught coelacanths

Local fishermen will continue to accidentally catch coelacanths which, once near the surface, are probably doomed. However, immediate recompression to native depth could possibly prevent their death and we have built a recompression cage in which the caught individual could be transported back by the submersible to the depth of its capture. In September 1988, it proved possible to keep a coelacanth alive in our recompression cage for a total of six days at a depth of 80 m.

Finally, all efforts should be taken to preserve some specimens for future investigations. Questions and techniques might arise which we are still not aware of. Therefore, long-term preservation of several specimens in liquid air or nitrogen would be necessary to permit e. g., biochemical and physiological studies. Of course, this is a very expensive undertaking. Nevertheless, it is an investment which is essential if we are to keep a 400 million year old creature available for the scientific community of coming generations.

The new submarine, Jago, *which will be used for the continuation of Hans Fricke's research.*

Long-term ecological field research in Greenland

Benoît Sittler

Forschungsstelle für Experimentelle Landschaftsökologie, Werderring 8, 7800 Freiburg, Federal Republic of Germany

French, born 13 June 1950. Research Scientist at the University of Freiburg. Educated in France and Federal Republic of Germany; Maîtrise en Géographie from Université Louis Pasteur, Strasbourg, in 1973.

The *Groupe de Recherches en Ecologie Arctique* is a registered not-for-profit association of scientists set up to promote knowledge of the ecology of arctic areas; since 1973, it has organized an expedition each year to various arctic sites, such as Svalbarden, the Canadian Arctic and northeast Greenland, to collect scientific data and compile audiovisual materials for widespread viewing. The participating scientists come from French, German and Swiss universities and are accompanied by experienced technicians.

These surveys on the status and ecology of arctic species have made a significant contribution to our knowledge of arctic ecosystems and have given the group wide and valuable experience on the implementation of arctic field research. The know-how that has been gathered includes: extensive knowledge of ecological conditions prevailing in various arctic sites; an up-to-date bibliography on arctic biology, ecology, geography, etc.; and comprehensive photographic documentation.

A long-term project of Arctic studies

The Karupelv Valley Project has been designed to carry out long-term ecological field research in high arctic tundra and has evolved as a major programme from these former undertakings. It was started in 1987, and aims at improving knowledge of the ecology of the tundra and of how ecosystems work. It is expected that the project will be completed by 1993.

The purpose of the research programme is to assess and interpret biological productivity of tundra ecosystems on the basis of long-term population surveys of all vertebrates belonging to the community. The research should provide insight into: the carrying capacity of the tundra ecosystem; fluctuations of consumer populations in time (cycling of lemming populations, etc.); the factors involved in population fluctuations (role of competition among primary consumers such as musk-ox, lemming, arctic hare, geese, etc.); predator-prey rela-

Lemming winter nests revealed by snow melt are inspected by members of the expedition. The information collected will lead to a broader understanding of the marked population fluctuations (Photo: J. L. Klein and M. L. Hubert).

tionships; impact of climatic variations upon the population studies over a period of consecutive years; behavioural responses, etc.

In an attempt to achieve these objectives, we have and will continue: sampling of data on herbivore and predator populations, including observation of population structure and seasonal trends; sampling of data on bioenergetics which are basic to any productivity investigation; assessment of abiotic factors, especially of the climatic conditions (for example snow-cover pattern).

Northeast Greenland – a particularly suitable study site

Northeast Greenland was chosen for this research since it has not been the site of any long-term ecological research, and the presence of a national park in this region reduces human interference to a minimum. The Karupelv Valley on Traill Island was particularly suitable as a study site because it is – geographically – a well-delimited site with a large valley floor opening on the south side, with raised beaches, basaltic cliffs and offshore islets; the background data confirm that it is typical high-arctic tundra; and the logistics are favourable (possibility of landing on an unprepared runway with a twin-engined aircraft, and the presence in the vicinity of a trapper hut which may be used as insulated shelter in late winter).

Based on census work previously carried out, an area of 1,000 hectares (called the "restricted study area") has been earmarked for the study and will be the site of the main research. In order to obtain more reliable data on species known to have a greater range (musk-oxen, geese, arctic fox, etc.) we will also carry out population level studies in adjacent areas.

Surveys supplemented by field work

These surveys will be supplemented by field work to record climatic parameters with particular reference to snow-melt pattern. Surveying will be carried out during the summer when all migratory species breeding in the study site are present, and observers will have to stay in the field from at least June to August.

However, we also need to collect data on winter processes; consequently, the programme will include both indirect methodology (i.e. for lemmings), and direct surveys (sample surveys taking place in late winter and early spring designed to provide data on range use and predatory relationships among sedentary species) during two field seasons from March through May in both 1991 and 1992.

It is expected that field work will be completed after the summer surveys in 1992. However, depending on results, additional activities may be required during the following year. Thereafter, data processing and production of scientific papers will take at least another two years.

The arctic fox is the most common mammalian predator in the tundra. In northeast Greenland, it relies mainly on lemming. A shortage of this rodent will cause it to prey predominantly on birds (eggs and young) (Photo: J. L. Klein and M. L. Hubert).

The survival of ethnic minorities; Two Indian tribes in South America

Peter Elsass

Klinisk Psykologisk Afdeling, Aarhus Amtskommune Psykiatrisk Hospital, Skovagervej 2, 8240 Risskov, Denmark

Danish, born 11 March 1947. Chief clinical psychologist at the University Hospital of Aarhus, Denmark. Educated in Denmark; Ph.D. (Clinical Psychology) from University of Copenhagen in 1976.

In order to build a strong nation-state, the authorities often demand great sacrifices from the different ethnic groups. Hunters and pastoralists are especially vulnerable, partly because the state sees the expansion of agricultural areas as a necessity for national growth. The purpose of my project is to study why some ethnic minorities survive, while others disintegrate and disappear physically and culturally. This knowledge will be used to support the minorities themselves.

The survival of ethnic minorities depends on their ability to organize themselves and fight for their autonomy and land. The minorities are very unequal in this respect, not only because the surrounding state societies differ, but also because their own communities are structurally different. One aspect of the indigenous social structure seems particularly pertinent, namely that of power. There are no societies without power, but in some tribal communities power is constituted non-hierarchically and involves no threat of violence – the so-called "powerless" power. The hypothesis is that the more invisible and "powerless" the social organization of the ethnic minority, the greater the problem of surviving the contact with Western society without being absorbed in ethnocide.

Building a picture of ethnic minorities

I have stayed 12 times among two South American Indian tribes with different survival capacities. Over the period 1973–1988, the Baris, living in the lowlands on the border between Colombia and Venezuela, illustrate the non-coercive society, egalitarian and without chieftainship. They express little knowledge of their own history and, although they have lost almost 90% of their land since 1900, they have not made any public claims to land or autonomy. Their culture is almost totally englobed by the Catholic mission.

The Arhuacos, living in the mountains of Colombia, illustrate a society of both coercive and non-coercive structures, where the coercive elements have been strengthened and exposed in the confrontation with the state society. They have

Peter Elsass has been studying two indian tribes in South America (the Bari Indians and the Arhuaco Indians) since 1973.

expelled the missionaries and have established their own education, underlining their traditions and history. They are well organized with a hierarchical structure and have elected spokesmen who meet the government officials in the big cities. In recent years they have increasingly emphasized the visible expressions of their ethnicity, for example their traditional dress and their original language.

At the very start in 1973 I had a clear-cut purpose for visiting the Indians: I wanted to document their suppression. I travelled around with a tape recorder and made the Indians talk about their problems of survival. Thereafter I travelled to the white state authorities and played back the Indians' statements to the officials of the local or state government, missionaries and landowners. They answered back in my tape recorder, and the answers were later played back to the Indians. By travelling to and fro crossing the borders I collected concrete material about the suppression of the Indians. All that I later delivered back to the Indians without interfering by giving interpretations and explanations.

Observing an ethnic minority react to stimuli

As time has passed, the situation of the Indians has been more and more difficult to describe. But in the process I have had possibilities to gain insight into the structures which determine their ability to survive, and I have reached some conclusions as to why violence and terror have intruded their society. I have published this knowledge in scientific journals and, in 1989, a book was published in which the disciplines of anthropology and psychology are combined to give a general theoretical framework for understanding the survival of ethnic minorities.

459

However, scientific and academic work with foreign cultures has changed over recent years and subjectivity has gained a new status. I have now made a film which not only presents the situation of the Arhuaco and Bari Indians, but also reflects the presence of the movie team. The film was made in collaboration with the Indians and used as an advocacy for their survival. It was sold to European television companies and the money and the film are now in the hands of the Indians who want to make another film, this time on their own. Some money for instance has been used for the organization of meetings and to cover travel expenses of leaders. The film has also supported a group attempting to establish regional organizations.

The role of the anthropologist and psychologist

As anthropologists and psychologists, we must deliver sound social-scientific arguments that can be used to support the people and societies we study. However, as soon as our expert role generates the complementary role of the Indian as a client, we have extended our role too far in pleading the cause of another people. This problem represents a theoretical challenge of the utmost practical importance. My work with the Arhuacos and the Baris may provide an outline for a new role of self-determination within the state.

My long-lasting acquaintance with the Arhuaco and Bari Indians has given new opportunities for developing projects which might give hope for their survival. The attitude has been a non-political and non-missionary advocacy, where I use my scientific knowledge to strengthen the Indians' autonomy and survival. The aims of my work among the Arhuaco and Bari Indians have been – through comparative scientific analyses – to enable indigenous peoples as well as anthropologists to determine the kind of mechanisms that lead to oppression of indigenous peoples and their culture. I now wish to further develop a science of anthropology and psychology which will strengthen this aim.

By returning to the same indian villages and families regularly, it has been possible for Peter Elsass to study the mechanism that has caused the survival of the Arhuaco Indians and the demise of the Bari Indians.

The Otter Centre

Claus Reuther

Honourable Mention
The Rolex Awards for Enterprise – 1990

Sudendorfallee 1, 3122 Hankensbüttel, Federal Republic of Germany

German, born 7 November 1950. Secretary, Aktion Fischotterschutz and Director, Otter-Zentrum. Educated in Federal Republic of Germany; M. Sc. from College of Forestry, Lower Saxony, in 1974.

In 1979, I founded a registered charity to save the otter (*Lutra lutra*), a highly endangered mammal, and proposed to my employer – the Forestry Department of Lower Saxony – the construction of an otter research station. Two years later, I was able to start transferring the results of the station's research programme to the habitat management of over 6,000 km of rivers in Lower Saxony; I also organized an education programme, initiated an international otter symposium, etc.

Our expenses were paid mainly by the Government and, when we tried to transfer our scientific studies into every-day practice, we met with fierce resistance; eventually the financial support that had been given to us by the Forestry Department of Lower Saxony was suspended and the otter research station was closed down.

Going it alone for the otters

My answer was to go it alone and, in 1986, I left the Forestry Department and set up an independent Otter Centre which I intended should be devoted to research, habitat management and education. The research is carried out in co-operation with over 20 different universities and colleges, and is financed and supervised by the Otter Centre itself. The programme covers not only ethology, physiology, morphology and environmental toxicology, but has also become involved in water economics, agriculture, electronics, industrial design, teaching and marketing. The scientific work is done in the field, in the Otter Centre's own laboratories and in its own special research enclosures.

The preservation of endangered species requires various measures of habitat protection which entail biotope conservation and restoration, and the development of a habitat network. Consequently, the Otter Centre has set itself the task of restoring canalized rivers. A section of a river close to the Centre, which had been turned into a drainage ditch during the l960s, is being renaturalized so that

461

Claus Reuther, the director of the Otter Centre, with a litter of three six-week old otter cubs.

it can provide otter populations with an intact habitat. Particular attention here is being paid to finding a stable compromise between agricultural, forestry and recreational interests on the one hand and environmental interests on the other. At the same time, this long-term conservation programme is aimed at re-uniting the otter populations from the western part of the German Democratic Republic with those still existing in eastern Lower Saxony.

An extensive research and education programme

Since 1987, the Otter Centre has employed a team of six scientists and three assistants who survey the ecological and economic baseline data for the area. In 1990, our next major step will be to buy some areas of landed property and then, over the next 5–10 years, we will undertake the restoration of the River Ise system; the project will be scientifically documented so that the experience and knowledge acquired can be transferred to other areas and river systems.

The education programme starts from the concept that effective long-term conservation cannot be achieved solely through restrictions, regulations and sanctions. What is needed is environmental knowledge, insight and understanding amongst the population, and the Otter Centre consequently emphasizes the emotional aspect of experiences with animals, habitats and problems of conservation, in order to avoid merely imparting dull facts in its educational activities. Its guiding principle is: "Learn by playing!" Having confronted the problems and potential solutions of environmental protection through games and experiments, visitors are then able to convert experiences into practical guidelines for their day-to-day life at home or at work. Moreover, we at the Centre want to demonstrate that, although environmental problems are serious ones, education does not have to be put across in a moralizing way – in fact, learning about the environment can be fun. In 1988, some 100,000 people had the opportunity to enjoy this experience.

An innovative approach to financial independence

Since tradition has it that nature conservation organizations are supported mainly by donations, the concept has developed that the know-how these organizations have built up is of no intrinsic financial value. In contrast, what the Otter Centre has done is to develop a commercial market for its know-how in nature conservation, field research, habitat management and education; in just two years, it has been able to finance a staff of over 60 together with the equipment they require to function correctly. However, two of our problems have been our level of credibility as a professional partner to governmental bodies or commercial or industrial organizations, and the difficulty of finding staff qualified in a specialized ecological approach not taught in the traditional education system. Consequently, we have discovered the importance of learning and of convincing others of our competence by doing our job well and by achieving good results.

A typical example is the River Ise restoration project which originally attracted no interest since it was considered unfeasible. Now that we have proved our abilities, we are discussing with the Government a multimillion deutschmark contract for the restoration programme even though government financing for subsequent scientific supervision is still being refused. What we need is to accumulate experience and develop ever more know-how that we can sell in the future.

The otter is an important indicator for the ecological state of river-systems, and an effective medium in nature conservation policy and education.

The Belihuloya multi-purpose project

Gamini Samarasinghe

Halbarawa Estate, Talahena, Malabe, Sri Lanka

Sri Lankan, born 4 January 1940. Farmer and vegetable seed production researcher. Educated in Sri Lanka and Sweden; Ph. D. (Zoology) from University of Lund in 1974.

On my return to Sri Lanka from my university studies in Sweden in 1972 we set up a small farm and began growing fruit and vegetables at that time unknown in my country. We later moved to an isolated mountain property at an altitude of 2,000 m near to the Belihuloya River. The project that I developed to construct a dam on the Belihuloya, deviate its waters and use the resulting fall of over 1,500 m to generate 10 megawatts of electricity, was submitted to The Rolex Awards for Enterprise 1987.

Using the turbine water for drinking

This Belihuloya Hydropower project, starting as it does from the highest dam in Sri Lanka, will be using the purest and finest-quality surface water in the country to drive the generator turbines. However, as this water descends to the sea it finally joins the Walawe Ganga which is heavily polluted and consequently this vast quantity of pure water would go to waste. Nevertheless since I developed the concept of my electricity generation project, I learnt that another large dam is to be constructed in quite close proximity, although at a lower altitude (about 1,600 m below). I have therefore suggested to the Government of Sri Lanka that the quarry necessary for the extraction of rock for the building of the Samanalaweva Dam (a dam-fill of 4.5 million cubic metres) be shaped as a basin and not as an open L-shaped quarry as planned. This would then provide storage capacity for over a billion gallons of the finest water from the upper reaches of the Belihuloya River exiting from the hydroelectric generating plant of the Belihuloya Power Project. The shaping of the quarry in the form of a basin will merely entail that the trucks carrying the rock for the dam-fill travel up a small slope, and the cost involved would be negligible. The outflow once stored could be used to supply drinking water to the south and southwest of the island which badly need good water. Due to the altitude at which it is stored, the water could also be distributed under gravity flow, thus saving on pumping.

*Millions of litres of pure,
uncontaminated potable
water flow daily from the
upper reaches of the
Belihuloya river.*

Gaining official support for the plan

My first thoughts were that another, adjacent valley could be dammed for this purpose, and I wrote to the Director-General of NARESA (National Aquatic Resources Agency) in June 1987 putting this proposal to him. My subsequent idea of using a quarry which was being constructed for an entirely different purpose came to me suddenly and unexpectedly in the early hours of the morning; I wasted no time and telephoned the Director-General of NARESA at about 7 am the same morning. We met at about 10 am and decided to have a meeting with the Secretary for Power and Energy (also Chairman of the Ceylon Electricity Board) a few days later to discuss this point. The Samanalaweva Project is being constructed by the Ceylon Electricity Board and is estimated to cost a total of US$ 450 million. We subsequently met and discussed my concept and confirmed our discussions in writing.

I then contacted the National Water Supply and Drainage Board, the Government body in charge of all the piped water supply of Sri Lanka to inform them about my proposal, and contacted the United States Aid expert in Sri Lanka, Dr. Robert Bradley (US Aid is funding some of the major water works and piped supply in Sri Lanka). The water is free of human or industrial contamination and is extremely pure and of fine quality in taste and smell; it is the largest available amount of surface water in our country and amounts to about 30% of the supply of piped water presently available in Sri Lanka. I also informed the press about my proposal and they gave me useful coverage.

Developing a concept into a viable plan

I then carried out a careful review of the Belihuloya Hydropower project so that it would be possible to fully exploit the available head for power generation. After careful consideration, I have now produced a basic design for the whole project utilizing the unique topography of the project area and the expertise of Norwegian tunnelling technology; we then presented to the public and the experts a new design which takes into account a head of 1,567 m, a unique tail pond and a delivery pipe (instead of the normal tail race tunnel) based on a siphon system, delivering the drinking water – after further oxygenation in the impulse turbine – into the basin-shaped quarry by means of an 8 km long pipeline. I have also been invited by the Institute of Engineers in Sri Lanka to give official talks on the alternate design, which I have done.

The final feasibility study will, therefore, take account of this design and I am still awaiting the Presidential Committee's final decision on the privatization of this hydropower part of the project. The present political situation will have to improve and new elections are expected soon. A final decision on the privatization will have to await the new Government, but the water resource is, of course, there for the Government to incorporate into their planning for Sri Lanka's water supply.

World experts on water-supply who have been brought in by the Government have recommended the plans I have envisaged, and I feel strongly that they will be implemented, giving Sri Lanka an additional, cheap and pure water supply.

The Samanalaweva Dam on the left and the main quarry on the right, with the Belihuloya Mountains in the background.

Preserving and restoring the living environment of the Kathmandu Valley

Dwarika Das Shrestha

Dwarika's Kathmandu Village Hotel Ltd, Post Box No. 459, Battisputali, Kathmandu, Nepal

Nepalese, born 25 December 1925. Chairman of Kathmandu Travels and Tours Ltd. Educated in India; Bachelor of Law from Lucknow University in 1951.

I hope to make a significant contribution towards the restoration of the living architectural environment of a Kathmandu valley. Governments and other organized entities are doing important work in restoring old buildings, monuments, temples and other structures. However, these are static affairs, and once completed, they become beautiful objects to behold, but, "Please do not touch". My project – a single-handed effort begun 14 years ago – is to recreate a 15th-17th century environment where tourist and Nepali alike would have a sensation of the original.

A 17th-century world centre

Culminating in the 17th century, the Kathmandu Valley, then known as "Nepal", became a world centre of art, architecture and craftsmanship. The pagoda temple style originated here. Outstanding examples of brass and bronze casting, stone sculpture, painting, brick masonry work and wood carving exist in unimaginable quantities which now exhibit every degree of deterioration.

A dramatic change in life-style began in the 18th century when the valley and other parts of modern Nepal were conquered and brought under the rule of one man. A decline in the social and economic structures accelerated and, in the years between 1845 and 1950, one family took political and economic control, closed the country to the outside world, forbade education, imported what aesthetics seemed desirable, and shattered the old life. In 1952, I, a young man fresh from college, organized and opened the first youth organization under the name of "Nepal Youth League" with a passion to build a new Nepal. I began realizing that great values were being lost. Artisans were moving to other professions. Old, beautiful structures with great character were falling apart. Intricately carved wood used in all forms of architecture became firewood. The more I travelled the valley, the more I could see the devastation in the environment and I felt a great humiliation and injustice. One day I saw carpenters demolishing a beautiful wooden pillar; without knowing to what ultimate use the pieces would be put,

467

Wood carvings collected by Dwarika Das Shrestha stored awaiting restoration.

but knowing they must be saved, I began collecting old, carved windows, doors, pillars, columns, tympanums, mouldings, bricks of various types and age and stone work, everything I could afford to buy from the owners of the buildings being destroyed. I started a travel agency in 1970 as a means of using tourism for the employment of Nepalese people. Several years later, friends, aware of my collection, encouraged me to use some of it in the construction of a small rental house on the property containing my home and the cowshed. The idea of using rental income for the financing of the collection and later restoration work slowly developed, along with ideas for the most appropriate use of the collection.

The building of a Village Hotel

In 1975 work began on what has become the gradual fulfillment of a passion. The cowshed was removed and construction began on a tourist hotel complex to be named Dwarika's Kathmandu Village Hotel. The doors opened in 1977. Dwarika's was born, people came, stayed and applauded the hotel's ambiance, and most importantly, provided the financial means of continuing and expanding the collection and restoration.

Problems and challenges appeared as the first new building went up. Practically all the old wood pieces needed restoration of some kind. Portions of window frames had rotted away. Corners of carved doors have broken off and disappeared. Where could I find more old style bricks to complete a wall when that style had not been made for a century or more? The same was for the roof tiles. Where was a brick mason familiar with construction techniques of the 17th century? I became a researcher, studying ancient buildings in the old section of Kathmandu, Patan, Bhaktapur and Kirtipur, comparing carvings on my windows with those on existing buildings of known age, talking with the older craftsmen for bits of information on how and why it was done that way and what was the significance of that scroll or succession of figures, there being no books or written information available.

468

The more I studied the greater became the urge, indeed the necessity, to build authentically and not just incorporate old things into modern construction. So I hired and trained wood carvers and carpenters and masons. A wood carving workshop has been on the premises continuously since 1977, wherein young craftsmen are learning old traditions by meticulously copying 15th century pieces on to new wood. Bricks are being specially made in valley kilns. Roof tiles are obtained as old buildings are demolished.

Dwarika's has become an asylum and hospital for the care of wounded master-pieces in wood, where they are restored to their original beauty, a school for training and practice of traditional arts and skills, a laboratory to research old techniques, and a living museum where people may enjoy and understand this heritage which is not only Nepali but, that of the human race.

A vehicle for future dreams

For the future, I would like to say that the hotel as a commercial enterprise is merely a vehicle to finance and carry my dream forward. The Kathmandu Valley once had an unparalleled environment. I expect to create a non-profit founda-tion, financed by donations and by the hotel, as a permanent institution to carry my work forward in the future. The foundation's task would be preservation, divided into the categories of materials, skills and culture.

I would like to see a training institute for craftsmen established to teach the old techniques of wood, metal and stone work, a school operated on an economic basis that allows a student the opportunity of support without having to mend fenders in the local garage. In the absence of authentic history and documenta-tion, my conservation work would lead me in preparing a catalogue and history of carvings and architecture in the valley. Its unique environment and great values for all mankind must not be lost.

The woodcarving workshop and training centre that D. D. Shrestha has established.

469

Developing practical methods of arid land revegetation

Dean Stephen Hill

Honourable Mention
The Rolex Awards for Enterprise – 1990

Australian Revegetation Corporation, Ltd., 51 King Edward Road, Osborne Park, 6017 Western Australia, Australia

Australian, born 19 January 1945. Managing Director, Australian Revegetation Corp. Ltd. Educated in USA; B. A. (Agricultural Economics) from University of New England in 1967.

Practical solutions to desertification must be implemented quickly and proven seeds, machinery and techniques have to be used in large quantities if the world is to stem the tide of 27 million hectares becoming unproductive each year.

During the 1970s and 1980s considerable research was carried out on the rehabilitation of arid lands. Much of this work was done in Western Australia, where climatic conditions match those in the Middle East and North Africa in many respects. However, it is in the nature of research that results often do not get translated into practice for many years. Through Australian Revegetation Corporation Limited, which I set up, I have worked with researchers and land users to focus on the fast development of practical and effective techniques for the revegetation of arid lands. The essence of this co-operation has been to speed up the commercial availability of new techniques.

Practical machines and techniques

This close liaison between researchers and our company may be illustrated by four programmes we have undertaken in seeder machinery design and construction, plant production and planting technique improvement. We developed the Kimseed contour seeder as a versatile furrow seeder designed to produce acceptable germination conditions for seeds planted in arid and saline conditions and it is used in particular for direct seeding of tree seeds such as eucalyptus. The Kimseed camel pitter is a low-cost arid-land seeder which creates micro-catchments for water harvesting. It does not need a tractor, but can be trailed behind a pick-up truck. It has been used for research on the selection of appropriate revegetation species at given sites and for large-scale revegetation plantings by pastoralists, and an animal-drawn version is being developed for Africa.

Acacia saligna (Cyanophylla) has been identified by researchers in North Africa as suitable for fodder in dry and saline areas, and our company has now sourced large quantities of this plant, and is using it successfully throughout Australia and

470

The tree seeder developed by Dean Stephen Hill's Australian Revegetation Corporation Ltd.

North Africa. We have also undertaken a joint venture with the University of Western Australia to develop seeding and management techniques for tagasaste (*Cytisus proliferus*), a leguminous, tap-rooted, fast-growing wind break/fodder shrub that is ideal for barren, deep sands. Our company has provided seeds, seeding and harvesting machinery and other technology.

Top skills for effective solutions

An essential feature of our machinery is the quality of our design and, from an early date, the company has benefited from the services of a top agricultural engineer who has now designed over 20 revegetation machines. The machines are of three basic types: rangeland seeding machines, which form soil contours that collect water and wind-carried topsoil for seed placement; pitters which form discontinuous hollows for collection; and contour seeders which form continuous furrows and mounds for collecting run-off water. All these machines have been designed to be: effective; up-to-date in their techniques; simple to operate; and robust. The design excellence of our machines has been recognized through ten industry awards presented at Australian national and regional field displays and the Greening Australian Award for Innovation.

Desert revegetation seeds are germinated in hostile conditions of salinity, wind blasting, and extremes of heat and water availability, and consequently it is necessary to select the right seeds for a given environment. Australia has an abundant supply of the appropriate seeds and Greg Hill, our Operations Director, built up reliable sources of seeds, in many cases inventing methods for harvesting seeds that have never before had commercial value.

The future

In Western Australia, after 19 years of developing awareness, the market has matured. Kimseed revegetation seeds, machinery and contracting services are now well know and accepted. Revegetation is currently seen as a viable way of increasing farm profitability through drought proofing and fodder management. The world market is far more complex and difficult to service. Although we have sold seed and machinery to 90 countries worldwide, the market is spasmodic and unco-ordinated. In many cases, the cost of time and travel is greater than the return, while most larger projects require substantial funds to proceed through tendering systems.

Two additional major requirements that have been identified are education and soil conservation. We are now developing short courses in soil conservation in conjunction with Australian Departments of Agriculture and Curtin University. This is a practical and effective way of providing information on low-cost solutions to soil erosion problems. Although the company has been recognized within Australia as the leader in the field, international acceptance of the available revegetation technology would be helped by the prestige attached to the Rolex Awards for Enterprise.

The Kimseed camel pitter, a low-cost, low-maintenance rangeland seeder.

Health mission at 5,000 m above sea level

Carlos Santa Maria

El Bosque 386, Lima 27, Peru

Peruvian, born 1 November 1959. General Practitioner and Surgeon. Educated in Peru; M. D. from Universidad Nacional Federico Villareal, Lima, in 1987.

This project operates a mini-mobile medical unit, mounted on a four-wheel-drive station wagon, to take professional care to those otherwise unable to receive medical attention due to sickness or lack of transport to reach the nearest medical post. In a three-day ride, starting at sea level, medical help and medicines are taken to small-community dwellers who live in the Andes at altitudes of up to 5,000 m.

Haloxylon persicum for feed, firewood and environmental improvement in semi-arid regions

Yaakov Orev

18 Hogla Street, 84 722 Beer-Sheva, Israel

Israeli, born 27 March 1921. Retired Desert Range Development Specialist. Educated in Israel; M. Sc. (Agriculture) from the Hebrew University, Jerusalem, in 1951.

This project is studying *Haloxylon persicum* (white saxaul) in the 40–100 mm rainfall zone of Israel (Negev and Arava), and will attempt to introduce it and make it spread in the winter rainfall area of Africa, north of the Sahara. It is also planned to introduce it to the summer rainfall areas south of the Sahara as forage for camels and goats, and for firewood, sand dune stabilization and environmental improvement.

Project Aeolus – volcano surveillance using ultra-light planes

Marino Martini

Department of Earth Sciences, University of Florence, Via La Pira 4, 50121 Florence, Italy

Italian, born 29 January 1935. Professor of Geochemistry, University of Florence. Educated in Italy; Degree (Geology) in 1961.

This project aims to develop a simple procedure for the surveillance of volcanic activity by means of infrared imagery of volcanoes taken from ultra-light planes which can approach the craters at a very low altitude. Experiments to date appear to confirm that ultra-light planes may offer a simple, cheap and effective tool for forecasting changes in active volcanoes well in advance of eruptive events.

Sewage pollution and marine communities along the coast of Buenos Aires Province, Argentina

Juan Lopez Gappa

Museo Argentino de Ciencias Naturales, Avenida Angel Gallardo 470, Casilla de correo 220, Succursal 5, 1405 Buenos Aires, Argentina

Argentine, born 30 October 1954. Marine Biologist/Researcher at the Argentine Museum of Natural Sciences. Educated in Argentina; Doctor en Ciencias Naturales from La Plata University in 1979.

This project aims to evaluate the impact of sewage pollution on marine communities in the vicinity of coastal towns of Buenos Aires Province. To heighten awareness of the problem, the project will contact municipalities, undertake field work in affected areas, train local groups to carry out sampling and monitoring, inform the public through local press and broadcasting, publish findings, and draw up technical reports.

Collecting Mexican birds to conserve a major resource

Aldegundo Garza de León

Calle Real 603, Colonia Jardines de Valle, P. O. Box 150 C, Saltillo, Coahuila, 25000 Mexico

Mexican, born 15 November 1939. Stores Manager. Educated in Mexico; Administrator's Degree from Instituto Panamericano de Alta Administración de Empresas.

This project has, with government authorization, set up a collection of endangered Mexican bird species. The collection already contains 650 of the possible 1,000 species, and has 1,280 specimens with a view to presenting the life cycle and characteristics of the various species. This is the only collection in Mexico or in any other country of Mexican birds presented for display in their natural postures.

"Nuestra Señora de Guadalupe" – a small-farm development project

Frank X. Klamet

Parroquia de Nuestra Señora de Guadalupe, 03005 Chirilagua, San Miguel, El Salvador

American, born 6 January 1952. Roman Catholic Priest for the Diocese of Cleveland. Educated in United States; B. A. (Social and Behavioural Sciences) from the Borromeo College of Ohio in 1974.

This project, which began in 1985 in one of the most war-torn areas of El Salvador, is designed to help poor farmers to cultivate basic grains using the best organic and environmentally safe methods, especially prohibiting the use of herbicides. Also, the project promotes a space-saving and soil-preserving vegetable and fruit cultivation technique adapted from Dr. Jacob Mittleider's hydroponics method.

Environmental and geo-scientific mapping of Austrian alpine karst areas

Rudolf Pavuza

Breitenseerstrasse 64, 1140 Vienna, Austria

Austrian, born 3 April 1955. Geologist in an oil exploration and production company. Educated in Austria; Doctorate (Geology) from University of Vienna in 1982.

Since 1977, this project has been preparing environmental and geo-scientific maps of the Austrian alpine karst regions. The work consists in extensive field mapping, literature searches, chemical analyses, and preparation of the maps and the explanatory booklet. The maps are in the form of transparent overlays to official topographic maps. Currently, two maps are available and five are in preparation.

Conservation of the Mediterranean seal in North Africa

Francisco J. Avella

Fondo Para La Foca de Mediterraneo, Palau 10, 20, 07001 Palma de Mallorca, Spain

Spanish, born 26 August 1957. President of Fondo Para La Foca de Mediterraneo. Educated in Spain; graduated (Biological Sciences) from Autonomous University of Barcelona in 1979.

This project is carrying out an extensive public information and education campaign on the Mediterranean coast of Algeria, Libya, Morocco and Tunisia to increase awareness of the endangered Mediterranean seal (*Monachus monachus*) of which there are thought to be only 500 survivors. It is also determining the status of the seal in this area and attempting to find a suitable location for a seal reserve.

A new eco-agro-system at Liu Min Ying Village, Beijing

Bian Yousheng

Beijing Municipal Research Institute of Environmental Protection, Fu Wai Avenue, 100037 Beijing, People's Republic of China

Chinese, born 14 October 1938. Environmental Protection Researcher. Educated in People's Republic of China; attended Fu Dan University, Shanghai, from 1956 to 1961.

This project is carrying out a systematic, quantitative study of ecological agriculture, taking a village as an ecological system. On the basis of ecological principles, agricultural production is being systematically organized to make full use of natural resources and to ensure continuous and steady yield growth while protecting and improving the environment and maintaining ecological equilibrium.

Eskimo language survival through the 21st century

Roy Dean Iutzi-Mitchell

University of California at Berkeley, P. O. Box 60490, Fairbanks, Alaska 99706, United States

American, born 1 December 1958. Ph. D. candidate at University of California, Berkeley. Educated in United States; M. A. (Anthropology) from University of Alaska, Fairbanks in 1981.

Many indigenous minority peoples are facing linguistic and cultural extinction. This project proposes to apply research findings from cognitive anthropology, interactional sociolinguistics and language planning by establishing Eskimo Language Survival, a non-profit association of Alaskan Eskimos dedicated to designing scientifically based language policies, and aiding Eskimo villages in their implementation.

Space-based Verification, Inspection and Surveillance System

Daniel Robert Schaubacher

Eigerstrasse 44, 3007 Bern, Switzerland

Swiss, born 31 December 1937. International Trade Adviser. Educated in Switzerland; studied at the Ecole supérieure de commerce et d'administration, Lausanne.

This project aims to establish an integrated management system, using the combined resources of remote sensing, *in-situ* inspections and information/signal processing technology for the observation, prediction, mitigation and/or control of global conflictual or ecological threats. The project has tentatively been called Space Verification, Inspection and Surveillance System (SVISS).

Conserving the *Cracidae*: Latin America's most endangered avian family

Stuart Strahl

Wildlife Conservation International, New York Zoological International, 185th Street and Southern Boulevard, Bronx, New York 10460, United States

American, born 30 July 1955. Programme Co-ordinator for Tropical South American Region Wildlife Conservation International. Educated in United States; Ph. D. (Biology/Ecology) from State University of New York, Albany, in 1985.

The avian family *Cracidae* (guans, curassows and chachalacas) comprises 50 species of large galliform birds endemic to the Neotropics, and is the most endangered family of large birds in this region. This project has a comprehensive plan for *Cracidae* conservation and management, including promoting cracids as "indicator species" for monitoring protected areas, supporting field research on these birds, etc.

Restoring the Caribbean queen conch by a hatchery in Puerto Rico

Dietmar W. Fuchs

Riedererstrasse 10, 8045 Ismaning, Federal Republic of Germany

German, born 20 September 1958. Chief Editor of the Swiss magazine Aquanaut. Educated in the Federal Republic of Germany; M. A. (Marine Biology) from the Ludwig-Maximilians-Universität, Munich, in 1990.

The marine snail *Strombus gigas* is on the verge of extinction due to over-fishing. This project plans to restore the conch population through natural breeding in hatcheries. The released animals will revive the natural stock and should support small local conch-fisheries. The hatcheries will be financed by selling to new markets, e.g. in Europe. It is proposed to establish the programme in Puerto Rico.

The takin and musk-ox: A comparison of two species

Pamela Groves

Institute of Arctic Biology, University of Alaska, Fairbanks, Alaska 99775, United States

American, born 24 July 1954. Graduate student. Educated in United States and Alaska; B. A. (Animal Behaviour and Ecology) from Hampshire College, Amherst, in 1976.

This project is comparing the takin and musk-ox – two related large ungulates that live in China and the Arctic, respectively. The takin is rare, probably endangered, but has never been intensively studied. The musk-ox has successfully recovered from extirpation in Alaska. Comparative studies on these two species may answer basic scientific questions, as well as helping in effective management.

Using dune-mole rats for poverty-reduction

Petrus Hendrik Van Rooyen

4 Paul Kruger Street, 7600 Stellenbosch, South Africa

South African, born 17 July 1953. Senior lecturer at University of Stellenbosch. Educated in South Africa; Ph. D. (Developmental Studies) from University of Stellenbosch in 1983.

In South Africa, agriculturalists are combating infestations of dune-mole rats (*Bathyergus suillus*) which reduce livestock and crop productivity. The project will investigate the future possibilities of utilizing dune-mole rats for home-industry fur manufacturing and the production of protein for human and livestock consumption in areas of unemployment and poverty. A pilot project has given promising results.

A community-based research programme for regional conservation

Geoffrey Wayne Clarfield

National Museum of Kenya, P.O. Box 40658, Nairobi, Kenya

Canadian, born 21 June 1953. Project Manager. Educated in United States, Kenya and Canada; M. A. (Social Anthropology) from the University of Toronto in 1982.

Without an understanding of how people around Lake Tarkana perceive nature, any attempt at conservation there will fail. This project aims to train educated Turkana, Arial and other tribe members to discover their vision of nature, i. e. how plants, animals, landforms and people are classified, and how these ethno-biological understandings are expressed in language, material culture, ceremony, song, etc.

The optimal tree to fight erosion in the Tropics

Karsten Werner Jochims

Apartado postal 2389, Carretera Vieja a León, Managua, Central America, Nicaragua

German, born 10 March 1934. General Manager of the Foundation for Non-traditional Energy and its Technology. Educated in Federal Republic of Germany; B. Sc. (Economics) from University of Cologne in 1961.

This project proposes reforestation with *Crescentia alata* trees for the control of tropical soil erosion. The tree: is low in cost; has a direct-sowing seed survival rate of 80%; resists droughts, hurricanes, permanent flooding, and open forest fire; and produces large quantities of fruit for 80–100 years. The fruit can be processed to replace petroleum as an energy source, and yield high-quality protein.

Preserving the voices of a subcontinent

Muhammad Luthfullah Khan

75 15th Street, Khayaban-e-Sahar, Phase VI, D. H.A., Karachi 75500, Pakistan

Pakistani, born 25 November 1916. Advertising Chairman. Educated in India; matriculated in Madras in 1936.

Since 1951, this project has been collecting on magnetic tape recordings of musicians, writers, scholars and other personalities of the Indian subcontinent. The library is divided into five sections: music, literature, religions, speeches of the famous, and education. Much of the collection has been catalogued, cross-referenced and stored for easy retrieval. Further recordings are in progress.

Migration of cetaceans through the Straits of Gibraltar

Luca Marini

Via Pio Foà 23, 00152 Rome, Italy

Italian, born 7 October 1960. Environmental analyst for the State Administration of Rome. Educated in Italy; Degree in Natural Sciences from the University of Rome in 1986.

This project will investigate the migrations of cetaceans through the Straits of Gibraltar by the establishment of an international sighting base on the coast of Spain and/or Gibraltar. The aim is to assess the status of the cetacean populations that enter and leave the Mediterranean basin each year with a view to managing and protecting threatened species that probably use the Mediterranean as a "nursery" area.

Evaluating the reconstruction of a town destroyed by a natural disaster

Mario A. Noriega

Apartado Aereo 18991, Bogotá, Colombia

Colombian, born 22 April 1949. Architect and Urban Planner. Educated in Colombia.

In 1985, mudflows from the Ruiz volcano wiped out the town of Armero, Colombia, killing 20,000 people. This project, based on five years of involvement in national and international efforts for the recovery of Armero, seeks to evaluate those efforts. The ultimate objective is to arrive at general conclusions and principles for orienting and co-ordinating rebuilding efforts in similar cases of large-scale natural disaster.

Photographing "jewels" of the European alpine flora

Guy Bonfils

avenue Agirond 66, 26400 Crest, France

French, born 25 March 1939. Education adviser. Educated in France; studied (Biology) at Grenoble University.

This project aims to publish a photographic compilation of European alpine flowers in need of protection. A voyage will be made through the relevant European countries and the collection of photographic material will be accompanied by on-site botanical research, the taxonomy of the species encountered, and close-up photography. The project will commence in Greece and move on to other European countries.

Vermiculture technology for bioprocessing of organic waste

Uday Bhawalkar

A/3 Kalyani Building, Pune Satara Road, Pune 411037, India

Indian, born 16 February 1951. Proprietor, Bhawalkar Earthworm Research Institute. Educated in India; B. Tech. (Chemical Engineering) from Indian Institute of Technology, Bombay, in 1973.

This project will further develop its vermiculture technology for converting solid and liquid organic wastes into usable resources. Agricultural residues and non-toxic domestic and industrial waste can be converted to biofertilizers and proteins. Using the project's Vermifilter, agricultural, municipal and non-toxic industrial waste water can also be converted to biofertilizer, protein and reusable water.

Saving the green monkeys of Barbados

Jean Baulu

Barbados Primate Research Centre and Wildlife Reserve, Farley Hill, St. Peter, Barbados

Canadian, born 9 September 1944. Director and Founder of the Barbados Primate Research Centre and Wildlife Reserve. Educated in United States and Canada; M. Sc. (Psychology/ Primatology) from the University of Georgia in 1973.

The Barbados Primate Research Center and Wildlife Reserve is a non-profit organization focused on the production, optimal utilization, research and conservation of the island's primate species (*C. aethiops sabaeus*). It has an expansion plan for the Wildlife Reserve in which an adjoining large forest would be stocked with endangered neo-tropical primates; it also runs programmes to benefit other sectors.

A park for one of the world's last unprotected wild horse herds

Marcelo Carvalho de Andrade

Euclides Figueiredo 76, 22261 Rio de Janeiro-RJ, Brazil

Brazilian, born 15 November 1958. President, Brazilian Institute for Environmental Research. Educated in Brazil and United States; M. D. from Universidade Gama Filho in 1985.

This project aims to set up a private park in northern Brazil to preserve the region's ecosystem and save from extinction what is probably the world's last remaining herd of wild horses that is not officially protected. These horses originated from Spain and have undergone over 200 years of natural selection. The project also plans to study the specific genetic characteristics of these horses.

Education programme to save the Kunzas in the Atacama desert

Hector Santiago Garcés Hill

Sucre 1085, Antofagasta 1137, Chile

Chilean, born 22 May 1941. Director, Institute of Archaeological Investigations. Educated in Chile and Mexico; Degree (Anthropology) from Universidad de Concepción in 1972.

The Kunzas in the Atacama desert are threatened by development of mineral deposits in their area, exploitation of their water resources, and the likelihood of nearby gas and/or oil discoveries. This project has set up a self-instruction programme at an archaeological museum in San Pedro de Atacama to enhance the Kunzas' consciousness of their heritage and stimulate awareness of the problem among the population.

Saving the world's largest *Crocodylus niloticus* from skin hunters

Jean Christophe Peyre

B. P. 563, Antananarivo, Madagascar

French, born 20 November 1961. Crocodile breeding research worker. Educated in France, Zimbabwe and Mauritius; attended University of Nice-Valrose from 1980 to 1984.

Having located three enormous crocodiles each between 6 m and 7 m in length, i.e. amongst the world's largest, which are under threat from skin hunters and poachers, this project plans to set out and capture these animals and to release them in a farm. In this way it will be possible to protect them and allow visitors to have a glimpse of the last survivors of the gigantic crocodiles that peopled prehistory.

Fondation Soleil – a unique primary health care organization

Christian Tal Schaller

Fondation Soleil, Bois des Arts, 38, 1225 Geneva, Switzerland

Swiss, born 11 September 1944. President of Fondation Soleil. Educated in Switzerland; M. D. from University of Geneva.

The Fondation Soleil promotes holistic health studies and has adopted a global, non-sectarian approach to public information on health maintenance and restoration, with special reference to individual independence and self-responsibility. Its key message is that – through lifestyle and habit adjustments – it is possible to experience physical, mental, emotional and spiritual health at the level of the individual.

Methane production to combat deforestation in rural Africa

John Warner Jarman

P. O. Box UA 295, Union Avenue, Harare, Zimbabwe

Zimbabwean, born 2 August 1934. Partner in a firm of personnel consultants. Educated in United Kingdom; Degree from School of Surgical Chiropody in 1959.

This project is promoting methane as a viable alternative to wood or dried animal dung as a cooking fuel in rural Africa. The project will: design, construct and test methane digesters that operate efficiently on a manure/water mixture, are cheap and easy to construct, and simple and safe to operate; and disseminate and demonstrate to rural communities the advantages of methane as an alternative cooking fuel.

Educational development programme for the *Atlantis* submarine

Dennis Hurd

Sub Aquatics Development Corp., 191 West 6th Avenue, Vancouver, British Columbia, Canada V5Y 1K3

Canadian, born 11 January 1942. President and Chief Executive Officer, Sub Aquatics Development Corp. Educated in Canada; B. Sc. (Applied Science) from Queens University, Kingston, in 1965.

Atlantis submarine operations have carried approximately 400,000 people on underwater excursions through coral reef areas and brought people face to face with the underwater world and environment. This project has instigated school programmes aimed at introducing children to the underwater environment, and now intends to develop the necessary educational systems and materials for this experience

The world of wood

Giovanni Borgognoni

Via A. Cammelli 55, 51100 Pistoia, Italy

Italian, born 4 June 1937. Pointsman for the Italian State Railway. Educated in Italy; after graduating from secondary school, has been responsible for his own education.

This project has put together a collection of over 1,500 different types of wood derived from all parts of the world. The collection has been classified, and each specimen is marked with its Latin name, common name, origin, special characteristics and uses (both as a wood and as a plant). The wood samples are also accompanied by specimens of the related resins, photographs of the tree in its natural surroundings, etc.

Ride for the rhino – a 22,000-km conservation bicycle ride

Charlene Hewat

Melfort Farm, c/o P. O. Box UA 460, Harare, Zimbabwe

Zimbabwean, born 28 July 1963. Conservationist. Educated in Switzerland and Zimbabwe; studied French at American College of Leysin in 1982.

In order to create worldwide public awareness of the way in which African animals are being butchered every day by armed poachers, this project involves two young women cycling 22,000 km through snow, ice, desert and rough terrain from Britain to Zimbabwe, on a "Ride for the Rhino" campaign. The women will raise funds and give talks. The project aims to create sanctuaries for these endangered animals.

A simple, low-cost system for upland rescue and improvement

Warlito A. Laquihon

Mindanao Baptist Rural Life Center, Kinuskusan, Bansalan, Davao del Sur, Philippines

Filipino, born 26 November 1942. Associate Director/Director of Training, Mindanao Baptist Rural Life Centre. Educated in Philippines; Masters Degree (Agriculture) from University of the Philippines, Los Baños, in 1974.

This project has developed the Sloping Agricultural Land Technology (SALT) – a legume-based agroforestry model – to help save eroded uplands in the Philippines. After ten years' successful operation, SALT has a sound reputation; to determine its suitability for other tropical uplands, 100 volunteer small-scale upland farmers from throughout the tropical regions will be helped in setting up pilot SALT farms.

Project preservation – Lake George's sunken bateau fleet

Joseph W. Zarzynski

P. O. Box 2134, Wilton, New York 12866, United States

American, born 1 July 1950. Social Studies Teacher at Saratoga City School. Educated in United States and Hong Kong; M. A. (Social Sciences) from State University of New York in 1975.

This project has researched and carried out underwater fieldwork on the sunken bateaux of Lake George, USA; these vessels are some 230 years old, and are threatened by boat anchors and inconsiderate scuba divers. The goal is to preserve these vessels by lobbying the State of New York to set up an underwater preserve, and have one or more bateaux listed on the National Register of Historic Places.

A development project involving interaction of indigenous communities

Hernán Eusebio Lechuga Farías

Teatinos 371, Of. 301, Santiago, Chile

Chilean, born 17 February 1941. Chief Surgeon, Paediatric Surgery Service, "El Pino" Hospital. Educated in Chile; M. D. from University of Chile in 1966.

This project intends to promote the development of indigenous ethnes threatened with extinction, whilst respecting their way of life, traditional work and organization. The project will be based on financial and technological support from non-governmental organizations and social and organizational development catalysed by interaction with more advanced indigenous communities in the region.

World Ecologists Foundation – working for environmental conservation

Beatrice Isabel Barretto

#15 Annapolis Street, Greenhills, Metro Manila, Philippines

American, born 5 April 1939. President and Founder, World Ecologists Foundation. Educated in United States; attended Louise School of Hotel Management, Washington D. C.

The World Ecologists Foundation is dedicated to conserving natural resources, improving the environment and maintaining ecological balance in the Philippines. It disseminates information, sets up seedling banks, establishes livelihood programmes, provides technical consultancy, lobbies for legislation to improve the environment, designs educational programmes on ecology, reforests depleted areas, etc.

Alcañiz botanical refuge

Gustavo Alvarez Gardeazábal

Apartado 400, Tualá, Valle, Colombia

Colombian, born 31 October 1945. Municipal Mayor, Tuluá. Educated in Colombia; Licenciate (Belles Lettres) from Universidad del Valle in 1970.

This project has, over the past 12 years, installed a botanical refuge in the centre of the Cauca River valley, Colombia, intended for native species and for species adapted to the local climate. The tasks involved include: ensuring a summer water supply; building transit roads and trails; classifying and naming the on-site species; preserving the general layout of the landscape, etc.

A self-sustaining tribal livelihood project

Benedict Ballug

Defence of Democracy Movement Foundation, P. O. Box 368, Garcom Mails, Maharlika Building Lobby, Session Road Cor., Abanao Street, Baguio City 2600, Philippines

Filipino, born 8 July 1958. Farmer, and coffee and tea producer. Educated in Philippines; B. Sc. (Political Science) from Baguio Colleges Foundation in 1984.

Starting from a 20-ha model farm, this project now covers some 1,050 ha of tribal land holdings belonging to the "Baliwon" tribe; it aims to constitute a self-sustaining project that matches local skills and integrates tribal culture and practices. It involves: alternative livelihood sourcing; gradual change-over from kaingin farming to plantation farming and use of coffee proceeds to finance tribal rice requirements.

Joint American-Soviet saturation mission in an underwater habitat

Mark Robert Patterson

Division of Environmental Studies, University of California, 3150 Wickson Hall, Davis, California 95616, United States

American, born 3 April 1957. Assistant Professor, University of California. Educated in United States; Ph. D. (Biology) from Harvard University in 1985.

This project proposes to bring a team of Soviet scientists to the United States for a joint mission with a team of American marine scientists in the underwater habitat, Aquarius. This unique facility is the only habitat in the world currently devoted to scientific research. The project would address some fundamental problems in coral physiology with a view to using coral ecosystems as barometers of the environment.

Transferring water to the desert

Fan Changxin

Department of Physics, 44–603, 2nd Dormitory, Fudan University, Guo-Nian Road, 200433 Shanghai, People's Republic of China

Chinese, born 27 February 1937. Associate Professor of Physics, Fudan University. Educated in People's Republic of China; graduated from Fudan University, Department of Physics, in 1960.

This project proposes transferring 10^{10} m^3 per year of water from the Yangtze River to the Qaidam Basin in northern China by means of a dam 50 m high and 1 km wide and a culvert 100 km in length. It is hypothesized that precipitation will increase, the increment of total collectable water in northern China will be over 10^{10} m^3 per year, and that millions of hectares of sandy land will converted to oases.

Native river shrimp farming in Oaxaca, Mexico

Donald Rohan Cerutti

c/o Alfonso Hernandez, Insurgentes Sur 1677, Desp. 903, Mexico D. F. 01020, Mexico

Swiss, born 8 March 1964. Biochemical Engineer. Educated in Switzerland and Mexico; Degree (Biochemical Engineering) from Instituto Tecnologico y de Estudios Superiores de Monterrey in 1986.

The population of native river shrimp (*Macrobrachium americanum*) in Oaxaca, Mexico, has decreased alarmingly. This project proposes to rebuild this shrimp population. The use of local techniques and materials will ensure preservation of cultural values, promote training and participation in environmental improvement, raise nutritional levels, create jobs and coherently focus the efforts of local communities.

Name Index

Country Index